Towards an Understanding of
the Mechanism
of Heredity

"How odd it is that anyone should not see that all observation must be for or against some view if it is to be of any service!"

Charles Darwin, 18 September 1861, in a letter to Henry Fawcett. (More Letters of Charles Darwin, edited by Francis Darwin and A. C. Seward (1903). London, John Murray, vol. 1, pp. 194–196.)

Fawcett had just addressed the Botany and Zoology Section at the Manchester Meeting of the British Association for the Advancement of Science 'on the Method of Mr. Darwin in his Treatise on the Origin of Species'. In the discussion that followed, Edwin Lankester expressed the opinion that the facts which Darwin had brought forward in support of the hypothesis of evolution by natural selection were of more value than the hypothesis itself. This gave rise to the remark in Darwin's letter.

Towards an Understanding of

the Mechanism
of Heredity

H. L. K. WHITEHOUSE
M.A., Ph.D.
Fellow of Darwin College, Cambridge
and University Lecturer in Botany

Foreword by
Professor G. PONTECORVO
Dr. Agr., Ph.D., F.R.S.
Professor of Genetics, University of Glasgow

 EDWARD ARNOLD (Publishers) Ltd. London

First published 1965

Reprinted 1967

To my MOTHER and FATHER
who first aroused my interest in the
scientific study of plants and animals

Printed in Northern Ireland at The Universities Press, Belfast

Foreword

Genetics—the study of heredity and variation—is going through a phase of obvious success. It is inevitable that a proportion of the young and more able artificers of this success should have come to think that what matters in genetics dates, say, from 1953. That was the time of the remarkable elucidation by Watson and Crick of the structure of DNA with its all embracing implications. In the last two years quite a number of books, some of them admirable, have been written with that conscious or unconscious attitude.

Dr. Whitehouse's book is refreshingly different. It traces the basic ideas of Genetics through their development and describes concisely, yet without omitting any essential detail, the critical experiments which led to the establishment of each of those ideas. This historical approach, invaluable for teachers and no doubt appealing to the more thoughtful students, is not at the expense of keeping abreast with the advancing frontiers. Suffice it to say that in one chapter Dr. Whitehouse deals with the latest genetical and biochemical approaches to recombination—a stagnant field since about 1930—which gives hope that this basic biological process may soon become understood.

To the honour of having been asked to write this foreword I can add the pleasure of having been compelled to read a most valuable book.

Glasgow
September, 1965   G. Pontecorvo

Preface

This publication is intended as an account of the primary evidence for current beliefs concerning the mechanism of heredity. Other aspects of genetics are referred to only if their study has illuminated fundamental features of heredity. Thus, the book deals only with the central core of genetics, omitting the more peripheral components. There is no discussion of how the hereditary mechanism may have evolved, nor of how evolutionary divergence of populations and species may have come about, and discussion of the many applications of genetics, such as to medicine, and to crop and livestock improvement, is omitted. The aspects of genetics which are included occupy such a central position in biology that in varying degrees all the rest of biology may be said to be related to them. In consequence, if the contents were not restricted to basic aspects, the book would have to be greatly enlarged.

The theme of the book has been to trace the development of ideas about heredity from the earliest times. The approach, however, is not strictly historical. Each of the 16 chapters deals with a particular hypothesis concerning a fundamental feature of the hereditary mechanism, and sets out to show how experimental evidence has either confirmed the theory, or led to its modification or its abandonment. The classic experiments which gave rise to major advances are described, together with the inferences drawn from them. Particular trouble has been taken to distinguish observation from deduction. In this way it is hoped that the nature of the scientific method will be clearly demonstrated. The chemical and physical evidence for the structure of the components of DNA (Chapter 11), and the evidence from biochemical studies for the steps in protein synthesis (Chapter 14), are not given. On the other hand, some idea of the nature of the evidence for all the conclusions reached about the hereditary mechanism is included, with the exception of some of the inferences about genetic recombination in bacteria (Chapter 15, § 15.2). An author's work may be referred to a number of times in different contexts, since only matter relevant to a particular hypothesis is discussed in any one section of the book. Another consequence of this method of presentation is that, within each chapter, data from a wide variety of organisms, often ranging from bacteria to man, may be discussed. This means that aspects of, for example, the study of human heredity are considered in a number of places scattered through the book, wherever such studies have provided fundamental information relevant to the hypothesis under discussion.

Some features of the study of the hereditary mechanism are rather complex, but no attempt has been made to omit them on that account. In consequence, certain parts of the book are not easy reading; for instance, those concerned with the inheritance of quantitative characters (Chapter 4, § 4.8), the evidence that crossing-over occurs after chromosome duplication (Chapter 8, § 8.6), the origin of structural changes in chromosomes (Chapter 9, § 9.8), and some aspects of genetic recombination (Chapter 15).

The book is intended for any interested person who has some background knowledge of biology and chemistry. No attempt has been made to describe the structure or life-cycle of the organisms mentioned in the text, but a systematic list of the many different plants and animals referred to is included (Appendix 1). It is hoped that the book will be usful to Biology students at Universities, including research students in the more marginal branches of genetics or in cognate subjects, who may wish to read about the basic aspects of heredity. Much of the book is based on the courses of lectures in genetics which I have given to first-, second- and third-year students reading Botany at Cambridge University. A glossary of genetical terms is included (Appendix 2) for the benefit of readers unfamiliar with the subject, and an extensive bibliography of original papers for those wishing to obtain more detailed information about the topics discussed.

The book has been written in the hope that an account of the remarkable progress that has been made (beginning with Mendel just a century ago) in understanding the mechanism of heredity, will give some readers the pleasure of intellectual stimulation. The immense advances of the last 20 years have greatly illuminated many of the earlier discoveries by revealing their molecular basis, and I hope readers will be able to recapture something of the intellectual excitement that this has caused. Much of the basic fabric of living organisms now stands revealed, with its central enigma of how the extraordinary interlocked system of nucleic acids and proteins (both of which, in different ways, are necessary for the synthesis of each) first evolved.

I wish to thank all those who have helped me in the preparation of this book. Dr. D. Briggs, Mr. M. H. V. Cooray, Dr. S. A. Henderson and Dr. G. Meyer have provided photographs, and I am indebted to them for their generosity. I am grateful to Dr. Sydney Smith for tracing the source of the Darwin quotation on p. (ii), and I owe a special acknowledgement to Professor G. Pontecorvo, F.R.S., for his kindness in writing the Foreword. I would like also particularly to thank Mr. G. J. Clark for the substantial help he has given me in the preparation of many of the diagrams. Mrs. Pamela Landshoff kindly typed part of the manuscript, and Mr. F. T. N. Elborn took the photographs reproduced as Plate 4 (b)–(e). I thank Messrs. Oliver and Boyd for permission to publish Table 4.2. In thanking my Publishers, I should like to mention especially their unfailing courtesy and helpfulness. Finally, I would express my gratitude to Pat, my wife, not only for the assistance she has given me, but also for putting up with my many hours of study.

Cambridge
1965   H. L. K. W.

Contents

1. The classical theory of direct inheritance of characters

§ 1.1 The ideas of Hippocrates

Among the earliest known writings on the subject of heredity are those of Hippocrates (ca. 400 B.C.). He believed that the reproductive material came from all parts of the individual's body and hence that characters were directly handed down to the progeny. As evidence in support of this hypothesis he referred to a race of mankind called the Macrocephali, who, immediately after a child was born, fashioned its head by hand to give it an elongated shape. He also said that, at a later period, the elongated head was formed naturally, without the necessity of moulding it after birth. Hippocrates asked why, since such characters as baldness and blue eyes are inherited, should not the long-headed character be similarly handed down. Since he believed that the reproductive material coming from unhealthy parts of the body was correspondingly unhealthy, he was willing to accept the notion that mutilations, such as the moulding of the head, would in the course of one or a few generations become inherited. Hippocrates must have relied on hearsay for supporting his theory of heredity, as he could hardly have made direct observations of a change in a human population over a number of generations.

§ 1.2 The views of Aristotle

Aristotle (ca. 350 B.C.) questioned the Hippocratic view and pointed out the difficulties, even impossibilities, which it presented. He referred to the inheritance of such characters as the voice, nails, hair, and way of moving, which he believed could not contribute to the reproductive material, since they were intangible or concerned dead tissues, and he also referred to characters such as a beard or grey hair which may not be present at the time of reproduction. Further, Aristotle pointed out that children may resemble a grandparent more closely than they resemble their parents. He also drew attention to the dilemma which the Hippocratic theory presents when applied to plants, where, for various reasons, a part may be absent at the times of reproduction and yet be inherited. He was puzzled, too, as to how the two parents could each contribute something from all their parts, and yet their progeny have but one and not two of each part.

Aristotle argued that the reproductive material, instead of being derived

1

from all the parts of the individual as Hippocrates thought, should be regarded as made up of nutrient substances which, while on their way to the various parts, had been diverted to the reproductive path. These nutrient substances would differ from one another depending on the part of the organism for which they were originally destined. He also favoured the idea that the contributions to the progeny from the two sexes were not the same, the female contributing the material and the male something to define the form that the embryo is to assume, just as the carpenter's contribution to the making of a chair is merely its shape and form.

The ideas of Hippocrates and of Aristotle concerning heredity differ, but share the notion that inheritance is direct: that is, that substances derived from or intended for specific parts of the individual are handed down to the progeny. Hypotheses of this kind represent the simplest theory of heredity which one can postulate.

§ 1.3   Darwin's theory

Over the centuries many variations of the theories of Hippocrates and Aristotle have been proposed, but the basic idea that characters are in some way transmitted directly from parent to offspring was never effectively challenged until the year 1883 when Weismann proposed his theory of the continuity of the germ-plasm. Mendel's conclusions (1866) implied the discarding of the classical view of heredity, but this was not appreciated at the time, as his contribution was largely overlooked until 1900. Thus, Darwin (1868, Chapter 27) suggested that all the cells and tissues of an organism threw off minute granules, both during development and when the individual had reached maturity. He further supposed that these granules circulated through the plant or animal, multiplied, and were passed to the reproductive cells, which thus contained a multitude of components thrown off from each individual part of the organism. In this way, hereditary characters were thought to be transmitted to the progeny. In the offspring the granules were regarded as responsible for the development of cells or tissues corresponding to those from which they had been derived in the parent. The granules were supposed to be transmitted occasionally in a dormant state for several generations before developing to reveal an ancestral character. As Darwin (1875, Chapter 27, footnote 42) himself remarked, this theory of heredity resembles that of Hippocrates. It differs chiefly in specifying that granules were responsible for the hereditary transmission.

§ 1.4   Experimental results obtained by Knight and by Goss

Experimental evidence which appeared to establish the existence of a hereditary mechanism of the kind which Hippocrates described has been obtained on a number of occasions. One of the most recent concerns the effect of fertiliser treatment on *Linum usitatissium* (Flax) (Durrant, 1962). Rigorous attention to many points of detail is necessary in order to exclude the possibility of selection, and no claim for the existence of a direct adaptive influence of the environment on inheritance has gained general acceptance. In view of this lack of confirmation, it is remarkable that Hippocrates' hypothesis remained unchallenged for 23 centuries. Numerous experiments on the crossing of different species or varieties of plants and animals were performed during the 18th and 19th centuries, but although these studies failed to provide support for the classical theory, they did not lead to any alternative hypothesis. That is, of course, with the notable exception of Mendel's work. Some of the most promising earlier experimental studies were made by Knight and by Goss with *Pisum sativum* (Edible Pea) and since this was the plant which Mendel subsequently used so successfully, their work will be described.

Knight (1799) lived near Ludlow, England, and his primary intention was to obtain new and improved varieties of fruits and vegetables. He chose the Edible Pea as his initial experimental material, because of its short generation time, the numerous varieties available and the self-fertilizing habit, which made the protection of the flowers from insects carrying pollen unnecessary.

He crossed two varieties which differed in colour. One was unpigmented, having green stems, white flowers and colourless (white) seed-coats, while the other had purple stems and flowers and grey seed-coats. He found that when an unpigmented plant was pollinated by a pigmented one, only pigmented progeny were obtained the next year (the first filial generation), but these on self-pollination, or on pollination by unpigmented plants, produced some pigmented and some unpigmented plants in the succeeding year. This diversity was manifest even when the peas from within one pod were sown. However, he did not record the numbers of the two kinds, either in the progeny of individual plants, or in total, and so failed to discover the underlying mechanism of heredity and was able merely to deduce that there was a 'stronger tendency' to produce coloured than colourless plants.

Knight also established that reciprocal crosses gave identical results. Thus a tall variety pollinated by a dwarf one, and *vice versa*, gave plants which were the same as regards their vigour of growth, the size of the seeds and the season of maturity. Unknown to Knight, the identity of the progeny from reciprocal crosses had already been discovered by Kölreuter (1763) using species of *Nicotiana* and other flowering plants.

Goss (1824) made similar discoveries to those of Knight, but took the analysis a little further. He lived at Hatherleigh in Devonshire, and had also been attempting to produce new varieties of vegetables. He had removed the stamens from a normally green (blue) seeded pea, pollinated it from a yellow (white) seeded variety, and had been surprised to find that the seeds set (the first filial generation) were yellow like the male parent (Fig. 1.1). He sowed these the following year and was equally surprised when, after self-pollination, he found some pods with all green, some with all yellow, and many with both green and yellow peas in the same pod (the second filial generation) (Fig. 1.2). On sowing these the next year, he found on further 'selfing' that whereas the green peas bred true and gave only green progeny, the yellow yielded some pods with all yellow and some with both green and

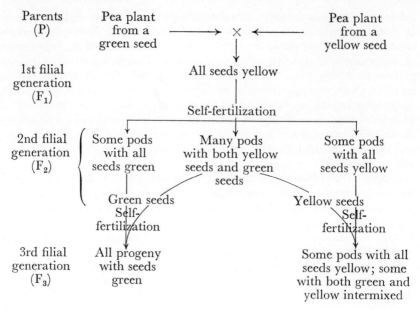

| Parents (P) | Pea plant from a green seed | → × ← | Pea plant from a yellow seed |

1st filial generation (F₁) — All seeds yellow

Self-fertilization

2nd filial generation (F₂)
- Some pods with all seeds green
- Many pods with both yellow seeds and green seeds
- Some pods with all seeds yellow

Green seeds Self-fertilization   Yellow seeds Self-fertilization

3rd filial generation (F₃)
All progeny with seeds green

Some pods with all seeds yellow; some with both green and yellow intermixed

FIGURE 1.1   Goss' results from crossing green and yellow peas (*Pisum sativum*).

yellow peas intermixed (the third filial generation) (Fig. 1.1). Forty-two years later, Mendel (1866) reported similar results. However, Goss, like Knight, did not count the numbers of the two kinds of peas (or if he did count them, he failed to see the significance of the figures and did not publish them), and so he failed to discover the hereditary mechanism which Mendel found.

The studies by Knight and by Goss with peas illustrate the kind of result that was obtained in the 18th and 19th centuries with many organisms. The experimental work at this time appears to have been designed, either to obtain new and improved varieties of animals and plants for use in agriculture or

FIGURE 1.2   Drawing of a pea pod with seeds of two colours, similar to that used to illustrate Goss' paper.

horticulture, or with the object of understanding the nature of species by means of artificial hybridizations, rather than with the specific intention of obtaining information about the mechanism of heredity. Probably this is the reason that the experimental results were not recorded with sufficient detail and precision for anything about heredity to emerge except 'an inscrutable medley of contradictions' (Bateson 1909, page 2). To take one example, Goss states that his second generation yellow peas produced, on selfing, some pods with a mixture of green peas and yellow peas, and some with all the peas yellow. If he had studied the plants more carefully he would have found no doubt, as Mendel did, that one can substitute 'plants' for 'pods' in the previous sentence; in other words some of the second generation yellow peas breed true. He would then have been much nearer to understanding the underlying mechanism of inheritance.

2. The hypothesis of indirect inheritance through particulate determinants

§ 2.1 Mendel's experimental results

Mendel (1866) had made crossing experiments with *Pisum sativum* similar to those of Knight, Goss and others but, unlike them, he recorded the numbers of progeny of each kind. This was the rewarding advance which enabled him, by a stroke of genius, to detect the underlying mechanism and so to put forward an entirely new hypothesis concerning heredity.

One of the character-differences which Mendel studied was the same as Knight had used about 60 years earlier, namely the presence or absence of pigmentation in the plant (stems, flowers and seed-coats). Like Knight, Mendel found that the progeny from a cross between the two forms were pigmented (the first filial generation), and that, on self-pollination of these, both pigmented and unpigmented plants were obtained (the second filial generation). But Mendel went further and counted the numbers of each kind. He found that among 929 plants, 705 were pigmented and 224 were not, and he observed that these frequencies closely approximate to $\frac{3}{4}$ and $\frac{1}{4}$ of the total (696·75 and 232·25), respectively. The character—presence of pigment, in this instance—which is manifest in all the immediate progeny of the cross, and in $\frac{3}{4}$ of the following generation, Mendel called the *dominant* character, the other being the *recessive*. He also confirmed Kölreuter's and Knight's observations that reciprocal crosses (*A* female × *B* male, and *B* female × *A* male) give similar results.

Mendel also worked with the character-difference which Goss (1824) had used, confirming that yellow seed (embryo) is dominant to green, and that both kinds appear in the second generation after crossing. Unlike Goss, Mendel counted his peas, and recorded that out of 8023, 6022 were Yellow* and 2001 green, or again a very close approximation to $\frac{3}{4}$ (= 6017·25) and $\frac{1}{4}$ (= 2005·75). Mendel confirmed Goss' third-generation observations, namely, that the green peas bred true, whereas the Yellow often did not. But Mendel went much further than this. Of 519 such Yellow seeds, he found that 166 bred true, while 353 did not (but gave Yellow and green seeds in the proportion of 3 to 1 like the previous generation). Mendel observed that the frequencies 166 and 353 are a close fit with $\frac{1}{3}$ (= 173) and

---

* A capital initial letter is used for dominant characters, lower case for recessive ones.

6

$\frac{2}{3}$ (= 346) of the total, respectively. This implied that the second-generation
ratio of 3 dominants to 1 recessive was really a ratio of 1 pure-breeding
dominant to 2 impure dominant to 1 recessive (always pure-breeding).
Mendel pursued his inheritance studies through 5 or 6 generations and
showed that the pure-breeding types in the second filial generation remained
pure-breeding, and the others gave a 1:2:1 ratio in each generation.

Essentially similar results to those just described were obtained by Mendel
for a total of 7 character-differences in *P. sativum*. In the first generation from
a cross, one character was always dominant to its alternative, and in the
second generation showed a 3 to 1 ratio, and this, on further analysis, was
shown to be a disguised 1 to 2 to 1 ratio. What was the significance of these
simple numerical ratios?

§ 2.2 Mendel's theory

In building an hypothesis to account for his results, Mendel introduced
symbols, *A* for the dominant and *a* for the recessive character. This use of

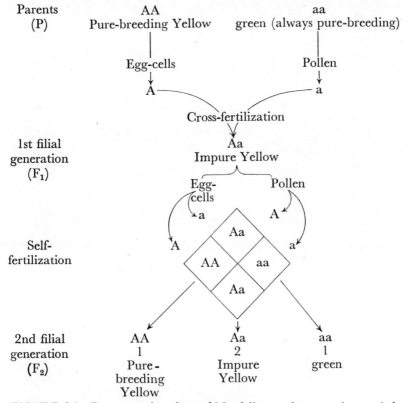

FIGURE 2.1   Representation of one of Mendel's experiments, using symbols
(*A* and *a*) for the hypothetical hereditary determinants (*A* for
Yellow, *a* for green seed-colour).

symbols is most significant, as it implies the existence of something which 'stands for' the character. Although Mendel used 'Charakter' or 'Merkmal' almost throughout his paper, it is clear that he was thinking in terms of 'factors' or 'determinants' responsible for the manifestation of the character. This is the crucial feature of his theory of heredity, that characters are not 'transmitted' directly from generation to generation as the classical theory supposed, but that there exist discrete particles responsible for the appearance of particular characters. Furthermore, each individual receives one particle from each of its two parents in respect of a particular character-difference; and these particles do not influence one another in any way but separate uncontaminated at the time of formation of the reproductive cells. If *A* denotes the particle which determines Yellow seeds and *a* that for green seeds, then on this hypothesis, Mendel's experiment described above can be represented as in Fig. 2.1. A further corollary implicit in the hypothesis was that egg-cells carrying *A* were equally likely to be fertilized by pollen cells carrying *A* or those carrying *a*, and similarly with egg-cells carrying *a*. In other words, fertilization was at random between egg-cells and pollen-cells, irrespective of what factors they carried.

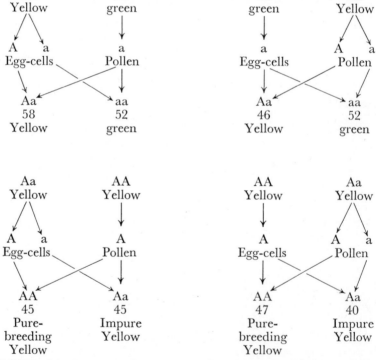

FIGURE 2.2   Representation of a set of back-cross experiments used by Mendel to test the validity of his theory of heredity. *A* = determinant for Yellow seed-colour, *a* for green.

In order to test the validity of this theory of heredity, Mendel devised a series of experiments. The Yellow peas obtained in the first generation from a cross between pure-breeding Yellow and green (necessarily pure-breeding) were germinated and the flowers on the resulting plants, instead of being allowed to self-pollinate, were crossed with the parental forms. On Mendel's hypothesis, from such a 'back-cross' to the green parent, a 1 to 1 ratio of Yellow to green peas is expected and this prediction was confirmed experimentally: the first generation Yellows as female parent crossed with green as male parent gave 58 Yellow and 52 green peas as progeny, and the reciprocal cross (green as female parent, first generation Yellow as male parent) gave 46 Yellow and 52 green. Comparable results were obtained on back-crossing the first generation Yellow peas to the Yellow parental type, but here it was necessary to grow the progeny and allow them to self-pollinate in order to reveal the 1:1 ratio of pure-breeding and impure Yellows. These experiments confirming the hypothesis are shown diagrammatically in Fig. 2.2. Mendel made similar tests with all the 7 character-differences in peas with which he worked, and in every case he obtained the expected 1:1 ratio.

§ 2.3   The rediscovery of Mendel's work

Mendel's work made no impression on contemporary thought and indeed was almost entirely overlooked for 34 years. It was 'rediscovered' independently by De Vries (1900), Correns (1900) and von Tschermak (1900). Each of these authors had made experiments similar to those of Mendel and obtained comparable results. Thus, De Vries had found that various character-differences in a whole range of species of flowering plants showed dominance in the first generation from a cross and 3:1 ratios in the second generation. The species and characters are listed in Table 2.1. Correns had worked with *Zea mays* (Maize) and both he and von Tschermak with *Pisum sativum*. The characters in *P. sativum* which they studied included those used by Knight and by Goss and which, unknown to them, had also been used by Mendel. Correns introduced the expression 'Mendels Regel' (Mendel's law) for the basic principle, namely, the separation or segregation at the time of formation of the reproductive cells of the discrete particulate determinants of alternative characters, and their reassociation at fertilization.

So, when Mendel's work was rediscovered, a number of his experiments had already been repeated and his results confirmed independently by two observers. The truth of Mendel's work was thus immediately established. Moreover, its wide applicability was demonstrated by De Vries' experiments. Further evidence for this came from the work of Bateson and Saunders (1902)*, who established that Mendel's law applied to *Gallus*

* Bateson and Saunders introduced several terms which have since been generally adopted: *allelomorph* (now often abbreviated as *allele*) for each of the alternative factors responsible for a particular character-difference; *heterozygote* for the product of fertilization of gametes differing by an allelomorph; and *homozygote* for the product of fertilization of gametes carrying the same allelomorph. They also proposed the symbols P for the parental generation, F_1 for the first filial generation, F_2 for the second filial generation, and so on.

TABLE 2.1   Character-differences found by De Vries (1900) to show Mendelian inheritance as indicated by 3:1 ratios in the second filial generation.

Name of Plant	Characters	
	Dominant	Recessive
Agrostemma githago (Corn Cockle)	Normal reddish-purple petals	Petals pale-coloured
Aster tripolium (Sea Aster)	Normal blue flower-colour	White flower-colour
Chelidonium majus (Greater Celandine)	Normal pinnately cut leaves and petals	Laciniate leaves and petals
Chrysanthemum roxburghi	Normal yellow flower-colour	White flower-colour
Coreopsis tinctoria	Normal yellow flower-colour	Brown flower-colour
Datura tatula and D. stramonium (Thorn Apple)	Purple stem- and flower-colour	Green stem- and white flower-colour
——	Thorny fruit	Unarmed fruit
Hyoscyamus niger (Henbane)	Normal purple-veined corolla	Corolla pale-coloured
Oenothera lamarckiana De Vries (Evening Primrose)	Normal style	Short style
Papaver somniferum (Opium Poppy)	Dark spot at base of petals	Petals without basal dark spot
——	Normal single flower	Double flower
Silene alba (White Campion)	Normal hairy shoots	Glabrous shoots
Silene dioica (Red Campion) and *S. alba*	Red petal colour	White petal colour
Solanum nigrum (Black Nightshade)	Normal black fruit	Green fruit
Trifolium pratense (Red Clover)	Normal red flowers	White flowers
——	Quinquefoliate leaves	Normal trifoliate leaves
Veronica longifolia	Normal blue flower-colour	White flower-colour
Viola cornuta	Normal blue flower-colour	White flower-colour
Zea mays (Maize)	Normal starchy endosperm	Sugary endosperm

domesticus (Domestic Fowl), as well as to further plants. In *G. domesticus* they found an extra toe was dominant to the normal foot; pea comb was dominant to single comb; rose comb was also dominant to single comb; and white shanks and bill were dominant to yellow. Each of these character-differences appeared in a $3:1$ ratio of dominants to recessives in F_2. Simultaneously and independently, Cuénot (1902) also established that Mendelian inheritance occurred in animals, when he showed that the normal grey coat-colour in *Mus musculus* (House Mouse) was dominant to albino in F_1 from a cross, and segregated to give 198 grey and 72 albino in F_2.

(a)   (b)

FIGURE 2.3   Drawings of (*a*) normal, and (*b*) peloric *Antirrhinum majus* (Snapdragon).

Bateson and Saunders (1902) drew attention to the fact that many studies on inheritance dating from before 1900, previously inconclusive, were now explicable in terms of Mendelian inheritance. They quoted, for instance, the work of Darwin (1868, vol. 2, Chapter 14) with peloric *Antirrhinum majus* (Snapdragon). This form differs from the normal in having a regular radially-symmetrical flower instead of the normal irregular two-lipped structure (Fig. 2.3). Darwin's results are shown in Fig. 2.4. They were interpreted by him as indicating that the tendency to produce normal flowers prevailed in the first filial generation from the cross between the two forms, whilst 'the tendency to pelorism appeared to gain strength by the inter-mission of a generation', and prevailed to a large extent in the second filial generation. But on Mendel's theory of heredity it is merely necessary to postulate that the factor for pelorism is recessive to the normal. Darwin's F_2 frequencies, omitting the two intermediate plants, are in good agreement with the $3:1$ ratio expected on the Mendelian hypothesis. Later studies have confirmed the Mendelian explanation.

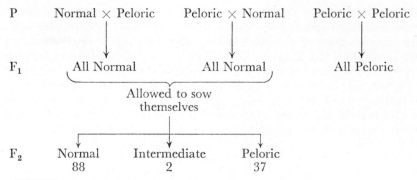

FIGURE 2.4   Darwin's results from studies of the inheritance of peloric *Antirrhinum majus* (Snapdragon).

§ 2.4   The difference between the classical and Mendelian theories

The example from Darwin's work provides a good illustration of the difference between the classical and Mendelian theories of heredity. On the classical theory, something is transmitted directly from each part of the organism, for example, the flower of the *Antirrhinum*, to the corresponding part in the progeny. On the Mendelian hypothesis, on the other hand, inheritance is indirect through the agency of particulate determinants. It is these determinants which are transmitted from generation to generation, and the character of the flowers which develop in any individual is merely the fortuitous consequence of the set of determinants which it happens to receive at fertilization. Thus, the classical theory deals with the tendencies of characters to gain strength or lose strength, while Mendel's is concerned with chance combinations in pairs of dominant and recessive particulate determinants of characters. The fundamental difference is that on the classical theory inheritance is direct and hence the extent of transmission of a particular character to the progeny may be influenced by the character itself, whereas on the Mendelian theory the determinant of a character is considered to be in no way modified by its presence in an organism, whether it possesses that character or not, and hence the inheritance of a character is thought to be unaffected by the character itself. Thus, on the Mendelian theory, the inheritance of mutilations, such as Hippocrates quoted in support of the classical theory, is impossible.

§ 2.5   The diversity of Mendelian characters

Bateson, Saunders and Punnett (1905) established one of the first instances in Mendelian inheritance of the occurrence of incomplete dominance, that is, where the heterozygote is intermediate between the two homozygotes. They found that the so-called 'blue' Andalusian variety of *Gallus domesticus* (really a grey) is the heterozygote from a cross between a black and a white variety. Many further instances of incomplete dominance were established soon afterwards, both in animals and in plants. Dominance and recessiveness were thus seen not to be an essential part of Mendel's theory of heredity, the central notion of which is the coming together at fertilization, and the separation at gamete-formation, of pairs of particulate determinants.

Within a few years of the rediscovery of Mendel's work, innumerable examples of Mendelian inheritance had been established. Bateson (1909), without any attempt at completeness, listed about 100 examples in plants and a similar number in animals. Both the organisms and the characters involved were highly diverse, including susceptibility to *Puccinia glumarum* (Yellow Rust) in *Triticum aestivum* (Wheat); eye-colour in *Homo sapiens* (Man); waltzing behaviour in *Mus musculus*; and shell colouring in *Helix hortensis* and *H. nemoralis* (Snails).

§ 2.6   The Hardy-Weinberg equilibrium

Confirmation of Mendelian inheritance for particular character-differences can sometimes be obtained from study of the frequencies in a population of individuals of different genetic constitutions. Hardy (1908) and Weinberg (1908) showed independently that, in the absence of mutation* or selection, the frequencies of the two homozygotes and the heterozygote for a pair of alleles will remain constant from generation to generation, provided the population is large enough for chance fluctuations in their proportions to be neglected, and provided crossing is at random with respect to the alleles. If the pair of alleles is denoted by A and a, and their frequencies in the population by p and q, respectively, where $p + q = 1$, then with random crossing the frequencies of AA, Aa and aa individuals in the population will be given by the terms of the expansion of $(p + q)^2$, that is, by p^2, $2pq$ and q^2, respectively. The frequencies of all the possible crosses, such as $AA \times Aa$, $Aa \times Aa$, and so on, can then be expressed in terms of p and q, and likewise with their progeny. When the frequencies of AA, Aa and aa progeny from the various crosses are summed, it is found that they are given by the expressions p^2, $2pq$ and q^2, respectively. In other words, the population is in equilibrium, and the relative proportions of individuals with the different genetic constitutions are the same as in the previous generation.

Snyder (1931) discovered that ability to taste phenyl-thiocarbamide was due to a single dominant Mendelian gene, and that in 440 individuals from 100 American families, 301, or 68·5%, could taste it and 139, or 31·5%, could not. There were 9 families in which both parents were taste-deficient, and their 17 children were all taste-deficient also, as expected if this is a recessive character. Assuming that the Hardy-Weinberg equilibrium conditions apply (that is, large population size, random mating with respect to tasting, no differential viabilities or fertilities of the heterozygote or homozygotes, and negligibly low mutation rates), the frequency of non-tasters (q^2) is $0·315$. It follows that $q = 0·561$, $p = 1 - q = 0·439$, $p^2 = 0·192$ and $2pq = 0·493$; that is, $19·2\%$ of the total population are expected to be

---

* Mutation is an abrupt change from one allele to another: see § 9.2.

homozygous and 49·3% heterozygous for the dominant gene for tasting ability. This means that $\dfrac{0\cdot192}{0\cdot685}$ or 28% of the tasters are homozygous and 72% heterozygous. It is evident that in 72% of families where one parent is a taster and the other not, there will be equal numbers of tasters and non-tasters among the children, while in the other 28% of such families, the children will be expected all to be tasters. Snyder tested 117 children from 51 such families and found that 37 were taste-deficient. The expected number is half of 72% of 117 = 42·1, in agreement with the observed number. In 40 families where both parents were tasters, he found 16 taste-deficient children out of a total of 106. The expected number is $\frac{1}{4} \times \left(\dfrac{72}{100}\right)^2 \times 106 = 13\cdot7$. Thus, the numbers of tasters and non-tasters among the children in both these classes of families are in agreement with the Hardy-Weinberg predictions. This confirms that the taste deficiency is due to one recessive gene, and this confirmation has been obtained without the need to test tasting ability over several generations.

One of the conditions for Hardy-Weinberg equilibrium is that there shall be no selection favouring one or other allele. In practice, the maintenance of a pair of alleles in a population, if not due to recurrent mutation, is likely to be due to *balanced polymorphism*, that is, the possession by each allele of certain advantages over the other, depending on the conditions. It is a simple possibility if the heterozygote has an advantage over either homozygote. An example of this is provided by heterozygotes for a pair of alleles, *A* and *S*, affecting human haemoglobin. Allele *A* gives normal adult haemoglobin, and *S* gives sickle-cell haemoglobin (see Chapter 13). Allison (1954) showed that the heterozygote, *AS*, has increased resistance to malaria compared with normal *AA* individuals. On the other hand, sickling homozygotes, *SS*, suffer from a severe anaemia which is usually lethal in childhood. As expected, the *S* allele occurs in human populations only where malaria is endemic, such as in West Africa, or in populations recently derived from such areas.

§ 2.7   Non-Mendelian inheritance

Although Mendelian inheritance appears to be so widespread, it is not universal. One of the first exceptions to be established was through the work of Correns (1909). He had been studying the inheritance of a number of pale-leaved or variegated forms in various flowering plants. A strain of *Urtica pilulifera* (Roman Nettle) with yellowish-green leaves, and a variegated strain of *Lunaria annua* (Honesty) with white-margined leaves were found to be inherited as Mendelian recessives. In *Mirabilis jalapa* (Marvel of Peru), a strain called *chlorina* with leaves wholly yellowish-green, another called *variegata* with leaves variegated with yellowish-green, and a third called *striata* with striped flowers, were all found to show Mendelian inheritance. However, a fourth strain of this plant, called *albomaculata*, with leaves variegated with yellowish-white, was found to show a different kind of inheritance. Correns observed that, in addition to the variegated ones, occasional shoots on the *albomaculata* plants were normal, being wholly green, while others were wholly white. He found that flowers on green shoots gave only green progeny, irrespective of whether the pollen came from green, white or variegated shoots. Similarly, whatever the source of pollen, flowers on white shoots gave only white progeny, which necessarily died soon after seed-germination owing to the lack of chlorophyll for photo-synthesis. Flowers on variegated shoots, again irrespective of the type of shoot from which the pollen was obtained, gave three kinds of progeny: wholly green; wholly white; and variegated; and moreover, the proportions of the three kinds were highly variable, never consistently fitting any particular ratio. Plants or branches with only traces of white gave a higher proportion of wholly green progeny than did strongly variegated individuals or shoots.

Here were results differing markedly from those expected on Mendel's hypothesis, notably in the maternal inheritance, with divergent results from reciprocal crosses, and in the lack of constant proportions of the different kinds in segregating progenies. Hypotheses which have been put forward to explain these results will be discussed in Chapter 5, when other examples of non-Mendelian inheritance will be described. However, it has been evident ever since this work by Correns that Mendelian inheritance, although widespread and abundant, is not the only method of inheritance in living organisms. The relative importance of the different methods of inheritance is discussed in § 16.4.

3. The hypothesis of independent inheritance of determinants for different characters

§ 3.1 Mendel's results for two character-differences

Mendel (1866) in his classic paper on inheritance in *Pisum sativum* did not confine himself merely to the study of the inheritance of various character-differences considered in isolation. He made experiments in which the parents differed in two or three characters. Thus, a pure-breeding strain with round (that is, smooth) yellow seeds was crossed with a pure-breeding strain with wrinkled green seeds. The F_1 seeds were all Round Yellow, these being the dominant characters. In F_2 he obtained 556 seeds, which comprised 315 Round Yellow, 101 wrinkled Yellow, 108 Round green and 32 wrinkled green. These figures are in good agreement with a ratio of $9:3:3:1$. Similar results were obtained with all the combinations of character-differences in peas which Mendel chose to test, apart from such features as presence or absence of pigment in the seed-coat and flower, where Mendel confirmed Knight's observation that these are merely two aspects of one character-difference: the presence or absence of pigment in the plant as a whole.

§ 3.2 Mendel's hypothesis

As an hypothesis to account for his results, Mendel postulated that when two character-differences are present each is inherited independently. The $9:3:3:1$ ratio is then predicted, for it is the consequence of superimposing two $3:1$ ratios, one for each character-difference. Its derivation is shown in Table 3.1, where R represents the determinant for Round seeds, r for wrinkled, Y for Yellow and y for green. Mendel assumed that at pollen formation in the F_1 plants, pollen-grains with the four possible combinations of the two pairs of factors, that is, RY, Ry, rY, ry, arise with equal frequency, and similarly at egg-cell formation. Mendel also assumed that fertilization is at random between the different kinds of pollen and egg-cells. It then follows, as indicated in Table 3.1, that on the average $\frac{9}{16}$ of the combinations will carry both R and Y, $\frac{3}{16}$ will carry R but not Y, $\frac{3}{16}$ Y but not R, and $\frac{1}{16}$ neither R nor Y.

TABLE 3.1 The proportions of progeny of different kinds expected in F_2 from a cross between pure-breeding strains differing in two characters, on Mendel's hypothesis that in the double heterozygote the four possible combinations of two pairs of factors arise with equal frequency, both in the formation of the pollen and of the egg-cells, and that fertilization is at random. R = factor for Round, r for wrinkled, Y for Yellow, y for green seeds in *Pisum sativum*. (*a*) Individual frequencies. (*b*) Totals.

(*a*)

Reproducive Cells from F_1 Heterozygote		Pollen			
		RY 1	Ry 1	ry 1	rY 1
Egg-cells	RY 1	$RRYY$ 1	$RRYy$ 1	$RrYy$ 1	$RrYY$ 1
	Ry 1	$RRYy$ 1	$RRyy$ 1	$Rryy$ 1	$RrYy$ 1
	ry 1	$RrYy$ 1	$Rryy$ 1	$rryy$ 1	$rrYy$ 1
	rY 1	$RrYY$ 1	$RrYy$ 1	$rrYy$ 1	$rrYY$ 1

(*b*)

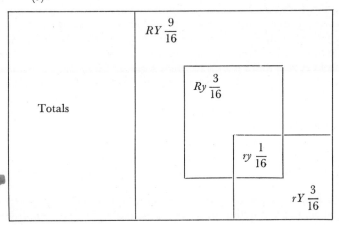

Totals

$RY \dfrac{9}{16}$

$Ry \dfrac{3}{16}$

$ry \dfrac{1}{16}$

$rY \dfrac{3}{16}$

Mendel confirmed this hypothesis in two ways. Firstly, he bred from his F_2 plants, and showed that the Round Yellow, Round green and wrinkled Yellow peas consisted of the appropriate mixture of pure-breeding and impure types and moreover in the appropriate proportions, while the wrinkled green peas bred true. Secondly he backcrossed the F_1 plants to the parental forms, and demonstrated that such crosses gave a $1:1:1:1$ ratio in the progeny. Thus Round Yellow F_1 crossed with wrinkled green gave a progeny of 55 Round Yellow, 51 Round green, 49 wrinkled Yellow, and 53 wrinkled green seeds.

When Mendel's work was rediscovered, confirmation of the independence of inheritance of different character-differences was immediately available. Thus, De Vries (1900) reported an approximation to a $9:3:3:1$ ratio in F_2 from a cross between a white trifoliate and a red quinquefoliate strain of *Trifolium pratense* (Red Clover), the latter two characters being dominant; and von Tschermak had unknowingly confirmed Mendel's results for Round Yellow and wrinkled green Peas. Bateson and Saunders (1902) established $9:3:3:1$ ratios in F_2 in respect of flower-colour and fruit prickliness in *Datura* (Thorn Apple), and in respect of type of comb and number of toes, and other pairs of character-differences, in *Gallus domesticus*.

§ 3.3 Bateson, Saunders and Punnett's discovery of partial linkage

Bateson, Saunders and Punnett (1905), working with *Lathyrus odoratus* (Sweet Pea) were the first to discover an exception to the law of independence. In an F_2 progeny 381 plants with coloured petals comprised 305 with a purple pigment and 76 with a red pigment. These figures are a rather poor fit with a $3:1$ ratio, but later work established this ratio, indicating that purple differs from red by a single dominant factor. The plants also showed diversity in respect of another character-difference, namely, shape of pollen-grain, whether elongated (long) or disc-shaped (round). This character-difference had been chosen for study in the hope (unavailing as it transpired) that it might reveal more precisely when segregation of character-differences took place, for Mendel had postulated its occurrence at the time of formation of the pollen and egg-cells. However, all the pollen-grains on any individual plant were found always to be alike.* By a coincidence, the 381 plants showed the same proportion with the two different shapes of pollen (305 long, 76 round) as for the two different flower colours. Although the fit with a $3:1$ ratio is poor, later work confirmed its truth, and hence established that long-pollened plants differ from round-pollened by a single dominant factor.

When the 381 plants were classified simultaneously for pigment colour and pollen shape, a startling discovery was made. The relative frequencies of the four classes were quite different from those expected on the basis of all

* Pollen characters do not always behave like this—see § 5.4.

previous work. The results obtained were:

284 (74·6%) with Purple flowers and Long pollen
21 (5·5%) with Purple flowers and round pollen
21 (5·5%) with red flowers and Long pollen
and   55 (14·4%) with red flowers and round pollen.

More precise frequencies, based on 6952 F_2 plants derived from the same cross (Purple Long × red round) gave:

4831 (69·5%) Purple Long
390 (5·6%) Purple round
393 (5·6%) red Long
and   1338 (19·3%) red round   (Punnett, 1917).

This *coupling* of 'Purple' with 'Long' (the two dominant characters), as Bateson, Saunders and Punnett called it, implies that at the time of pollen

TABLE 3.2   The proportions of progeny of different kinds expected in F_2 from a cross between pure-breeding strains of *Lathyrus odoratus* with purple flowers and long pollen and with red flowers and round pollen on the assumption that reproductive cells of constitution *PL* and *pl* each have a frequency of 44%, and *Pl* and *pL* of 6%, and with fertilization at random. P = factor for Purple, p for red flowers; L for Long, l for round pollen. (*a*) Individual frequencies. (*b*) Totals.

(*a*)

Reproductive Cells from F_1 Heterozygote			Pollen			
			PL 4·4	*Pl* 0·6	*pl* 4·4	*pL* 0·6
	PL	4·4	19·36%	2·64%	19·36%	2·64%
Egg-cells	*Pl*	0·6	2·64%	0·36%	2·64%	0·36%
	pl	4·4	19·36%	2·64%	19·36%	2·64%
	pL	0·6	2·64%	0·36%	2·64%	0·36%

(*b*)

Totals	*PL* 69·36%		
		Pl 5·64%	
			pl 19·36%
			pL 5·64%

and egg-cell formation in the F_1 plants, the four different combinations of the factors P (Purple) and p (red flower-colour), and L (long) and l (round pollen) do not arise with equal frequency, but that PL and pl are of appreciably higher frequency than the other two combinations (Pl and pL). Frequencies of 44% for each of PL and pl, and of 6% for Pl and pL, instead of the 25% for each which Mendel would have expected, were found (Haldane, 1919) to give a close fit with the data from the 6952 plants (see Table 3.2).

As Bateson, Saunders and Punnett continued their breeding work with *Lathyrus odoratus*, several other examples of such *partial linkage* between different character-differences were soon found. The cause of partial linkage will be discussed in Chapter 7.

§3.4   Doncaster and Raynor's discovery of sex-linkage

Linkage of another kind, in which two of the four possible ways of associating two character-differences appeared not to arise at all, was discovered

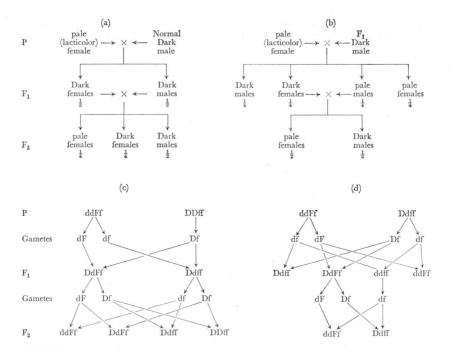

FIGURE 3.1   Doncaster and Raynor's results ((a) and (b)) from study of the inheritance of the pale (*lacticolor*) form of *Abraxas grossulariata* (Magpie Moth), and Punnett and Bateson's hypothesis ((c) and (d)) to explain them. D = dominant factor for normal Dark form of the moth, d = recessive allele for pale form, F = dominant factor for Femaleness, f = recessive allele for maleness. The hypothesis was later modified: see §6.11.

by Doncaster and Raynor (1906) working with *Abraxas grossulariata* (Magpie Moth). They studied the inheritance of a pale form of this moth called *lacticolor*, which first appeared in a female individual. They established that the pale character behaved as a normal Mendelian recessive, disappearing in F_1 and reappearing in one quarter of the F_2 and in one half of the back-cross progeny, that is, the progeny from crossing the F_1 males (normal) with their mother (pale) (see Fig. 3.1(*a*) and (*b*)). However, the following results were unexpected:

(i) The quarter of the F_2 which were pale were all female, and hence resembled their grandmother (Fig. 3.1(*a*)).
(ii) Pale males from the backcross progeny, when crossed with their normal sisters, gave only pale females and normal males (the grandparental forms), instead of equal numbers of each form in each sex (Fig. 3.1(*b*)).

Earlier work by Cuénot with albino *Mus* and by Bateson and Punnett with comb characters in *Gallus* had always shown character-differences to be equally distributed between the sexes, so this *sex-linkage* in *Abraxas* was unexpected.

For linkage between two pairs of characters (factors A/a and B/b) to be detected it is necessary to have an individual heterozygous for both char-acter-differences, in order to provide the four possible kinds of gamete (AB, ab, Ab, aB). Hence, to explain Doncaster and Raynor's results, in addition to accepting that the pale form is recessive, Punnett and Bateson (1908) made two postulates:

(1) Sex in *Abraxas* is a Mendelian character, with femaleness dominant to maleness, such that all Females are heterozygous for the sex factors (Ff), and all males are the homozygous recessive (ff).

The 1:1 ratio of the sexes in each generation was thereby explained, and the normal females, which provide one parent for both the aberrant progenies (i) and (ii) above, would be the double heterozygote, $DdFf$, where D is the dominant factor for the normal Dark insect and d the recessive factor for paleness.

(2) The double heterozygote ($DdFf$) produces eggs of only two kinds, bearing the factors for Dark male (Df) and for pale Female (dF), respectively, the other two combinations (DF and df) not being pro-duced, for some unknown reason.

Punnett and Bateson spoke of this kind of linkage as *repulsion* since the dominant factors stayed apart, and as complete linkage unlike the partial linkage of the *Lathyrus* example discussed earlier. Their hypothesis was found to explain satisfactorily the sex linkage data in Doncaster and Raynor's results (see Fig. 3.1(*c*) and (*d*)).

However, shortly afterwards, Doncaster (1908) made a remarkable discovery. He found that whenever a pale male was crossed with a normal Dark female, all the male offspring were normal and all the females pale.

This was true even when the normal female parent came from a part of the country where the rare pale form had never been seen. This result was totally unexpected as it implied, on Punnett and Bateson's hypothesis, that all female Magpie Moths were heterozygous for the pale character! As will be shown in § 6.11, their hypothesis was later modified so as to make this unlikely deduction unnecessary.

Morgan (1910) reported results with *Drosophila melanogaster* (Fruit Fly) essentially similar to those of Doncaster and Raynor with *Abraxas*, except in one important respect. Morgan studied the inheritance of white eye-colour in *Drosophila* and found this to differ from the normal dull red eyes by a single recessive factor. The white-eyed condition first appeared in a male individual, unlike *Abraxas* where, as already mentioned, the pale form first appeared in a female. This difference was reflected throughout the inheritance studies on the white-eyed condition in *Drosophila*, where the role of the sexes appeared to be exactly reversed compared with *Abraxas*. To explain these results, Morgan put forward an hypothesis identical to that of Punnett and Bateson for *Abraxas*, except that the position of the sexes was reversed, that is, maleness was regarded as dominant to femaleness and the male *Drosophila* was postulated to be heterozygous for the sex factors, instead of the female *Abraxas*. Furthermore, Morgan found that when a white-eyed female *Drosophila* was crossed with a normal Red-eyed male, even if the latter came from an unrelated stock with no known ancestry of white eyes, the progeny always consisted of Red-eyed females and white-eyed males. This was the exact counterpart of Doncaster's discovery with *Abraxas* and implied that all normal red-eyed *Drosophila* males were heterozygous for white eyes! As with *Abraxas*, the hypothesis was subsequently modified to eliminate this unlikely deduction (see § 6.11).

§ 3.5   Conclusion

In spite of a number of exceptions such as those just described, Mendel's hypothesis of independent inheritance of the determinants for different characters was found to hold quite widely, and ultimately was christened 'Mendel's Second Law' by Morgan (1919), the 'First Law' being the fundamental concept of the coming together of the determinants for a particular character-difference at fertilization, and their separating again unchanged at gamete formation.

4. The hypothesis of Mendelian inheritance for characters showing a continuous range of variation

§ 4.1 The analysis of quantitative data

The method which Mendel used so successfully to obtain information about the mechanism of heredity was to find a well-marked character-difference in the chosen organism and to cross pure-breeding strains of each kind. The method is clearly dependent on the existence of sharply defined character-differences. However, many characters are not suitable because they do not reveal clear-cut discontinuities. The most familiar

TABLE 4.1 Johannsen's data for the weight-class of 5494 F_2 beans (seeds of *Phaseolus vulgaris*), obtained by self-pollination for two successive generations of 19 beans of diverse origin.

Weight-class in Centigrams	5–15	15–25	25–35	35–45	45–55	55–65	65–75	75–85	85–95
Number of Beans	5	38	370	1676	2255	928	187	33	2

examples of characters which in most organisms commonly show a continuous range of variation are size measurements such as height or weight. In order to study the inheritance of such characters statistical methods are required. Before describing some of the results obtained from study of the inheritance of characters showing a continuous range of variation, it is necessary to consider the techniques for analysing quantitative data. Only a superficial account is given below of a few statistical methods. For a sound treatment of these and other methods, reference should be made to standard works such as Fisher (1963), Bailey (1959) or Snedecor (1956).

Data of Johannsen (1909) for the weight of dwarf bean (*Phaseolus vulgaris*) seeds will be used as an illustration. He weighed 5494 beans and classified them into 9 categories depending on their weight (see Table 4.1). Such data can be plotted as a frequency histogram, as illustrated in Fig. 4.1. Such histograms for biological data commonly approximate to a smooth curve of a

FIGURE 4.1   Frequency histogram for bean weight in *Phaseolus vulgaris* from the data of Johannsen. The number of beans is plotted as ordinate and the weight in centigrams as abscissa. A normal curve has been fitted to the data.

particular kind called the *normal* curve. Non-biological data also frequently fit a normal curve, for example, the frequencies of different numbers of 'heads' (or 'tails') after repeatedly tossing a number of coins simultaneously. With a small number of coins, a stepped graph (histogram) is obtained approximating to the 'binomial distribution' (Fig. 4.2(*a*)), but as the number of coins tossed simultaneously is increased the graph of number of 'heads' (or 'tails') in the throw plotted against the frequency of occurrence of that number approaches the smooth curve of the 'normal distribution' (Fig. 4.2(*b*) and (*c*)). With the coins, whether a 'head' or a 'tail' shall turn up depends on a number of causes which in the long run act with equal frequency in two opposite directions. Similarly, bean weight may be supposed to depend on many factors, such as the position of the seed in the pod, the fertility of the soil and the hereditary constitution of the plant, which again may be supposed on the average to act equally in two directions, some favouring an increased and some a decreased weight.

A set of data which show an approximately normal distribution, such as bean weight in Johannsen's experiment, may be specified by two quantities: firstly, the *mean*, which is the sum of the measurements divided by the total number; and secondly, the *variance* (or its square root, the *standard deviation*) which are measures of the extent to which the various measurements differ from the mean value. The variance is calculated by finding the deviation of each individual measurement from the mean value, squaring each deviation, then summing these squared values, and dividing by the total number of measurements (or strictly speaking, by one less than this total number). On the normal curve, the standard deviation is represented by the horizontal distance from the position of the mean to the point of steepest slope of the curve on either side. Thus a wide curve, implying considerable variability in the quantity measured, will have a correspondingly large standard deviation. However, the area under the curve measured out as far as the standard deviation on each side is always the same fraction of the total area under the curve, namely 68·26% or approximately $\frac{2}{3}$. This means that $\frac{2}{3}$ of the observations will differ from the mean by less than the standard deviation, and the remaining $\frac{1}{3}$ will exceed it.

A further quantity of use in the analysis of quantitative data is the *co-variance*. Suppose pairs of related measurements are available, such as heights of a number of men and of one adult daughter of each of them. Data on human stature usually fit a normal distribution. The covariance of fathers' and daughters' height is obtained by the same method as for variance except that instead of squaring deviations, the deviation of each father's height from the fathers' mean is multiplied by the deviation of the corresponding daughter's height from the daughters' mean. A positive value for the covariance means that on the average when the fathers are tall so are the daughters, and when the fathers are short so are the daughters. A negative value would mean that tall fathers tend to have short daughters, and *vice versa*. If the covariance is zero, a tall father is equally likely to have a tall or short daughter. The co-variance of fathers' and daughters' height divided by the vaiance of the fathers is called the *regression coefficient* of daughters on fathers; if the covariance is divided by the variance of the daughters, this is the *regression coefficient* of fathers on daughters; and if the covariance is divided by the geometric mean (that is, the square root of the product) of the

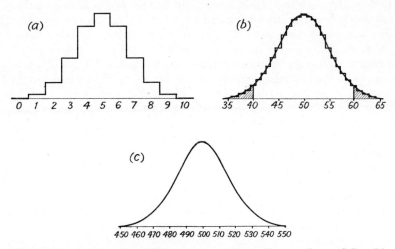

FIGURE 4.2   Frequency histograms or curves for numbers of 'heads' (or 'tails') when (*a*) 10, (*b*) 100, and (*c*) 1000 coins are tossed simultaneously. In (*b*) the shaded areas indicate the probability of obtaining 60 heads and 40 tails or a larger deviation from equality.

two variances (the fathers' and the daughters'), this gives the *correlation coefficient* of the fathers' and daughters' heights. These three coefficients are all measures of the degree of association between the two variables. A value of zero for the correlation coefficient means no association, of $+1$ means complete positive association, and -1 complete negative association. Intermediate values between -1 and 0 and between 0 and $+1$ would indicate the appropriate degree of association between the fathers' and daughters' heights.

§ 4.2　The significance of experimental data

The fact that data from the tossing of coins (in sufficient numbers) fit a normal distribution illustrates how the effects of chance can be assessed in testing the significance of experimental data in biology (and elsewhere). Suppose 100 coins are tossed simultaneously. Assuming the coins are not biassed, 50 heads and 50 tails is the most likely result, but there are so many other possibilities such as 49 heads and 51 tails, or 52 heads and 48 tails, that are individually only slightly less likely to occur, that in fact one would be surprised if in a single throw exact equality were achieved. Indeed, on the average 50 heads and 50 tails is expected only about once in every seven or eight throws of 100 coins. The likelihood of each alternative turning up can be precisely calculated. Now suppose at the first toss 60 heads and 40 tails are found. Is this a reasonable result, or should one suspect that the coins are biassed? The probability of this particular ratio turning up by chance is obviously quite low, but this has no significance because, as just indicated, there are so many possible alternative ratios that the probabilities are low for all of them. In order to judge the significance of the 60:40 ratio it is necessary to group together the alternatives, and consider the probability of getting by chance not only 60 heads and 40 tails, but all ratios showing a deviation from 50:50 as great or greater than the one observed, such as 61 heads and 39 tails, 62 heads and 38 tails, 40 heads and 60 tails, and so on. To find this probability is equivalent to finding the area under the tails of the normal curve (that is, the sum of the two shaded regions in Fig. 4.2(b)) compared with the total area under the curve, since as already indicated coin data as extensive as these tend to fit a normal curve.

Statisticians have derived formulae and tables to enable one to calculate the approximate area under the tails of the normal curve in specific instances with the minimum of trouble. The most generally useful method is that developed by Pearson (1900). It involves calculating a variance ratio called *khi squared* (χ^2). To calculate χ^2, take each observed frequency, find its deviation from expectation, square this deviation and divide by the expected value, and then sum the figures so obtained. In the present instance, the observed frequencies are 60 and 40, the expected 50 and 50, so the deviations are 10 and 10, and $\dfrac{(\text{deviation})^2}{\text{expected}}$ is $\dfrac{100}{50} = 2$ in each instance, and $\chi^2 = 4$. One must then refer to a table showing the values of χ^2 associated with particular areas under the tails of the normal curve. From the way in which

χ^2 is calculated, it is evident that the larger the difference between observed and expected values the larger will χ^2 be, and hence the smaller the area in question. Moreover, since χ^2 is obtained by adding a series of numbers one for each class, in general, the larger the number of classes the larger the value of χ^2. Evidently the number of classes must be taken into account in finding the area under the tails. In the table of χ^2 values (Table 4.2), the quantity n in the first column is one less than the number of classes (technically n is the number of degrees of freedom, or the number of classes which can be filled up arbitrarily). In the present example there were two classes (heads and tails) and hence $n = 1$. The value 4 for χ^2 in the $n = 1$ row of the table corresponds to $P = 0.05$ approximately. In other words, the two

TABLE 4.2
Table of χ^2
(based on Fisher (1963) by permission of Oliver and Boyd.)

n	P								
	0·99	0·98	0·95	0·90	0·50	0·10	0·05	0·02	0·01
1	0·00016	0·00063	0·0039	0·016	0·46	2·7	3·8	5·4	6·6
2	0·020	0·040	0.10	0·21	1·4	4·6	6·0	7·8	9·2
3	0·12	0·19	0·35	0·58	2·4	6·3	7·8	9·8	11·3

shaded areas under the tails of the normal curve in Fig. 4.2(*b*) represent in total approximately $\frac{1}{20}$ ($\frac{1}{40}$ each) of the total area under the curve. Thus once in 20 times of throwing 100 coins one can expect to obtain a deviation from equality at least as large as 60:40. It is usual to say that a 1 in 20 probability such as this indicates a suspiciously large departure from expectation and to describe the deviation as significant. However, if one made the deduction that the coins were biassed there is a distinct possibility that one would be wrong since with unbiassed coins this deviation is equalled or exceeded once in every 20 times purely by chance. Thus a probability of 0·05 suggests further experimenting is needed, before reaching a conclusion as to whether the hypothesis of 1:1 for heads:tails is true or not. A deviation giving a P value of 0·05 is equal to approximately twice the standard deviation.

§ 4.3 The significance of Mendel's data

In Chapter 2 Mendel's results were quoted from a back-cross of heterozygous Yellow peas with green peas. The expected ratio of Yellow:green peas in the progeny is 1:1. The situation is therefore strictly comparable to the example given above of tossing coins, and the effects of chance can be assessed in the same way. Thus, in one of the experiments quoted, Mendel found 58 Yellow and 52 green peas in the progeny. It was taken for granted in Chapter 2 that this was a satisfactory fit with a 1:1 ratio, but strictly speaking the χ^2 test ought to be applied in order to confirm this. The expected frequency in each class is 55, the deviation is 3 and so

$$\chi^2 = \frac{9}{55} \times 2 = 0\cdot33.$$

Reference to Table 4.2 shows that for $n = 1$, the probability of getting a deviation as large or larger than the observed one is between 0·5 and 0·9. In other words, more often than not one would expect a bigger difference from 1:1 purely by chance, and the data agree very well with the hypothesis.

The χ^2 test can also be applied when the expected frequencies of the classes are unequal. Thus, Mendel's F_2 data discussed in Chapter 2 are expected on his hypothesis to fit a 3:1 ratio. The observed frequencies for the seed colours were 6022 Yellow and 2001 green. The expected frequencies are 6017·25 and 2005·75 respectively. The deviation is 4·75 for each class and

$$\chi^2 = \frac{(4\cdot75)^2}{6017\cdot25} + \frac{(4\cdot75)^2}{2005\cdot75} = 0\cdot015.$$

Referring again to Table 4.2, for $n = 1$ the likelihood of getting a deviation as large or larger than that observed is approximately 0·9. Thus only once in 10 times would one expect to get so good a fit with the expected ratio.

The χ^2 method can also be used when the number of classes is more than two. Thus, Mendel's F_2 data quoted in Chapter 3 for the Round/wrinkled and Yellow/green character-differences were 315, 101, 108 and 32 in the four classes, where the expected frequencies on the hypothesis of a 9:3:3:1 ratio are 312·75, 104·25, 104·25 and 34·75 respectively. The deviations of the observed from the expected values are 2·25, 3·25, 3·75 and 2·75, respectively, and

$$\chi^2 = \frac{(2\cdot25)^2}{312\cdot75} + \frac{(3\cdot25)^2}{104\cdot25} + \frac{(3\cdot75)^2}{104\cdot25} + \frac{(2\cdot75)^2}{34\cdot75} = 0\cdot47.$$

Referring to Table 4.2, when $n = 3$, $P = 0\cdot90 - 0\cdot95$, implying a close fit with the hypothesis. Indeed 14 times out of 15 a larger deviation is expected by chance.

This finding points to a remarkable feature of Mendel's data discovered by Fisher (1936), namely, that Mendel's results taken as a whole fit the expected ratios better than they should! When the χ^2 test is applied to the results of his individual experiments, the probability values obtained usually lie between 0·5 and 0·95 as in the three examples just discussed. Individually, these are acceptable, but when one considers the data in the aggregate one's suspicions are aroused. For, with a series of experiments, the P values must on the average fall below 0·5 as often as above, assuming the data fit the hypothesis. From each experiment one reaches the conclusion that more often than not one would expect a bigger difference than that observed. Mendel's work was conducted on such a massive scale that the cumulative effect of the many experiments, each individually fitting the theory slightly better than expected on the average, is to produce an aggregate set of data which is exceedingly unlikely to be valid. Thus, Fisher found that Mendel's total data give a P value of 0·99993, or in other words only once in some 14,300 times would one expect to get so good a fit with expectation purely by chance!

This extraordinary discovery naturally raises the question of whether Mendel in fact carried out the experiments he describes! Fisher found that many points of detail were entirely consistent with the belief that Mendel did do what he says he did. Thus, the number of plants he would have to have grown in each year was reasonable for the size of the monastery garden at Brno (Brünn); and the scoring of embryo characters in the seed, such as yellow and green, covered an extra generation compared with mature characters, like tall and dwarf, as expected since the former but not the latter character-difference can be observed without germinating the seeds.

Accepting that Mendel conducted the experiments which he describes, why did he adjust the frequencies of progeny a little nearer to the theoretical values? Here a second puzzling feature of Mendel's paper may provide a clue. Fisher has pointed out that although Mendel's first experiments were with strains of peas differing by single characters (as described in Chapter 2), yet commercial varieties of peas, with which he started, always differ by many characters. The published experiments covered five years (1859–1863 inclusive), although Mendel states that the paper is the result of eight seasons' work. It is evident that the earlier work (1856–1858 inclusive), during which the strains differing by single characters were obtained, was never published. Fisher suggests that it was on the basis of these unpublished experiments, estimated to have involved the growing of nearly 7000 pea plants, that Mendel must have framed the entire theory of heredity. At the latest this would have been when he reviewed his 1859 results. The gigantic series of experiments upon which he then embarked, involving over the succeeding five years the cultivation, in Fisher's estimation, of over 26,500 plants and forming the basis of his classic paper, is then seen as a carefully planned demonstration of the conclusions which he had already reached before the outset. The slight adjusting of frequencies would then presumably have been done in order to make the conclusions a little more obvious. In this he was singularly unsuccessful, for no-one in his lifetime saw the significance of his epoch-making discovery. Even if the adjusted figures in his paper now make the recognition of the underlying mechanism look simple, yet Mendel himself would clearly not have had this advantage when he inferred that inheritance was particulate, with segregation at gamete-formation! His brilliant discovery, probably made in the very year that Darwin's 'The Origin of Species' was published, apparently remained unknown to Darwin and was not confirmed by anyone for 40 years.

§ 4.4 Further uses of the khi squared test

Mendel's results have been taken as an example of data which give an exceptionally high probability value with the χ^2 test. In general, P values within the range 0·1 to 0·9 cause no suspicion and indicate that the observations fit the hypothesis under test, although they may of course also fit other hypotheses. Values of 0·05 or less are conventionally said to indicate a real discrepancy, although this is quite an arbitrary line of demarcation and one would less often be misled if one took lower figures such as 0·02 or 0·01 as the significance level. Conversely values of 0.95 or more indicate an abnormally close fit with hypothesis, while probabilities as high as 0·98 or 0·99 would certainly arouse suspicion that, either consciously or unconsciously, the data had become biassed in favour of the hypothesis.

The χ^2 test can still be used when one does not know the expected proportions of the classes, but wishes to know whether the observed frequencies are in the same proportion following different treatments. Where there are two classes a and b and two treatments 1 and 2, the four observed frequencies may be denoted by a_1, b_1, a_2 and b_2 respectively. Then χ^2 is given by the expression

$$\frac{(a_1 + b_1 + a_2 + b_2)(a_1b_2 - a_2b_1)^2}{(a_1 + b_1)(a_2 + b_2)(a_1 + a_2)(b_1 + b_2)} \quad \text{and} \quad n = 1.$$

The application of this formula is called the *contingency* χ^2 test, and examples of its use are given in § 7.5 and § 8.6.

If the observed frequency in any class is less than 5, the χ^2 test becomes so inaccurate as a means of estimating the area under the tails of the normal curve that it should not be used. However, Yates (1934) pointed out that when there is only one degree of freedom $(n = 1)$, reasonable accuracy is restored if one adds 0·5 to the smaller observed value and subtracts 0·5 from the larger one before applying the test. With the contingency test there will be two small values and 0·5 should be added to each, and similarly there will be two large values from each of which 0·5 should be subtracted. An example showing the application of Yates' correction is given in § 4.8.

§ 4.5   Galton's and Pearson's studies on the inheritance of characters showing continuous variation

One of the first applications of statistical methods to the study of the inheritance of characters showing continuous variation was made by Galton (1889). His method was to obtain data on the attributes of relatives, notably in *Homo sapiens*, and then calculate regression and correlation coefficients. He obtained the data in several ways, but chiefly by offering prizes to anyone who would send in detailed particulars of their parents, grandparents, great-grandparents, brothers, sisters, uncles, aunts, great-uncles and great-aunts. The information asked for included stature, eye-colour, artistic aptitude, health and temperament. Data were received for about 150 families and concerned over 1000 individuals.

From the data on stature he obtained evidence of positive association between relatives. As one would expect, the parental and fraternal relationships gave the highest values for the coefficients, and cousins the lowest. He thus obtained the first sound evidence that human stature is to some extent an inherited character. Moreover, the coefficients for the two sexes did not differ significantly, indicating that their contributions to heredity were equal. From the values of the correlation coefficients he deduced that on the average a child receives $\frac{1}{4}$ of its heritage of stature from its two parents (total $\frac{1}{2}$), $\frac{1}{16}$ from each of its four grandparents (total $\frac{1}{4}$), and so on. This geometric scale continued indefinitely backwards would account for the total heritage. He found evidence that the other attributes for which he had data were inherited similarly. Later he called this geometric series of contributions the 'law of ancestral heredity'.

Pearson (1897) extended Galton's work in a number of ways, using his data. Thus, he showed that in assessing the significance of the correlation coefficients for human stature, allowance must be made for assortive mating, for it was evident from the data that tall husbands tend to have tall wives, and short husbands short wives. For some characters the marital correlation is remarkably high: for instance, Penrose (1963) has shown that for intelligence it may be as high as 0·5. Pearson and Lee (1903) collected further data on human stature in several hundred families, by the same means as Galton had done. They also obtained data on arm-span and elbow to finger-tip distances. For stature, the parental and fraternal correlation coefficients were 0·51 and 0·54 respectively; for arm-span they were 0·45 and 0·54 respectively; and for the forearm measurements they were 0·42 and 0·46 respectively*. It will be noted that in each instance the fraternal correlation is greater than the parental. Pearson and Lee's figures for both the parental and fraternal correlation coefficients for stature are appreciably larger than those which Galton had obtained.

Galton and Pearson also made statistical studies on the inheritance of characters such as coat colour in *Canis familiaris* (Dog) and *Equus caballus* (Horse), using the information in pedigree records. They found that the correlation coefficients were similar to those in man.

§ 4.6 The multiple factor hypothesis

With the rediscovery of Mendel's work, Bateson and Saunders (1902) raised the possibility that characters showing a continuous range of variation, such as human stature, might be determined by a large number of Mendelian factors. Pearson (1904) analysed this possibility mathematically, assuming that all the postulated Mendelian factors had equal and additive effects, and that there was complete dominance of each over its recessive allele when heterozygous, and that the two alleles of a pair were equally frequent. He found that, however many pairs of alleles were postulated, the expected parental correlation was 0·33 and the fraternal 0·42. Since these values did not agree with his observed values, he concluded that the Mendelian explanation was incorrect. Yule (1907) pointed out that the assumption of complete dominance was not necessarily justified, and that if the heterozygotes were intermediate between the homozygous dominants and the recessives, higher values of the correlation coefficients would be expected, such as had been found. However, much confusion of thought on the applicability of Mendelian heredity to continuous variation persisted until Johannsen (1909)

* The weighted means are given, as calculated by Fisher (1918).

published the results of his experiments with *Phaseolus vulgaris* (Dwarf Bean) and other plants, and drew for the first time a clear distinction between the hereditary determinant, or *gene*, as he called it, and its effect.

§ 4.7   Johannsen's experiments with *Phaseolus vulgaris*

Johannsen (1903) introduced the term 'pure line' for the progeny of single individuals in organisms which are regularly self-fertilised. Examples of such organisms are *Hordeum vulgare* (Barley), *Lathyrus odoratus* (Sweet Pea) and *Phaseolus vulgaris*. He found that the weights of the seeds of the members of a pure line of *P. vulgaris* fitted a normal curve, but whether he selected heavy, medium or light beans, the progeny of each by self-fertilisation in the succeeding year again fitted a normal curve, and moreover they all had the same mean value. In other words, within a pure line selection for heavy or light seeds had no effect: the mean weight remained constant. Thus, his pure line no. 2 gave him in the year 1901 beans ranging in weight from about 40 to 70 centigrams. He classified them into four groups according to their weight (35–45, 45–55, 55–65, and 65–75 cg) and the following year he sowed each group separately. Those in the 35–45 cg class produced 86 seeds in 1902, and they showed a normal distribution about a mean weight of 57·2 cg. Those in the 45–55 cg class (1901 seed) gave 195 seeds in 1902 with a mean of 54·9 cg. Similarly the 55–65 cg class gave 120 seeds of mean weight 56·5 cg and the 65–75 cg class produced 74 seeds with mean weight 55·5 cg. The mean weights of the seeds produced by the various classes clearly do not differ significantly. He concluded that the variation in bean weight within a pure line was entirely due to environmental factors such as the position of the seed in the pod.

Johannsen studied 19 different pure lines of *Phaseolus vulgaris*. Each had been obtained from a different source, and had a characteristic mean weight of seed ranging from 64·2 cg in no. 1 down to 35·1 cg in no. 19. Within each pure line he obtained results similar to those described above for no. 2. Each gave a normal distribution of bean weight about its characteristic mean value. Within a pure line selection for heavy seeds had no effect on succeeding generations.

The total population of bean seeds under observation also gave a normal distribution, with a mean of 47·9 cg (Table 4.1 and Fig. 4.1). This population was a mixture of the 19 pure lines. Selection for heavy beans within this population would produce a response, because one would tend to pick out seeds from the heavier pure lines and hence put up the average weight the following year. Selection would continue to have an effect until all the seeds belonged to the heaviest pure line, but thereafter it would be ineffective in stepping up the mean weight further.

Johannsen's work demonstrated the distinction between variation due to hereditary factors and that due to environmental factors. He coined the term *genotype* for the hereditary constitution of an individual, and *phenotype* for the appearance of the individual as a consequence of the interaction of genotype and environment. Thus a bean seed might be heavy, say of 60 cg,

as a consequence of favourable environmental conditions during development, even though belonging to, say, pure line no. 15 with a mean weight
of only 45·0 cg. Conversely, a bean of the same weight might belong to pure
line no. 1 grown under rather unfavourable conditions. Both beans would be
said to have the same phenotype, but the genotypic and environmental
contributions to this end-result would have acted in opposite directions in the
two examples. It is evident that the two kinds of variation, genetic and
environmental, cannot be distinguished by observation but only by experiment. Thus, it is necessary to study the progeny of two beans before one
can determine whether they belong to the same pure line or not. Differences
in genotype were responsible for differences in mean seed weight of the order
of 30 cg between the most extreme pure lines. This difference is of about
the same magnitude as the variation in weight within pure lines due to
environmental factors. It is evident that in a mixed population of a number
of pure lines the variation due the the environment will wholly obscure the
discontinuities in mean weight of the different lines, and give rise to a
continuous range of variation.

Johannsen was able to demonstrate the respective contributions of heredity
and environment to variation by choosing an organism in which, owing to
the regular self-fertilisation, many individuals have the same genetic constitution. In most organisms, where cross-fertilisation is the rule, it is more
difficult to distinguish the two kinds of variation. Nevertheless there is every
reason to suppose that the concepts of genotype and phenotype developed
by Johannsen with *Phaseolus vulgaris* are of general application. They are of
particular importance in plant and animal breeding, since his work showed
that selection for favourable characters in an organism will be unsuccessful
unless the character-difference in question has a genetic basis and is not
merely a consequence of favourable environmental conditions. Thus a first
essential in crop and livestock improvement is to have available sources of
hereditary variability such as strains of the organism from different regions
of the world, or allied species which will give fertile hybrids with that which
is being bred.

§ 4.8   Confirmation of the multiple factor hypothesis

From studies on crop plants, Nilsson-Ehle (1909) and East (1910) obtained
evidence in support of the multiple factor hypothesis to explain the inheritance of quantitative characters. Nilsson-Ehle had been studying the
inheritance of glume and ligule characters in *Avena sativa* (Oats) and of ear
and grain pigmentation in *Triticum aestivum* (Wheat). In *Avena* he found that
black glumes usually behaved as a simple Mendelian dominant to white
glumes, when strains with these characters were crossed, but in one instance
he obtained 630 plants with black and 40 with greyish-white glumes in F_2
from such a cross. He pointed out that this ratio approximated to 15:1
(expected frequencies 625·3 and 44·7, deviations 4·7, $\chi^2 = 0.53$, $n = 1$,
$P = 0.5$ approximately), and so could be regarded as a 9:3:3:1 ratio in

which the first three classes looked alike. Hence he postulated that the two strains differed by two independently-inherited genes, such that each alone or both together produced a black pigment in the glumes. Similarly, with ear pigmentation in *Triticum*, a brown variety crossed with white gave brown in F_1, and usually a 3:1 ratio of brown to white in F_2, but with winter wheats he obtained 15:1 ratios in F_2.

Nilsson-Ehle also crossed strains of *Triticum* having a red pericarp (which is maternal tissue surrounding the seed) with others having a white pericarp. All the crosses gave a red F_1 and some gave 3:1 ratios of red:white in F_2. However, a cross between an old red variety called Swedish Velvet-wheat and a white variety, produced only red plants in both F_1 and F_2. This unexpected result led him to obtain an F_3 generation by self-fertilisation of the 78 F_2 plants. He found that 8 of the 78 gave a 3:1 ratio in F_3 (aggregate frequencies 307 red, 97 white); 15 gave a 15:1 ratio (total progeny 727 red, 53 white); 5 gave a 63:1 ratio (total progeny 324 red, 6 white); and the remaining 50 F_2 plants bred true, giving in total 2317 red progeny. The 63:1 ratio is what is expected if 3 independently inherited pairs of alleles are segregating simultaneously and each of the dominants A, B and C, has the same effect. Nilsson-Ehle suggested that there were three such dominant genes responsible for the red pericarp colour in Velvet-wheat and that the white variety with which it was crossed carried the recessive alleles a, b and c. One would then expect a 63:1 ratio in F_2, with which the 78:0 ratio observed is in satisfactory agreement. (For the χ^2 test it is necessary to apply Yates' correction, since one of the observed frequencies is less than 5. The 'corrected' observed frequencies are 77·5 and 0·5, the expected frequencies on the 63:1 hypothesis are 76·8 and 1·2 respectively. Hence the deviations are 0·7 each, $\chi^2 = 0·41$, $n = 1$ and $P = 0·5$ approximately.) Moreover, Nilsson-Ehle showed that on his three gene hypothesis the expectations in F_3 agree satisfactorily with what he had found. On the average, out of every 63 red F_2 plants, 6 are expected to give 3 reds:1 white in F_3, 12 to give a 15:1 ratio, 8 to give a 63:1 ratio and the remainder to breed true.

Nilsson-Ehle suggested that the hereditary basis of continuous variation might be similar to what he had found in *Avena* and *Triticum* for discontinuous variation. In other words, if there were a number of genes affecting the same character, such that the discontinuities of phenotype were sufficiently small to be obscured by environmental variation, then continuous variation would be manifest.

East (1910) had studied the inheritance of various grain characters and of the number of rows of grains on the ear in *Zea mays*. Some of the grain characters gave 15:1 ratios in F_2 suggesting control by two independently-inherited pairs of alleles, but the number of rows of grains on the ear showed continuous variation. East found that there was always an even number of rows, and that the number of pairs of rows varied from 4 to 15. He made a number of crosses between strains differing in mean number of pairs of rows and studied the progeny. For example, he crossed a strain of *Zea* in which 28 ears had a mean of 4·14 pairs of rows and standard deviation 0·45 with one in which 107 ears had a mean of 6·59 pairs and standard deviation

0·79*. He obtained 21 F_1 ears with a mean of 5·62 pairs of rows and standard deviation 0·51. In other words, the F_1 was intermediate between the two parents and relatively uniform. He selected an F_1 ear with 6 pairs of rows and obtained 77 F_2 ears by self-fertilisation. These had a mean of 5·44 pairs of rows and standard deviation 0·82. Thus, although the F_2 mean was similar to that of the F_1, the F_2 plants were much more variable. East pointed out that this tendency to recover in F_2 some individuals that approached the parental forms in appearance is what would be expected if segregation of several pairs of alleles controlling row number was taking place, and hence he favoured the multiple factor hypothesis of inheritance of characters showing a continuous range of variation.

TABLE 4.3   Emerson and East's data for the frequencies of maize ears of various lengths from a cross between a short-eared and a long-eared strain.

Gener-ation	No. of Ears Measd.	Ear Length to Nearest Centimetre																	Mean Lgth. cm.	Standard Deviation cm.
		5	6	7	8	9	10	11	12	13	14	15	16	17	18	19	20	21		
P	57	4	21	24	8														6·6	0·8
P	101								3	11	12	15	26	15	10	7	2		16·8	1·9
F_1	69				1	12	12	14	17	9	4								12·1	1·5
F_2	401			1	10	19	26	47	73	68	68	39	25	15	9	1			12·9	2·3

An essential feature of this multiple factor hypothesis is that the effects of the different genes should be cumulative. If they merely duplicated one another, discontinuous variation would result, with F_2 ratios of 15:1, 63:1, and so on, as in the examples of these ratios found by Nilsson-Ehle and East. However, if the phenotype depends on the dosage of a series of different genes, then even with quite a small number of them, a considerable number of alternative phenotypes becomes possible, leading to greatly increased variability in the F_2 generation from a cross between two pure-breeding lines.

This increased variability in F_2, which Kölreuter (1763) was the first to discover, and which East (1910) had found, has since been amply confirmed for numerous characters showing continuous variation and in a great diversity of organisms. One of the clearest examples was from the work of Emerson and East (1913). They had studied the inheritance of numerous quantitative characters in *Zea mays*, such as lengths and diameter of ears, weight of grains, height of plant, number of nodes, internode length and duration of growth. From a cross between two strains differing markedly in ear length, the results shown in Table 4.3 and Fig. 4.3 were obtained. The

* From such data as these, it is possible to calculate the *standard error* of the mean, which is a measure of the precision of the estimate of the mean. The standard error of the mean is obtained by taking the standard deviation of the sample and dividing it by the square root of the number of observations. Thus the first parental strain has a mean of 4·14 ± 0·09 pairs of rows, since its standard error is $\dfrac{0·45}{\sqrt{28}} = 0·09$, and similarly the second parental strain had a mean of 6·59 ± 0·08 pairs of rows, since its standard error is $\dfrac{0·79}{\sqrt{107}} = 0·08$. The first mean does not differ significantly from 4, since once in twenty times one would expect a deviation of plus or minus twice the standard error or more. By a similar argument one would deduce that the second mean differs significantly from both 6 and 7.

short-eared parent was relatively uniform with a mean ear-length of 6·6 cm and standard deviation 0·8 cm. The long-eared parent was more variable (mean length 16·8 cm, standard deviation 1·9 cm). The F_1 plants were intermediate and relatively uniform (mean length 12.1 cm, standard deviation 1·5 cm) while the F_2 plants were much more variable (mean length 12·9 cm, standard deviation 2·3 cm).

FIGURE 4.3   Frequency histograms for ear length in *Zea mays* from the data of Emerson and East. The number of ears is plotted as ordinate and the ear length in centimetres as abscissa. (*a*) and (*b*) represent the two parental strains, (*c*) the F_1 generation, and (*d*) the F_2 generation.

Fisher (1918) took up the problem of testing the agreement between the observed values of the correlation coefficients between relatives and those expected on the multiple factor hypothesis, without making the arbitrary simplifications which had misled Pearson. Fisher made no assumptions about equality of effect of the various factors, nor about dominance or equality of frequency between alleles. He began by pointing out that when there are two or more independent causes of variability in a population, their contributions to the variance are additive. This necessarily implies that their contributions to the standard deviation are not additive. Hence, in considering the causes of variation in a population it is desirable to use the variance, rather than the standard deviation, as a measure of the dispersion about the mean value. He interpreted the fraternal correlation coefficient for human stature of 0·54, which Pearson and Lee had obtained, by saying that 54% of the variance of brothers is accounted for by ancestry. On the hypothesis of a large number of Mendelian factors determining stature, the greater part of the remaining 46% of the variance would be due to the segregation of factors for which the parents were heterozygous, and a small part to environmental differences during the brothers' childhood.

Fisher confirmed Yule's finding that the effect of dominance between the alleles is to reduce the parental correlation coefficient by a certain amount. But Fisher took the analysis much further and showed that the effect of dominance is to reduce the fraternal correlation to only half the extent to which the parental correlation is reduced. This enables the effects of dominance to be distinguished from the effects of environmental factors, and moreover explains why the fraternal correlation coefficient exceeds the parental. The observation of this excess by Pearson and Lee is thus in itself evidence in favour of the theory of cumulative Mendelian factors, and moreover with a considerable amount of dominance between the alleles. Fisher estimated that not more than 5% of the fraternal variance was due to environmental factors. His estimates for the correlation coefficients between relatives on the basis of the multiple factor hypothesis were in excellent agreement with the observations of Pearson and Lee, and others. Moreover, on making certain assumptions about assortive mating Fisher was able to deduce Galton's 'law of ancestral heredity'. Thus the controversial question of how far the inheritance of continuous variation could be attributed to Mendelian factors was finally resolved.

Much further support for the multiple factor theory has been obtained subsequently. Fisher's idea of partitioning the variance between the various causes of variability has been greatly extended, and has led to a much fuller understanding of the genetics of quantitative characters. Thus, Mather (1949a) has demonstrated that the genes responsible for the inheritance of continuously variable characters are not all inherited independently, but may show linkage, comparable to that known for certain genes controlling discontinuous characters. The method of establishing linkage is based on the analysis of variance. Consider two inbred lines differing in a quantitative character such as abdominal bristle number (*Drosophila*), or height or length of parts (plants), and assume that this character is determined by numerous genes. The character is counted or measured in a number of individuals of each line, and the means and variances calculated. Assuming that the two strains have each been inbred for a number of generations, the individuals of each will be almost uniform genetically, like Johannsen's pure lines of *Phaseolus*. In consequence, the observed variance can be attributed almost entirely to environmental factors. The two lines are then crossed and a number of individuals of the F_1 measured. The mean value for the character is expected to be intermediate in the F_1 between the two parents, as East (1910) and Emerson and East (1913) had found. Moreover, the variance of the F_1 will be due wholly to environmental factors, since all the individuals will have the same genotype, being heterozygous for the alleles by which the parents differ. An F_2 generation is raised by self-pollination (plants) or inter-crossing of F_1 individuals, and again the mean and variance are calculated from measurements of a number of individuals. The variance

4

will now have both genetic and environmental components, since segregation of alleles will have taken place. As a first approximation it may be assumed that the environmental variance is constant in the parental, F_1 and F_2 generations, if they have been grown under similar conditions, and hence the genetic contribution to the F_2 variance can be estimated. However, recent work has indicated that the F_1 generation commonly has a smaller variance than the initial inbred lines, indicating that the development of the latter is more readily modified by the environment. Some of the F_1 individuals are

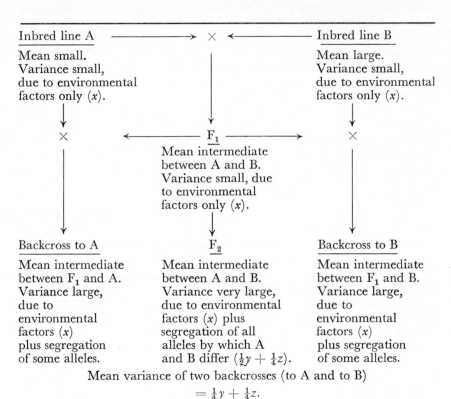

Inbred line A ————————→ × ←———————— Inbred line B

Mean small.   Mean large.
Variance small,   Variance small,
due to environmental   due to environmental
factors only (x).   factors only (x).

× ←———————— F_1 ————————→ ×

Mean intermediate
between A and B.
Variance small, due
to environmental
factors only (x).

Backcross to A F_2 Backcross to B

| Mean intermediate between F_1 and A. Variance large, due to environmental factors (x) plus segregation of some alleles. | Mean intermediate between A and B. Variance very large, due to environmental factors (x) plus segregation of all alleles by which A and B differ $(\frac{1}{2}y + \frac{1}{4}z)$. | Mean intermediate between F_1 and B. Variance large, due to environmental factors (x) plus segregation of some alleles. |

Mean variance of two backcrosses (to A and to B)

$$= \tfrac{1}{4}y + \tfrac{1}{4}z.$$

FIGURE 4.4   Diagram showing the means and variances expected when two inbred lines are crossed and the progeny inbred and also backcrossed. It is assumed that the environmental conditions are constant, that each population responds similarly to environmental effects (not necessarily true—see text), and that the character under study shows continuous variation determined by a number of independent Mendelian factors.
$x =$ environmental contribution to variance.
$y =$ measure of difference in phenotype between corresponding homozygotes, such as AA and aa.
$z =$ measure of dominance, that is, difference in phenotype between AA and Aa and between Aa and aa, and similarly with the other factors.

back-crossed to each parent, and the means and variances of the progeny determined. As with the F_2, the back-cross progeny will have genetic and environmental contributions to the variance, since the alleles by which the inbred lines differed will also segregate in the back-crosses.

The hereditary component of variance can be considered to consist of two parts. One is concerned with the magnitude of the effect of the various genes, that is, the difference of phenotype between AA and aa, and similarly for all the other pairs of alleles affecting the character. The other part is concerned with dominance, that is, how far the phenotype of Aa is intermediate between AA and aa, and similarly for the other pairs of alleles. If one compares the average variance of the progenies from back-crossing to each parent with the variance of the F_2, the environmental effects may be considered as a first approximation to contribute equally to each, and similarly with the dominance effects (Aa versus AA and aa). On the other hand, the homozygote differences (AA versus aa) will contribute much less to the average variance of the backcrosses than to the F_2 variance, because in the back-crosses one cannot have both homozygotes for a pair of alleles (for example, AA and aa) present at once. This explains why the variance of the back-crosses is less than that of the F_2 (see Fig. 4.4). From a comparison of the average variance of the backcrosses with the F_2 variance, the respective contributions of homozygote differences and of dominance can be estimated. In most experiments the former considerably exceeds the latter.

From the analysis of variance in F_3, further estimates can be obtained of the size of the various components of the variance. From studies of the variance for plant height in inbred lines of *Antirrhinum majus* and *A. glutinosum* and of the F_1, F_2, F_3 and back-cross progenies, Mather (1949b) found internal discrepancies in the various estimates for the components of the variance. However, by making allowance for the possibility of linkage between some of the genes, an excellent agreement with observation was obtained. He deduced that linkage was present. Confirmation of linkage between genes responsible for continuously variable characters has been obtained, for example in *Drosophila*, by studying quantitative characters in conjunction with one or more discontinuous characters.

§ 4.9   Conclusion

The hypothesis of multiple Mendelian factors, each with additive effects, has been found satisfactorily to explain data on the inheritance of many quantitative characters. The phenomena of dominance and of linkage, which are manifest in Mendelian inheritance of discontinuous characters, have also been demonstrated with characters showing a continuous range of variation. There is no reason, therefore, to suppose that the inheritance of quantitative characters differs in any fundamental way from that of qualitative characters which show Mendelian inheritance. There is evidence, however, that at least some of the genes affecting quantitative characters may occur in special regions of the hereditary material (see §16.2).

5. The hypothesis that Mendelian inheritance is determined by the cell-nucleus and non-Mendelian by the cytoplasm

§ 5.1 Weismann's theory of the continuity of the germ-plasm

The term *nucleus* was applied by Brown (1833) to the more or less spherical structure which usually occupies a central position in cells. He observed the nucleus in the cells of both the vegetative and reproductive parts of many flowering plants. He made particular mention of its occurrence in the leaf-cells of orchids and in the stigma and pollen of *Tradescantia*. The fate of the nucleus in cell-multiplication was a source of debate and speculation until Strasburger (1879) reached the conclusion that nuclei arise only from pre-existing nuclei. He had made extensive studies of the cells of the reproductive organs of numerous seed-plants. Meanwhile, Hertwig (1875) with *Paracentrotus lividus* (a species of Sea Urchin) and van Beneden (1875) with *Oryctolagus cuniculus* (Rabbit) had independently established that at fertilization there occurs not merely a fusion of cells but also of nuclei, and moreover these are derived from the egg and the sperm, respectively. Strasburger's discovery that the cell-nucleus has itself the property of heredity, in that it never arises afresh but is always handed down, led naturally to the conclusion that the nucleus is the vehicle of heredity.

It was against this cytological background that Weismann (1883, 1885) put forward his theory of the continuity of the germ-plasm. The essence of this theory was 'that heredity is brought about by the transference from one generation to another, of a substance with a definite chemical, and above all, molecular constitution' (1885, p. 168). He called this substance 'germ-plasm', and he supposed that in the development of the body or 'soma' of an individual from the fertilised egg-cell, this substance, or part of it, was 'reserved unchanged for the formation of the germ-cells of the following generation' (1885, p. 168). This notion had a considerable influence on contemporary thought. Weismann (1883) was the first person to challenge the existence of the inheritance of mutilations, or 'acquired characters', as they were called by Lamarck (1809), an idea which, as indicated in Chapter 1, had been widely accepted ever since the time of Hippocrates. For it was fundamental to Weismann's theory that this chemical (the germ-plasm) could not be

40

modified by the environment during the life of an individual, but was handed down unaltered. Weismann accepted the opinions of Hertwig and Strasburger that 'the nature of heredity is based upon the transmission of nuclear substance with a specific molecular constitution' (Weismann 1885, p. 180) and went on to equate this substance with his postulated germ-plasm.

§ 5.2   Boveri's experiments with echinoderms

Strong support for the view that the nucleus is the primary carrier of hereditary material in the cell was obtained by Boveri (1889) from studies on echinoderms. Working at the Zoological Station at Naples, he added sea urchin sperm to eggs which had been fragmented by shaking, and he found that even pieces of egg lacking a nucleus could sometimes be fertilised. The resulting larvae were quite normal in appearance, except that they were only about one-quarter of the size of those developed from unfragmented eggs or from fragmented eggs with a nucleus. He deduced from this experiment that

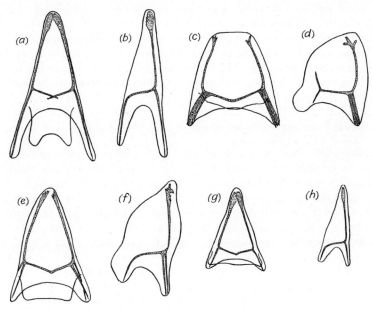

FIGURE 5.1   Posterior and side views (×100) of the calcereous skele-
tons of the larvae of sea urchins (from Boveri, 1889).
(a) and (b) *Psammechinus microtuberculatus*
             (a) Posterior view   (b) Side view
(c) and (d) *Sphaerechinus granularis*
             (c) Posterior view   (d) Side view
(e) and (f) *S. granularis* × *P. microtuberculatus*
             (e) Posterior view   (f) Side view
(g) and (h) *S. granularis* (enucleated) × *P. microtubercu-
             latus*
             (g) Posterior view   (h) Side view

the sperm nucleus possessed all the properties necessary to function like a fertilised egg-nucleus. This was an important conclusion as it implied that the egg-nucleus and the sperm-nucleus were essentially alike in their hereditary contributions.

Boveri made further experiments with even more striking results. He hybridised two species of sea urchin, *Psammechinus microtuberculatus* and *Sphaerechinus granularis*. The calcareous skeleton of the *Psammechinus* larva when seen in posterior view is shaped like a capital A of rather narrow outline (Fig. 5.1(*a*)) and the body is similarly shaped. In side view, the appearance is even narrower (Fig. 5.1(*b*)). On the other hand, the *Sphaerechinus* larva is much broader, the skeleton in posterior view almost resembling a capital H (Fig. 5.1(*c*)), but with the uprights slightly tilted towards the A shape. The body is correspondingly broad, and is almost as wide in side view (Fig. 5.1(*d*)). Boveri found that when normal *Sphaerechinus* eggs were fertilised by *Psammechinus* sperm, the resulting hybrid larvae were almost exactly intermediate in appearance between those of the two parents. The skeleton in posterior view was like a capital A of broad outline (Fig. 5.1(*e*)), and the body both in front view and in side view was of intermediate breadth (Fig. 5.1(*f*)). When the hybridisation was repeated using fragmented *Sphaerechinus* eggs, the enucleated fragments when fertilised with *Psammechinus* sperm developed into larvae exactly resembling those derived from *Psammechinus* egg and sperm, though dwarf in size (Fig. 5.1(*g*) and (*h*)). Boveri concluded that the maternal cytoplasm has no influence on the hereditary characters, and that these are determined by the nucleus alone.

§ 5.3 Hämmerling's experiments with *Acetabularia*

Another series of experiments which demonstrated the importance of the nucleus in determining heredity were those of Hämmerling (reviews 1953, 1963) with species of *Acetabularia*, small green plants of warm seas. These algae, in their vegetative condition, consist essentially of a single giant uninucleate cell. This cell may be 6 cm or more in length and is differentiated into a basal lobed rhizoid containing the nucleus, an erect photosynthetic stalk, and, in mature plants, a terminal cap up to 1 cm in diameter. Thus the full-grown plant has something of the appearance of a small green toadstool. In *A. mediterranea* which, as its name implies, is a native of the Mediterranean region, the cap has an average of about 81 rays (80·8 ± 3·2), and these have rounded tips (Fig. 5·2(*a*)). In *A. crenulata* from the W. Indies there are only, on average, 31 rays (30·7 ± 2·8) per cap, and the tips of the rays are pointed (Fig. 5·2(*b*)).

Hämmerling took immature plants of each species and grafted them together by cutting off the tops of the stalks (the caps had not yet developed) and bringing the cut surfaces into contact. A new stalk soon developed at the point of grafting, and this gave rise to a cap which was intermediate in appearance between the two parents. A number of such caps had an average of about 42 rays (42·3 ± 4·8) and hence approached *A. crenulata*, but with tips usually rounded like *A. mediterranea*. The intermediate character of this graft-hybrid is to be expected, since it contains two nuclei, one from each species. Control experiments in which two plants of *A. mediterranea* were grafted together gave caps resembling this species. Corresponding results were obtained with the other species.

Further grafts were achieved using the stalk of an immature plant of one

FIGURE 5.2   Drawings to show the appearance ($\times 2$) of (*a*) *Acetabularia mediterranea*, and (*b*) *A. crenulata*.

species and the rhizoid system (and hence nucleus) of the other. Such grafts contained only one nucleus. The type of cap which developed was found to depend on the length of stalk grafted. If it was about 1 to 2 cm. long, the cap was often of intermediate appearance between that of the two species, whereas if the piece of the stalk that was grafted on was about 0·5 cm long or less, the cap usually resembled that of the rhizoid (and hence nuclear) parent. It was noteworthy that, however long the stalk, the cap never wholly resembled the species from which the stalk was obtained. Hämmerling deduced that the nucleus in the rhizoid had an over-riding control over the form of the cap, but that the stalk also had some influence.

This result is not so clear cut as that obtained by Boveri with echinoderms. However, Hämmerling found that if in these graft-hybrids of the rhizoid of one species of *Acetabularia* with the stalk of the other, he cut off the first cap to form, in due course a second would develop and this invariably resembled the cap of the species which provided the rhizoid (and hence the nucleus). Hämmerling concluded that although substances in the cytoplasm are the immediate determinants of the form of the cap, these substances are ultimately controlled by the nulceus. It is to be noted that in these grafting experiments one cannot rule out the possibility that the cytoplasm in the rhizoid is playing a vital part. It seems more probable however, that it is the nucleus which is responsible, just as in Boveri's hybrid echinoderms from enucleated eggs. In the latter instance, there is so little cytoplasm in a sperm that one is fully justified in drawing the conclusion that the nucleus was responsible for the resemblance of the hybrid to the male parent.

§ 5.4   Delayed Mendelian inheritance

It will be recalled that one of the characteristic features of Mendelian inheritance is that reciprocal crosses give identical results. Such identity gives strong support to the hypothesis that the cell nucleus is the bearer of the Mendelian factors, since the nuclear contributions of sperm and egg appear to be the same, whereas their cytoplasmic contributions clearly differ. The over-riding importance in heredity of the nucleus compared with the cytoplasm, as demonstrated by Boveri's and Hämmerling's experiments, appears to be matched by the over-riding importance of Mendelian inheritance in living organisms compared with non-Mendelian. However, as will be discussed in § 16.4, the possibility that non-Mendelian inheritance does play a major part in heredity must not be overlooked.

Before discussing non-Mendelian heredity, some experiments will be described which demonstrate Mendelian inheritance, but with delayed action such that the effect of the nuclei presumed to be responsible is carried over in the cytoplasm into cells which may have a different nuclear constitution. Such an effect may resemble non-Mendelian inheritance, and needs to be carefully distinguished from it.

One example of such delayed Mendelian heredity has already been described in Chapter 3, namely, the inheritance of pollen shape in *Lathyrus odoratus* studied by Bateson, Saunders and Punnett (1905). Although segregation of factors must occur before the formation of the pollen grains, as first postulated by Mendel, yet when a pure-breeding strain of *Lathyrus odoratus* with long pollen-grains (Fig. 5.3(*a*)) is crossed with a pure-breeding strain with round grains (Fig. 5.3(*b*)), the F_1 plants as already mentioned have pollen grains which are all long in shape, and in F_2 three-quarters of the plants have long pollen and the remaining one-quarter have round pollen. It is evident from these results that long pollen-shape is determined by a dominant factor (L) and round pollen-shape by the recessive allele (1). It follows that the F_1 plants have the genetic constitution Ll and half their pollen grains must contain the L factor and the other half the l factor.

Nevertheless, all the grains from these plants have the *L* shape. It is evident that pollen shape must be controlled by the genetic constitution of the anther and not by that of the pollen grain itself. The simplest hypothesis is that some substance determining pollen shape is produced by the nuclei of the pollen

FIGURE 5.3   (*a*) and (*b*) Pollen (×175) of *Lathyrus odoratus* in the dry state (from Bateson, 1909).
(*a*) The normal Long (cylindrical) pollen-grains (usually with three germ-pores)
(*b*) The mutant round (disc-shaped) pollen-grains (usually two-pored)
(*c*) Pollen (×125) of *Oryza sativa* segregating for starchy (shown dark) and waxy (shown light) contents (from Parnell, 1921).

mother cells (or other anther cells) and carried over to the developing pollen-grains in the cytoplasm. This delayed manifestation of a nuclear effect is comparable to that found by Hämmerling in *Acetabularia* species grafts, where the second cap to form resembles that of the parent contributing the nucleus, whereas the first cap is more often intermediate. It is known that other characters of pollen in flowering plants may not show this delayed inheritance. Thus, Parnell (1921) discovered that in *Oryza sativa* (Rice) if a pure-breeding strain with normal starchy pollen-grains (staining blue with iodine) is crossed with a pure-breeding strain with waxy pollen-grains containing erythrodextrin (staining reddish-brown with iodine), the F_1 plants have half their pollen-grains starchy and the other half waxy (Fig. 5.3(c)). Evidently a single pair of alleles determines this difference, and the factors function after the formation of the pollen grains. A similar situation was discovered in *Zea mays* independently by Demerec (1924) and by Brink and MacGillivray (1924).

A second example of a delayed nuclear effect is provided by the work of Gossop, Yuill, and Yuill (1940) with *Aspergillus niger*. This asexual fungus normally has chains of black conidia (asexual spores), but a strain is known with cinnamon-coloured conidia and another with brown conidia. If the cinnamon strain and the brown strain are allowed to grow together, the hyphae may fuse so that the mycelium has within its cells nuclei from both strains (there is no nuclear fusion). The occurrence of nuclei of different genotype within one cell is called *heterokaryosis*. When such a heterokaryon produces conidia, the erect aerial conidiophores are composed of multinucleate cells, but the conidia produced from these are uninucleate. Hence

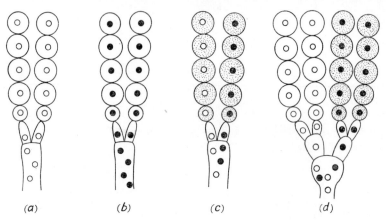

(a)   (b)   (c)   (d)

FIGURE 5.4   Conidia ($\times 2000$) of *Penicillium* and *Aspergillus* (from Pontecorvo, 1947).

(a–c) *Penicillium notatum*. Small open circles indicate nuclei carrying the gene for white conidia, solid circles those carrying the gene for yellow conidia, and dots in the cytoplasm indicate synthesis of the normal green conidial pigment. (a) White mutant. (b) Yellow mutant. (c) White-yellow heterokaryon with green conidia.

(d) *Aspergillus nidulans*. Small open circles indicate nuclei carrying the gene for white conidia, solid circles those carrying the normal allele for green conidia, and dots in the cytoplasm indicate synthesis of the green pigment. The white-green heterokaryon has some chains of spores white and others green.

in the formation of conidia, the heterokaryon breaks down and each conidium receives either a 'cinnamon' or a 'brown' nucleus. Nevertheless, all the conidia are black. Evidently the black pigment, or a precursor of it, is manufactured in the heterokaryotic conidiophore, where both types of nuclei can co-operate in its production, and is then transmitted in the cytoplasm to the conidia. The colonies derived from these conidia, if isolated, will be either cinnamon or brown in conidial colour according to the nuclei they have received. This is comparable to the long and round pollen shapes in *Lathyrus odoratus*. An even more striking example was described by Pontecorvo and Gemmell (1944), where white-spored and yellow-spored mutants of the normally green-spored *Penicillium notatum* were found to produce a heterokaryon which had green conidia, although these are uninucleate. When isolated, these conidia produced strains with either white or yellow conidia (Fig. 5.4(a)–(c)).

Other characters in fungi may not show this delay in the manifestation of the effects of nuclei. Thus, Gossop, Yuill, and Yuill found that in *Aspergillus nidulans* a heterokaryon between a white-spored mutant and the normal green-spored fungus produced mixed heads in which single chains of conidia were either green or white (Fig. 5.4(d)). This is analogous to starchy and waxy pollen in *Oryza* or *Zea*.

§ 5.5   Boycott and Diver's experiments with *Limnaea*

One of the best-known examples of delayed Mendelian inheritance concerns the direction of coiling in the fresh-water snail *Limnaea peregra* studied by Boycott and Diver (1923). The normal snail has the body and shell coiled in a right-handed spiral but in a pond near Leeds, Yorkshire,

a   **b**

FIGURE 5.5   *Limnaea peregra* (×2·5). (a) Normal dextral snail shell. (b) Sinistral snail shell.

along with the normal form another was found which was an exact mirror image of it (Fig. 5.5). Not only were the body and shell coiled in a left-handed spiral, but the positions of the heart and kidney were complementary to those in the normal animal, and the alimentary and reproductive openings were on the left instead of the right side of the neck. Earlier work by other authors had indicated that the difference between dextral and sinistral snails becomes apparent at the earliest stage of development, since the plane of the first cell-division in the fertilised egg is different in the two forms.

Limnaea peregra is hermaphrodite, and although cross-fertilisation is usual, self-fertilisation can also occur. Individuals which had not yet reached sexual maturity were isolated and allowed to fertilise themselves. Broods of several hundred snails were obtained in this way from each of 144 individuals, all of related ancestry. It was found that, apart from rare exceptions which were possibly due to environmental factors, all the snails in a brood were alike as regards their direction of coiling, but either type of parent (dextral or sinistral) could produce either type of brood!

Boycott and Diver explained these remarkable results by postulating that 'the appearance of the individual is the result of, and is determined by, the product of the parental nuclear composition . . .' (1923, p. 211). Sturtevant (1923), on the basis of their results, was more specific and suggested that in, view of the very early development of the difference between dextral and sinistral forms, it was likely to be the nuclear composition of the mother which determined the direction of coiling. Two further observations made by Boycott and Diver, namely, that sinistral snails obtained by self-fertilisation bred true, whereas dextral snails similarly obtained often did not, led Sturtevant to postulate that the dextral condition was dominant to sinistral.

Later work by Boycott, Diver, Garstang and Turner (1930) confirmed both of Sturtevant's postulates. In crosses between pure-breeding dextral and pure-breeding sinistral forms, the appearance of the F_1 progeny was the same as their mother, the F_2 snails were all dextral, and in F_3 1192 dextral and 401 sinistral broods were obtained. These results are intelligible as simple Mendelian inheritance, provided the direction of a snail's coiling is always regarded as a property of its mother. Evidently the mother's nuclear constitution leads to the production of some substance in the cytoplasm of the cells of the ovary or primary oocyte, and this substance reaches the next generation by way of the cytoplasm of the egg, where, after fertilisation, it determines the plane of the first cell-division, and hence the dextrality or sinistrality of the offspring.

§ 5.6 Kuhn's experiments with *Ephestia*

A rather similar example of delayed Mendelian inheritance concerns eye-colour in the moth *Ephestia kuhniella*. The eyes are normally black but a variant with red eyes is inherited as a Mendelian recessive. Kühn (1937) discovered that if red-eyed females (*aa*) are crossed with heterozygous black-eyed males (*Aa*), the black-eyed (*Aa*) and red-eyed (*aa*) progeny can be distinguished even in the young larvae. However, when the reciprocal cross is made, all the young larvae have black eyes, but in the individuals of constitution *aa* the colour gradually changes to red as they develop. Evidently a precursor of the pigment is carried via the cytoplasm of the egg to the progeny, but its effect does not persist to adult life, except in those progeny

(*Aa*) which carry the black-eye factor and hence can renew production of the precursor and pigment. Kühn confirmed this hypothesis by grafting testes from a black-eyed (*Aa*) larva into a red-eyed (*aa*) female one. It then developed a darker eye-colour which also appeared in the young *aa* progeny larvae. The substance which was shown by these experiments to be carried over in the cytoplasm of the egg to the next generation has been identified as kynurenine, which is also a precursor of *Drosophila* eye-pigment.

§ 5.7 Spurway's experiments with grandchildless *Drosophila*

A more extreme example of delayed Mendelian inheritance is provided by the mutant called *grandchildless* described by Spurway (1948) in *Drosophila subobscura*. During breeding work with this species of fly, all the males in a particular family were found to have abnormally small internal reproductive organs. These organs have an orange pigment and can be seen in living flies through the body wall. On dissection no testes or only the minutest rudiments were found. The same condition appeared in the progeny of sister cultures. Moreover, it was found that females were similarly affected, the ovaries remaining vestigial.

It was established that this sterility of the progeny was associated with particular female parents and was independent of the male parent. In order to determine the hereditary basis of the condition, brothers of grandchildless females were crossed with unrelated females and the progeny inbred. After two generations the sterile families reappeared, thus showing that their cause could be carried by males. Crosses were also made between brothers and sisters of 'sterile-progeny' females, and some the female progeny were found to show the condition by having sterile offspring. In this way the sterility was followed through more than twenty generations of flies. Grandchildless females formed a minority of the females in each generation.

On the evidence of the crossing experiments, it was postulated that the sterility was due to a Mendelian recessive gene called *gs*. The sisters with fertile offspring, by which the *gs* stock was maintained, were assumed to be heterozygous normals (+/*gs*)*, but it was impossible to determine whether the brothers with which these were crossed in the inbreeding experiment were heterozygous (+/*gs*) or homozygous (*gs*/*gs*). On the hypothesis just mentioned of a Mendelian recessive factor determining the grandchildless condition, in each generation following brother-sister mating, either a 3:1 or a 1:1 ratio of 'fertile-progeny' to 'sterile-progeny' females is expected, but the individual families were too small to distinguish these ratios. Taking Spurway's total data for fifteen consecutive generations (F_8 to F_{22} inclusive) comprising 23 brother-sister matings, the female progeny consisted of 309 with fertile offspring, 90 with sterile offspring and 112 themselves sterile. Since grandchildless females are less fertile than normal, it is probable that the 112 sterile females include many *gs*/*gs* females. With any reasonable distributions of the 112 between the other two classes, the ratio of the latter lies between 3:1 and 1:1, and hence is in agreement with the hypothesis.

* The + sign is used for the normal allele.

It thus appears that a Mendelian recessive factor, when homozygous, leads to the production of some substance in the ovary of female flies. This substance, or some other effect of the gene, may lower their fertility somewhat, but its main effect is on the progeny. It is presumably carried via the cytoplasm of the egg to the next generation, where it leads to a failure of development of the ovaries and testes. The abnormality cannot be detected before the last instar in male larvae, or the mid-pupal stage in females, and is most readily observed in the mature insects. This represents one of the most extreme instances known of the delayed effect of a Mendelian gene.

§ 5.8   Rhoades' experiments with iojap *Zea*

An instructive comparison can be drawn between the inheritance of grandchildless *Drosophila subobscura* and that of a particular kind of leaf-striping in *Zea mays* called 'iojap'. The name 'iojap' is abbreviated from 'Iowa', as the source of the maize strain, and 'japonica' as the name of a similar striped variety. Jenkins (1924) described experiments which established that the striped leaves found in iojap plants are due to a recessive Mendelian gene. Maize is usually cross-fertilised. Certain normal green plants when self-pollinated were found to give progenies segregating for iojap striping. Omitting one family where the stripes were very narrow and hard to recognise, Jenkins' total data for these segregating progenies were 2498 green and 782 iojap (including 12 white plants) (Fig. 5.6(*a*)) (Expected frequencies on 3:1 hypothesis:2460 and 820, deviations 38, $\chi^2 = 2 \cdot 3$, $n = 1$, $P > 0 \cdot 1$.) Furthermore, 26 of these 2498 green plants, on self-pollination, were found to consist of 9 which bred true and 17 which again

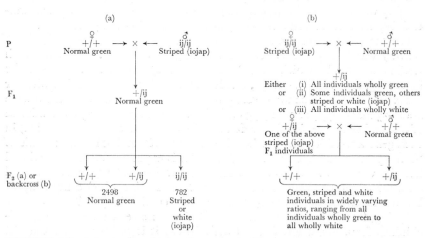

FIGURE 5.6   Inheritance of iojap character in *Zea mays*.
(*a*) Mendelian inheritance when iojap plants used as male parents (from Jenkins, 1924).
(*b*) Non-Mendelian inheritance when iojap plants used as female parents (from Rhoades, 1943).

segregated for iojap, in good agreement with the 1:2 ratio of homozygotes
to heterozygotes which Mendel would have expected. However, an unexpected result was obtained when female inflorescences of iojap plants
(obtained as above) were pollinated from a pure-breeding normal green
plant. The resulting F_1 plants often had striped leaves of typical iojap
appearance. Rhoades (1943) showed that so long as iojap plants are used as
female parents, the inheritance of the condition is similar to that of the
albomaculata variety of *Mirabilis jalapa* described by Correns (1909) and
discussed in § 2.7. Thus, widely varying ratios of green, white and striped
progeny were obtained in this way from iojap plants, and this result was
found irrespective of the male parent used (Fig. 5.6(*b*)).

Rhoades proposed the following hypothesis to account for these remarkable results. The nuclear gene, *ij*, when homozygous (*ij/ij*) causes striping of
the leaves, but this striped condition, once it has been initiated, is then
inherited through the cytoplasm. Cytoplasm is handed down only through the
egg-cell and not through the pollen, and so the iojap condition shows
maternal inheritance. Rhoades confirmed this hypothesis by crossing the F_1
striped plants as female parent with an unrelated normal green plant as
male parent (see Fig. 5.6(*b*)). The F_1 striped plants would be heterozygous
for the iojap gene ($+/ij$), the other parent would be homozygous for the
normal allele ($+/+$), and so the progeny from this cross would consist of
equal numbers of individuals homozygous for the normal allele ($+/+$) and
heterozygous ($+/ij$). Nevertheless, for some ears the progeny consisted
entirely of white seedlings, half of which by the above reasoning must not
have possessed the iojap gene at all. From other ears, there were green,
variegated and white progeny in diverse ratios, and here again many of the
iojap plants must have lacked the iojap gene.

The essential difference between the inheritance of grandchildless *Drosophila*
and iojap *Zea* is that in the former the cytoplasmic modification initiated by
the nuclear gene is passed only to the immediate progeny and no further,
whereas in the latter it appears to be capable of indefinite passage from
generation to generation. This distinction constitutes the essential difference
between Mendelian and non-Mendelian inheritance. It can of course be
argued that in grandchildless *Drosophila* there is no further opportunity for
cytoplasmic passage beyond the immediate progeny, on account of the
sterility induced. The initiation of iojap *Zea* shows Mendelian heredity, but
once it has been initiated, the inheritance is non-Mendelian. The ability
to be handed down indefinitely, independently of the nuclear constitution,
implies that whatever is responsible for non-Mendelian inheritance must
possess the ability to reproduce itself in the cytoplasm. The nature of such
reproducing structures is discussed later in this chapter and in § 16.4.

§ 5.9 Baur's experiments with *Pelargonium*

Almost simultaneously with Correns' (1909) discovery of the non-
Mendelian inheritance of the *albomaculata* character in *Mirabilis jalapa*
(see Chapter 2), Baur (1909) reported an example in *Pelargonium zonale*

(Geranium) which differed in an important respect from that in *Mirabilis*. Baur's example also concerned leaf-variegation, but he found that in *Pelargonium* reciprocal crosses gave similar results. It will be recalled that in 'albomaculata' *Mirabilis* (and also in 'iojap' *Zea*) such crosses give different results. Plants of a strain of *Pelargonium* with white-margined leaves when self-pollinated or inter-crossed gave wholly white progeny, which necessarily died young. Baur found that the sub-epidermal layer in white-margined plants was white. Since this is the layer which gives rise to the reproductive cells, the wholly white progeny could be explained. However, when the white-margined plants were crossed with normal green plants, the progeny consisted of green plants, white-margined plants and wholly white plants in widely-varying ratios, and this was true which ever direction the cross was made. Baur concluded that in *Pelargonium* cytoplasm is inherited from the male as well as the female parent. Thus the difference between reciprocal crosses, which in the *Mirabilis* and *Zea* examples was quoted as one of the distinctions from Mendelian heredity, cannot be maintained as an invariable feature of non-Mendelian heredity. The most striking feature of the latter kind of inheritance is the failure of the character-difference to segregate in a regular and predictable way at the time of formation of the reproductive cells.

§ 5.10   Renner's experiments with *Oenothera*

Further examples of non-Mendelian heredity of the *Pelargonium* type were found by Renner (1924) in *Oenothera* (Evening Primrose) hybrids. Thus, he found that when *O. hookeri* was crossed as female parent with the not very closely related *O. muricata* as male parent, the hybrids had yellow leaves and died. Plants of the same nuclear constitution obtained from the reciprocal cross* had green leaves with yellow flecks. He postulated that these yellow flecks represented cytoplasm contributed by the male parent (*O. hookeri*) and that in the presence of the hybrid nucleus, the *O. hookeri* cytoplasm became defective, giving the yellow colour. From self-pollination of flowers on wholly yellow shoots on the flecked plants, Renner was able to show that normal green progeny were recovered whenever the cytoplasm was restored to an *O. hookeri* nucleus. This result confirmed his hypothesis that the yellow colour was a consequence of lack of harmony between *O. hookeri* cytoplasm and hybrid nucleus, and showed that the change was reversible.

§ 5.11   Hypotheses to explain non-Mendelian inheritance of plastid characters

From the discussion of non-Mendelian heredity, both in this chapter and in Chapter 2, it is apparent that this type of inheritance is best explained as due to the transmission of some material in the cytoplasm. All the examples mentioned have referred to abnormalities of the green pigmentation of the

* To obtain such plants is more difficult than might be supposed, owing to the occurrence in *O. muricata* of an abnormal hereditary mechanism (see § 9.2).

leaves. The chlorophyll occurs in particles in the cytoplasm called plastids. The simplest hypothesis to account for the non-Mendelian inheritance of chlorophyll-pigmentation defects is therefore to postulate that plastids are autonomous self-replicating structures and that they may occur in abnormal yellow or colourless forms. This hypothesis was first proposed by Baur (1909) to account for his results with *Pelargonium*, and is supported by several pieces of evidence, notably that the white areas in variegated plants are found to have minute colourless plastids visibly different from the normal green ones characteristic of the green areas. However, it does not follow from this that the plastids are necessarily themselves the hereditary determinants. Indeed, the following observations made by Correns (1909) with 'albomaculata' *Mirabilis jalapa* suggest that cytoplasmic constituents other than the plastids are responsible. First, at the boundary between green and white areas in variegated plants, a gradation in plastid colour was observed from cell to cell, suggesting diffusion from the white areas of some substance which interferes with normal plastid development. Secondly, cells were rarely found to contain a mixture of two different kinds of plastids such as on Baur's hypothesis would be expected to occur frequently, particularly in the boundary zone between green and white areas. Thirdly, there are insufficient cell-divisions during development for the chance segregation of two types of plastids into different cells to occur often, yet green and white areas are constantly being initiated. Similar observations to these have been made in a number of other instances of non-Mendelian inheritance of variegation, for example by Rhoades (1947) with iojap *Zea*.

If the cytoplasmic hereditary determinants are not the plastids, what is their nature? In attempting to answer this question, an observation by Anderson (1923) is important. He was the first to discover non-Mendelian inheritance of leaf-striping in *Zea mays*, and in studying the progeny of such a striped plant used as female parent, he took care to record the position of each grain on the ear. He found that all the grains in one area of the ear produced green plants, and all those in another area produced white plants that died, while striped plants tended to come from grains forming a transitional zone between the 'green' and 'white' areas (see Fig. 5.7). These areas extended longitudinally up the ear and corresponded with the cell-multiplication during development, just as in the vegetative parts the striping reflects the way in which the leaf develops. It is evident that, in sexual reproduction as well as in leaf growth, green cells tend to give green, and white to give white. This behaviour suggests that the hereditary determinants do not readily diffuse from one cell to another, or in other words are particles rather than a fluid. It should be noted that the gradation in plastid colour at the boundary of green areas, referred to in the last paragraph, need not imply that the hereditary determinant is fluid but merely that its effects can diffuse from one cell to another. Similar gradations in plastid colour often occur when variegation shows Mendelian inheritance, and then one concludes that the hereditary determinant resides in the cell nucleus, and hence cannot be directly responsible for the gradation in colour in the cytoplasm.

5

FIGURE 5.7   Reconstruction ($\times$ 0·5) of an
ear on a striped plant of *Zea
mays* studied by Anderson
(1923). White (unshaded)
grains gave albino seed-
lings, cross-hatched grains
gave striped seedlings, and
black grains gave normal
green seedlings. All the
grains on the ear looked
alike. Almost all those on
the rear side of the ear gave
green seedlings.

This hypothesis of particulate cytoplasmic hereditary determinants,
capable of replication and indefinite passage from generation to generation,
appears to be consistent with the data on non-Mendelian inheritance of
variations in the green pigmentation of plants. However, these hypothetical
particles have not yet been identified with specific cytoplasmic structures.
Certain of the data, notably those of Baur for *Pelargonium* and of Renner for
Oenothera, are consistent with the equating of these particles with the plastids,
but this equation lacks confirmation.

§ 5.12   Further examples of cytoplasmic inheritance

Cytoplasmic inheritance in green plants is not confined to plastid characters. Michaelis (1954) studied cytoplasmic inheritance in *Epilobium*
(Willow-herb) by making reciprocal crosses between different species and

varieties, and then pollinating the progeny with the male parent, and repeating this in each successive generation. On the assumption that no cytoplasm is inherited from the pollen, plants will be obtained within a few generations which have essentially the nuclear constitution of one parent (that used as male in each generation), while the cytoplasm has all been derived from the other parent. Michaelis found that *E. luteum* as female crossed for 24 successive generations with *E. hirsutum* as male gave male-sterile plants resembling *E. hirsutum*. The reciprocal cross could not be continued for more than 3 generations of back-crossing because of sterility or inviability. Within the one species, *E. hirsutum*, similar back-crossing between strains from different parts of Europe also gave evidence of persistent cytoplasmic differences: such characters as male-sterility, stunted growth, or deformed flowers distinguished the back-cross progeny from their male parent. It is evident that some features of *Epilobium* cytoplasm are autonomous and persist, apparently indefinitely, in the presence of an alien nucleus.

Some cytoplasmically-inherited variants, for example, the killer character in *Paramecium aurelia*, and carbon dioxide sensitivity in *Drosophila melanogaster*, appear to be due to infection by a virus (cf. review in Jinks, 1964).

§ 5.13   The heterokaryon test

Many examples of non-Mendelian inheritance are known in Fungi. For this group of organisms, Jinks (1954) has devised a test for the occurrence of cytoplasmic variants, based on the phenomenon of heterokaryosis described in § 5.4. A mutant such as the white conidial character in *Aspergillus nidulans* is known to differ from the normal green conidial form by a nuclear gene, and a heterokaryon of the two produces conidia of each colour. These conidia are uninucleate, and so the colonies derived from them will be homokaryotic. If another character-difference also distinguishes the strains which give rise to the heterokaryon, these characters may reappear only in the parental combinations in the daughter homokaryons. It is then inferred that the second character-difference is also determined by the nucleus. However, it has been found that when a white sexually-fertile and a green sexually-sterile strain form a heterokaryon, the daughter homokaryons may all be sexually fertile whether white or green. It is then inferred that the sexual sterility of the green parent is of cytoplasmic origin. In a particular strain of *A. nidulans* which had been treated with ultraviolet light, a variant with red mycelium continually reappears in a proportion of the colonies derived from the conidia, even when these conidia are obtained from colonies of normal appearance. This is comparable to the origin of cytoplasmically inherited petite yeast described in § 5.15. Arlett, Grindle and Jinks (1962) isolated single conidia from a heterokaryon between this strain and a strain with white conidia. They found that recombination had occurred and the red variant now arose in some isolates of the white-conidial strain, as well as in some of those with normal green conidia. It was evident that the red variant was cytoplasmically inherited, since there is normally no recombination between nuclear factors in a heterokaryon.

§ 5.14   Specific agents which induce cytoplasmic variants

One of the characteristic features of cytoplasmic inheritance is the specific induction of variants by certain agents. This is in contrast to the production of Mendelian mutants, where mutagens produce a whole range of kinds of mutants, not one specific one (see Chapter 9). Agents known to cause specific cytoplasmic variants include acridine dyes, streptomycin, and high temperatures during growth. Treatment with streptomycin (Provasoli, Hutner and Schatz, 1948) or growth for 5 or 6 days at 34°C (Pringsheim and Pringsheim, 1952) can cause a permanent loss of the plastids in *Euglena gracilis*, which then becomes a colourless saprophytic organism, formerly regarded as a distinct species and called *Astasia longa*. Sager (1962) discovered that streptomycin caused cytoplasmic mutation in *Chlamydomonas reinhardi*. Such mutants are transmitted usually by one parent only, exceptionally by both. From study of the progeny of such exceptional zygotes, Sager and Ramanis (1963) found that segregation of two cytoplasmic differences (streptomycin dependence (sd) and sensitivity (ss), and acetate requirement (ac^-) and independence (ac^+)) occurred independently, the acetate character usually at an earlier stage of development than the streptomycin character.

§ 5.15   Ephrussi's experiments with yeast

One of the clearest examples of non-Mendelian heredity in Fungi concerns 'petite colonie' in *Saccharomyces cerevisiae* (Baker's Yeast) studied by Ephrussi and colleagues (see Ephrussi, 1953). When individual yeast cells are spread on culture medium, they soon grow to form small circular colonies containing many cells. Ephrussi observed that one or two out of every thousand such colonies were only about one-third or one-half the diameter of the remainder. Cells from one of the normal large colonies, when again spread on culture medium produced a further small proportion of 'petite' colonies, and this happened time after time. On the other hand, the cells from the small colonies bred true and gave only petites. Biochemical studies established that the slow growth of the petite strain of yeast was due to the loss of the ability to respire aerobically. In the absence of oxygen, the growth rate of large colonies was slowed to that of petites. Furthermore, the lack of aerobic respiration in the petite strain was found to be associated with the absence of a number of respiratory enzymes. These enzymes occur in particles in the cytoplasm called mitochondria. Ephrussi and associates discovered that in the presence of acridine dyes, such as acriflavine or euflavine, all the newly-formed daughter-cells in a yeast colony, if isolated, gave rise to petite colonies. This change from normal to petite, with its associated loss of respiratory enzymes, persisted indefinitely after the removal of the dye. When the petite strain, whether arisen spontaneously or induced by acridines, was crossed with a normal strain, the progeny did not show the petite character, and it did not reappear in subsequent generations apart from the low percentage of petite colonies which were always arising. Other character differences, when present, showed normal Mendelian inheritance, with precise ratios.

A number of similar variants with deficiencies in several respiratory enzymes are also known in *Neurospora crassa* (see Fincham and Day, 1965, and Jinks, 1964).

To account for his results, Ephrussi put forward the hypothesis that the petite strain differs from the normal in the loss of cytoplasmic particles postulated to be necessary for the synthesis of the respiratory enzymes. If these hypothetical particles are distributed at random between the parent cell and the daughter-cell budded off from it, and if it is further assumed that there are normally only about 10 of the particles per cell, then about one per thousand daughter-cells will contain none of the particles and will give rise to a petite colony. This would be in agreement with observation. The acridine dyes are assumed to destroy the particles or to prevent them from multiplying. When a petite strain is crossed with a normal one, the petite character is lost because some of the cytoplasm of the normal parent is passed to all the progeny, which therefore receive the postulated particles. Thus it can be seen that this hypothesis will account satisfactorily for all the observations.

It will be noticed that this hypothesis resembles that proposed to explain non-Mendelian inheritance of green pigment variants in flowering plants discussed above. Both theories invoke particulate cytoplasmic determinants. The resemblance may extend further, for the white areas in variegated plants may be composed of cells which have lost the particles necessary for the development of normal plastids, just as the petite yeast cells are thought to have lost particles necessary for the development of normal mitochondria. Moreover, just as plastid variants may show Mendelian inheritance (for example, yellow *versus* green seeds in *Pisum*), Ephrussi found a dwarf strain of yeast which showed Mendelian inheritance. This strain lacked the ability to respire aerobically, just like the non-Mendelian petite strain already described. It appears that particulate hereditary factors responsible for fundamental cell phenomena such as photosynthesis and respiration occur in both nucleus and cytoplasm.

§ 5.16   Conclusion

Evidence has been brought together in this chapter for the belief that Mendelian heredity, with its regular segregation of character-differences to give simple ratios of different kinds of progeny, and with its identical results from reciprocal crosses, is brought about by particulate determinants in the cell-nucleus, although their effects may sometimes be delayed. Conversely, non-Mendelian heredity, characterized by a lack of regular segregation of character-differences, by variable progeny ratios, and usually by maternal inheritance, appears to be determined by cytoplasmic particles. Whereas the identity of the nuclear particles is well-established and will be discussed in subsequent chapters, that of the cytoplasmic particles is unknown. The relative importance of nucleus and cytoplasm in heredity is discussed in § 16.4.

6. The chromosome theory of Mendelian inheritance

§ 6.1 Chromosomes

Thread-like structures which readily stain with many dyes had long been noticed at nuclear divisions before careful and detailed observations, notably by Flemming (1882) with *Salamandra maculosa* (Spotted Salamander), Strasburger (1882) with various plants, and van Beneden (1883) with *Parascaris equorum*) (*Ascaris megalocephala*, Horse Thread-worm), established the essential features of the division process. Flemming (1879) introduced the term *chromatin* for the deeply staining material of nuclei, and (1882) *mitosis* for the process of division. Various nouns such as 'threads', 'loops', 'segments' or 'elements', qualified by such adjectives as 'primary', 'nuclear' or 'chromatic' had been used for the structures seen during mitosis, until Waldeyer (1888), in reviewing what was known about nuclear division, proposed the name *chromosome* for them, because 'they are so important', adding that if this name 'is practically applicable it will become familiar, otherwise it will soon sink into oblivion' (English translation, p. 181).

§ 6.2 Mitosis

The key observations on mitosis were made by Flemming (1882) and van Beneden (1883). Flemming discovered in the salamander larva that the chromosomes divided longitudinally during mitosis, and van Beneden observed in *Parascaris equorum* that the two daughter-chromosomes derived from one original chromosome were exactly alike down to the smallest detail, and moreover that they separated and passed one to each daughter-nucleus. It thus became apparent that mitosis was essentially a mechanism for distributing the halves of longitudinally-split chromosomes equally to two daughter-nuclei. The longitudinal splitting was seen to be of such paramount importance that Strasburger (1884) coined the terms *prophases* and *metaphases* to refer to the stages of mitosis before (*pro-*) and after (*meta-*) the chromosomes had separated into daughter-halves, with *anaphases* for the stages when the daughter groups of chromosomes were going back (*ana-*) to the appearance of the original parent-nuclei. Subsequently, more careful observation revealed that the chromosomes divide earlier than was originally supposed, and indeed it is now generally accepted that the threads are double from the earliest stage of mitosis at which they can be seen. The term

58

telophase was added by Heidenhain (1894) for the final stages of mitosis, with
particular reference to human leucocytes, and about 1905 Strasburger
began to use his terms for earlier stages of mitosis than he had originally.
These revised usages are those now universally adopted.

The so-called resting-nucleus, prior to the beginning of mitosis, is a
more or less spherical structure, bounded by the nuclear membrane and
containing the nuclear sap, one or more *nucleoli*, and the chromatin. The
nuclear membrane has been shown from micrographs to contain pores
about 40 mμ in diameter (see Pl. 4(*a*)). When a cell is fixed and treated with
dyes, the nucleoli and the chromatin usually stain deeply whereas the nuclear
sap remains unstained. The nucleoli are small spherical structures. Each is
attached to a specific point called a *nucleolar organizer* on a particular
chromosome. A possible function for the nucleoli is discussed in §16.4.
The chromatin gives the appearance of a network of threads filling the
nucleus, but even at the time of Flemming and Strasburger's pioneer observations, the existence of a physical reticulum was questioned, and it is now
generally agreed that the chromosomes retain their identity through the
resting-stage, although invisible. The fact that there appeared to be characteristic chromosome numbers for each species argued in favour of the continuity of the chromosomes. Moreover, Boveri (1888) showed for the first few
mitoses in the fertilised egg of *Parascaris equorum* that the chromosomes
re-appeared at prophase in the position they had occupied at the preceding
telophase. In recent years this has been clearly shown by phase-contrast
photography of living nuclei, such as Bajer's ciné films of mitosis in the
endosperm of *Haemanthus katharinae* and *Clivia cytranthiflora* (see Bajer,
1957–58). The reticular appearance of nuclei in the resting-stage is thought
to be an optical effect associated with the existence of the chromosomes in
the form of threads so fine as individually to be beyond the resolving-power
of the microscope.

Mitosis is initiated (*prophase*) by the chromosomes gradually becoming
more distinct. It was formerly thought that all the chromosomes might
be joined end-to-end at this stage but here also it is now generally agreed
that they are not joined. The early studies were made by fixing the plant or
animal material, embedding it in wax, and then cutting a series of thin
sections with a microtome. The thickness of these sections was commonly of
the same order as the diameter of the nucleus, so that nuclei were frequently
cut open. If free ends of chromosomes were seen, it was often thought that
these were artefacts due to the cutting. Nowadays, squash techniques
rather than sections are usually employed.

The chromosomes become thicker and shorter during prophase through
spiral contraction. The direction of coiling is variable. As already indicated,
the prophase chromosomes are seen to be double structures, each having
divided longitudinally into two identical halves called *chromatids*. The two
halves, however, remain closely associated throughout their length (see
Fig. 6.1(*b*) and Pl. 1(*a*)), and are twisted round one another. In late prophase
this relational coiling disappears. The uncoiling is well seen in Bajer's film.
The nucleoli diminish in size and ultimately disappear, and shortly afterwards

FIGURE 6.1   Stages of mitosis in an
organism with two pairs of
chromosomes.
(*a*) Early prophase. The
small circles represent
nucleoli.
(*b*) Late prophase.
(*c*) Side view of metaphase.
(*d*) Polar view of meta-
phase.
(*e*) Side view of anaphase.
(*f*) Telophase.

the nuclear membrane breaks down, thereby releasing the chromosomes
in the cytoplasm of the cell. It is customary nowadays to identify this
relatively abrupt breakdown of the membrane with the end of prophase.

At the beginning of the succeeding stage, *metaphase*, a series of faint lines,
which do not stain with dyes, become visible forming a spindle-shaped
structure in the cytoplasm of the cell. In animals the spindle has well-defined
poles—star-like structures from which the faint lines radiate. In plants, the
lines fade away before the poles are reached. The chromosomes, now relatively short and thick, each with its two chromatids still closely paired
(Pl. 1(*b*)), become arranged in the equatorial plane across the middle of the
spindle. Each chromosome is usually bent at a sharp angle at one point to give

a shape like the letter V as seen from the poles of the spindle. The angles of the V's all point towards the centre of the equatorial plate. The tip of the angle in each chromosome coincides with a non-staining constriction called the *centromere*. It is the centromeres which appear to be responsible for the chromosome movement on to the metaphase plate. The spindle-fibres, as the fine non-staining lines in the cytoplasm are called, pass through individual centromeres. The chromosome arms, if long, usually point towards one or other pole (see Fig. 6.1(c)). In a few organisms, for example, species of *Luzula* (Wood-rush) and certain Hemipterous insects, chromosome movement appears to be determined through a generalized property of the chromosomes rather than through a discrete entity, the centromere. Such organisms are said to have diffuse centromeres. Their chromosomes do not show the characteristic V or L shape of normal chromosomes at metaphase.

Anaphase is said to begin when the daughter-centromeres start to separate, each moving along a spindle-fibre in opposite directions towards the poles. The daughter-chromosomes thus separate first at the angle between the two arms (Pl. 1(c)). The last point of separation is the tip of the longer arm (Fig. 6.1(e)). Mazia (1955) has isolated the spindle from fertilised eggs of the echinoderm *Strongylocentrotus purpuratus* undergoing mitosis, by removal of the rest of the cytoplasm with the natural steroid detergent digitonin. Chemical analysis showed that the spindle fibres are composed largely of protein, and the aminoacid composition of this protein was found to resemble that of the protein of animal muscles. It was therefore suggested that the shortening of the spindle fibres, which occurs in the anaphase movement, has features in common with muscular contraction. A second factor in the anaphase separation of the daughter-chromosomes is the elongation of the middle region or body of the spindle lying between the two groups of chromosomes. Ris (1949) showed that this elongation is inhibited by chloral hydrate, whereas the spindle fibre contraction is not.

Telophase is said to be initiated when nuclear membranes form round each group of chromosomes (Fig. 6.1(f)). Nucleoli re-appear within each daughter-nucleus, and the chromosomes, each now composed of a single chromatid, gradually become longer and thinner until the resting-stage or *interphase* is reached, when they can no longer be clearly seen.

From this brief outline of mitosis it is evident that the duplication of the chromosomes takes place during the resting-stage. This has been confirmed from isotope labelling and other experiments (see Chapter 11).

§ 6.3   Meiosis

An observation of great significance was made by van Beneden (1883) in his studies of *Parascaris equorum*. He noticed that the egg and sperm nuclei each contained two chromosomes, whereas at the mitoses in the fertilised egg four chromosomes were visible. He thus established that the gametes each contribute the *haploid* number of chromosomes to the zygote, which thus contains the *diploid* number in its nucleus. Weismann (1887) predicted that there must be a special nuclear division, repeated in every generation, at which the chromosome number is reduced again to half the number contained in the parent nucleus. It was already known that the nuclear divisions just before the maturation of sperm and eggs in animals, and before the formation of pollen-grains and embryo-sacs in flowering plants, were abnormal. Two nuclear divisions were found to occur in quick succession. Flemming (1887) called them *heterotype* and *homotype*, respectively, since the first was the more abnormal of the two. Strasburger (1888) observed in the pollen-mother-cells and in the embryo-sac-mother-cells of various flowering plants that at late prophase of the first of these divisions, when the chromosomes first become clearly visible, the haploid number is present. Whether these were individual chromosomes, or pairs of chromosomes, and if the latter, whether the chromosomes of each pair were associated laterally or terminally, were long disputed, but it soon became evident that Weismann's predicted reduction was occurring during these divisions, since at the preceding mitosis the diploid number of chromosomes was visible. Farmer and Moore (1905) gave the name *meiosis*, meaning reduction, to the whole process of two successive nuclear divisions. Grégoire (1904) had already suggested that the two divisions should be distinguished by the Roman numerals I and II.

§ 6.4   Von Winiwarter's observations on meiosis in rabbits

As already indicated, much difference of opinion persisted for many years about the precise sequence of events during the early stages of meiosis I. This was partly owing to the difficulty of distinguishing younger and older cells in fixed preparations. However, von Winiwarter (1900) discovered that the ovary of *Oryctolagus cuniculus* (Rabbit) provided ideal material, since meiosis was found to extend over a long period of time. By examining the stage reached in young rabbits of known age, an unequivocal seriation was achieved.

The majority of the nuclei in the ovaries of a half-day old animal were found to contain chromosomes in the form of exceedingly fine single threads (Fig. 6.2(a) and Pl. 2(b)). Cells at this stage he described as having *leptotene* nuclei, meaning that the chromosomes were in the form of a 'slender ribbon'. Later work showed that the leptotene chromosomes have a highly characteristic appearance resembling a string of beads of unequal size unequally strung. The granules are called *chromomeres*.

Nearer the centre of the ovaries of the half-day old rabbit, von Winiwarter found a few nuclei in which the chromosomes had associated in pairs side by side for part of their length, but remained independent elsewhere (Fig.6.2(b) and Pl.2(c)). These he called 'synaptene' nuclei, meaning 'uniting ribbons', but owing to confusion over the meaning of the term 'synapsis', the synonym *zygotene* was substituted by Grégoire (1907). In rabbits aged 1½ and 2½ days from birth, von Winiwarter found abundant zygotene nuclei, with leptotene nuclei also present but chiefly nearer the periphery of the ovaries.

In the inner parts of the ovaries of 4- and 5-day old rabbits he found nuclei in which the chromosomes were thicker than at the earlier stages, and

FIGURE 6.2   Stages of meiosis in an organism with two pairs of chromosomes.
(a) Leptotene stage. The small circles represent nucleoli.
(b) Zygotene stage.
(c) Pachytene stage.
(d) Diplotene stage.
(e) Diakinesis.
(f) Metaphase I (side view).
(g) Anaphase I (side view).
(h) Telophase I.
(i) Prophase II.
(j) Metaphase II.
(k) Anaphase II.
(l) Telophase II.

were associated in pairs throughout their length. To these he gave the name
of nuclei with 'thick ribbons', or *pachytene* nuclei (see Fig. 6.2(c) and Pl. 2(d)).
Outside these cells there was an extensive zone of cells with zygotene nuclei,
and near the periphery of the ovary a few still at the leptotene stage.
Wenrich (1916) observed in the grasshopper *Phrynotettix tschivavensis* (= *P.
magnus*) that the chromosome pairing at the zygotene and pachytene stages
was highly specific, with corresponding chromomeres closely associated
with one another. The mechanism of this specific pairing of homologous

regions of homologous chromosomes is not understood. Belling (1929) and Darlington (1929*b*) discovered that when three editions of each chromosome are present, as in some horticultural varieties of *Hyacinthus orientalis*, all three associate, but in any one region of the chromosome only two are in actual contact (see §8.14). Riley and Chapman (1958) and Sears and Okamoto (1958) discovered that in *Triticum aestivum* (Wheat) the pairing behaviour of the chromosomes is under genetic control. This plant is thought to have arisen by hybridisation of ancestral species, each with a similar set of chromosomes, and followed by doubling of chromosome number. In the absence of a particular chromosome (no. 5), it was found that each chromosome associated at meiosis with its counterparts from the other ancestral species, whereas normally the pairing is confined to the strictly homologous

TABLE 6.1   Appearance of nuclei in ovaries of rabbits (Von Winiwarter, 1900).

Age from Birth in Days	Tissue of Ovary			
	Extreme Outer	Outer	Middle	Inner
0·5	Resting	Resting	Leptotene	Zygotene
1·5 and 2·5	Resting	Leptotene	Zygotene	Zygotene
4 and 5	Resting	Leptotene	Zygotene	Pachytene
10, 11 and 12	Leptotene	Zygotene	Pachytene	Diplotene
18	Zygotene	Pachytene	Diplotene	Diplotene
28	Pachytene	Diplotene	Diplotene	Diplotene

chromosomes within the contribution from each ancestor. It was inferred that a specific gene in chromosome no. 5 determined the meiotic behaviour of all the chromosomes.

From rabbits aged 10, 11 and 12 days von Winiwarter found that the nuclei in the central parts of the ovaries contained chromosomes which were even shorter and thicker than the pachytene ones, and moreover had a very evident duality of structure, forming characteristic loops (see Fig. (6.2(*d*) and Pl. 2(*e*)). These nuclei he described as *diplotene*. The greater part of the ovaries of this age contained pachytene nuclei, with a peripheral zone at the zygotene and a few at the leptotene stage. An 18-day old rabbit had ovaries containing a thick zone of diplotene nuclei with many pachytene and a few zygotene nuclei near the outside, while at 28 days from birth there were no zygotene and only a few pachytene nuclei and the majority of the ovary cells showed nuclei at the diplotene stage. These results are summarised in Table 6.1, where the sequence leptotene–zygotene–pachytene–diplotene is clearly brought out. In the ovaries of vertebrate animals, meiosis commonly stops at the diplotene stage for a long period of time, so von Winiwarter was not able to follow meiosis beyond this stage in the young female rabbit. He observed the same stages as he had seen in the rabbit in the ovaries of a seven-month old human foetus.

Dispute continued for a further 30 years after von Winiwarter's pioneer studies, before general agreement was reached that his observations were correct and applied throughout the plant and animal kingdoms wherever meiosis took place. The reasons for this long drawn out controversy will be discussed in Chapter 8.

§ 6.5 Diakinesis

Prior to von Winiwarter's studies, Häcker (1897) had subdivided the prophase of the first division of meiosis into two parts. For the second of these, when the chromosomes are relatively short and thick and show characteristic loops or cross-shaped configurations, he coined the name *diakinesis*, meaning 'moving apart', since he saw that the chromosomes were well-separated from one another at this stage, whereas in the first part of the prophase he thought, like many others at the time, that they were joined end-to-end. He illustrated the diakinetic stage from both plants and animals, using the published diagrams of others. Since it is now established that the various chromosomes are not joined end-to-end in early prophase I, the term diakinesis is really a misnomer. It is also out of keeping with von Winiwarter's terms (with the suffix *-tene*) for the earlier stages. In the diakinetic chromosomes the successive loops lie at right angles to one another, whereas at the diplotene stage they are all in one plane. Otherwise the chromosomes do not differ in any important respect from the diplotene ones, apart from being shorter and thicker (Fig. 6.2(*e*) and Pl. 3(*b*)), and sometimes with fewer loops (see §8.18).

Observation of diplotene or diakinetic nuclei in favourable material soon established that the structures within them are not merely double but quadruple (Pl. 3(*a*)). In other words, each chromosome, in addition to being associated with a counterpart, is itself divided into two chromatids. How the four strands which make up the diplotene and diakinetic chromosome pairs have originated has been a source of prolonged debate and will be discussed in Chapter 8.

§ 6.6 Later stages of meiosis

With the disappearance of the nucleoli and of the nuclear membrane, prophase I gives way to *metaphase I*. Each chromosome pair takes up a position on the equatorial plate of the spindle such that the centromeres of the two component chromosomes lie one on each side of the mid-plane (Fig. 6.2(*f*) and Pl. 3(*c*)). Thus, whereas in metaphase of mitosis the centromeres of the individual chromosomes lie on the equator of the spindle, at metaphase I of meiosis the centromeres of a chromosome-pair lie one in the tropic of Cancer and the other of Capricorn and both on the same line of longitude. At this stage, the chromosomes are exceptionally short and thick.

Anaphase I is said to begin when the two whole chromosomes forming each pair start to move apart towards opposite poles of the spindle. At this stage the two chromatids of which each chromosome is composed are readily seen (see Fig. 6.2(*g*)). Nuclear membranes develop round each group of chromosomes at *telophase I* (Fig. 6.2(*h*)). After a brief *interphase*, when the chromosomes become difficult to observe, *prophase II* follows during which they become shorter and thicker again (Fig. 6.2(*i*)). *At metaphase II* the nuclear membranes have broken down again and two new spindles have formed (Fig. 6.2(*j*)). The second division of meiosis resembles mitosis in the centromeres of the chromosomes taking up a position on the equatorial plate, but differs in the two chromatids, of which each chromosome has been composed ever since prophase I, diverging somewhat from one another instead of being closely associated (Pl. 3(*e*)). At *anaphase II* the daughter-chromosomes separate and move towards opposite poles on each spindle with the centromeres as usual leading the way (Fig. 6.2(*k*)), and at *telophase II* nuclear membranes have formed round each of the four haploid nuclei which result from meiosis (Fig. 6.2(*l*)).

The essential features of meiosis which distinguish it from mitosis are, first, that whole chromosomes associate in pairs at prophase *I* and separate to opposite poles at anaphase *I*; and secondly, that there is no duplication of the chromosomes in the brief interphase between the two nuclear divisions, so that the daughter-chromosomes which separate at anaphase II were those first seen at prophase I. Thus, instead of the single nuclear division without chromosome division which Weismann (1887) had anticipated, when the details of meiosis were discovered, it was found that the process was less simple: as indicated above, there are two divisions of the nucleus associated with one of the chromosomes.

§ 6.7   Evidence that paternal and maternal chromosomes associate

Montgomery (1901), from studies of the chromosomes at meiosis in some 42 species of hemipterous insects, came to the conclusion that the chromosomes which associate in pairs at prophase I are of paternal and maternal origin respectively. His evidence for this important deduction was two-fold. First, whenever two chromosomes could be distinguished by their greater size, as for instance in *Protenor belfragei*, these two especially large ones were always found paired with one another at prophase I. Secondly, in *Euschistus variolarius* with 14 chromosomes visible at the somatic mitoses, 7 bivalent associations were always found at prophase I of meiosis. He argued that if chromosome association was paternal with paternal this would give 3 bivalent and 1 univalent association, and likewise with the chromosomes of maternal origin. The regular formation of pairs even when, as here, the haploid chromosome number is odd, led Montgomery to the conclusion that the bivalent associations at prophase I are always made up of one paternal and one corresponding maternal chromosome.

Sutton (1902) extended Montgomery's observations when he showed that in the grasshopper *Brachystola magna* all the chromosomes can be individually recognised. The somatic mitosis in the male showed 23 chromosomes which could be classified by size into 11 pairs and one odd one (the *X*-chromosome— see §6.10). The largest chromosomes were 5 to 6 times as long as the smallest.

At prophase I of meiosis, apart from the X-chromosome, 11 double chromosomes were visible in each nucleus and they showed the same size differences as at mitosis. Moreover, though the absolute lengths of the chromosomes varied greatly at different stages of meiosis, their relative lengths were approximately constant. It was evident that each chromosome was distinct and maintained its morphological individuality throughout successive cell-divisions, and that the meiotic pairing was strictly between paternal and maternal homologues, as Montgomery had suggested.

§ 6.8   Evidence of qualitative differences between chromosomes

Boveri (1902) found evidence that the individual chromosomes in *Paracentrotus lividus* (a Sea Urchin) possess different qualities. This remarkable conclusion was based on studies of abnormal progeny resulting from fertilisation of eggs by two sperms. Boveri showed that the first mitosis in such *triploid* eggs, that is, with 3 sets of chromosomes, was abnormal, and gave rise to an irregular distribution of the chromosomes to the daughter-nuclei. He was able to show that for normal development, a particular combination of chromosomes was more important than a particular number. It will be recalled that he had shown earlier (see Chapter 5) that haploid individuals (from enucleated eggs) were normal although dwarf. He now established that they were normal because they had the normal combination of chromosomes. This important principle has subsequently been confirmed in many other organisms. Thus, Blakeslee (1922) showed that in *Datura stramonium* (Thorn Apple) triploid and *tetraploid* individuals, having respectively 3 and 4 complete sets of 12 chromosomes in their somatic cells, only differed rather slightly in appearance from the normal diploid, whereas individuals which he described as *trisomic*, having one of the chromosomes represented three times but the remaining 11 represented twice, were abnormal. The discovery of individuals with each of the 12 different chromosomes in turn present in triplicate revealed that each had a different morphology. Thus, three doses of one chromosome gave rise to a variety called Globe with broader leaves than normal, a less toothed leaf-margin, and a spherical instead of ovate capsule with shorter spines than normal (Fig. 6.3(*a*) and (*b*)).

(*a*)   (*b*)   (*c*)

FIGURE 6.3   Fruits (×0·5) of normal and trisomic plants of *Datura stramonium* (from Blakeslee). (*a*) Normal. (*b*) Globe. (*c*) Cocklebur.

Individuals trisomic for a different chromosome gave a variety called Cocklebur with weak stems, narrow twisted leaves and a narrow short-spined capsule (Fig. 6.3(*c*)). Each trisomic variety differed from the normal in a whole range of characters affecting all parts of the plant.

Knowledge of the abnormality of trisomic individuals has recently been extended to man. From squash preparations of mitosis in cultures of lung tissue from 4 embryos of unknown sex after legal abortion, Tjio and Levan (1956) showed that the human somatic chromosome number was 46. Confirmation of this number was obtained by Ford and Hamerton (1956) from study of meiosis in fresh operative specimens of testis tissue from 3 individuals. Human chromosomes are readily classified by size into 7 classes, and within these classes the individual chromosomes can be recognised by the relative lengths of their arms (Pl. 1(*e*)). By international agreement, the largest of the 23 pairs is called no. 1, and the others have been allocated identification numbers in order of decreasing size. Lejeune, Gautier and Turpin (1959) discovered that mongolism is associated with the presence of an additional small chromosome. It appears that mongols have three editions of chromosome no. 21 in their somatic cells, instead of the normal two.

§ 6.9   The chromosome theory of Mendelian heredity

Sutton (1903), on the basis of his studies on *Brachystola magna* and with the support of Montgomery's and Boveri's findings, gave the first clear formulation of the chromosome theory of Mendelian heredity. He drew attention to the resemblance between the separation of homologous chromosomes at meiosis and Mendel's postulated separation of character-differences at gamete-formation. Moreover, Sutton pointed out that in all probability each homologous pair of chromosomes is orientated on the metaphase I spindle independently, so that any pair of chromosomes may lie with maternal or paternal chromosome indifferently towards either pole irrespective of the orientation of other pairs. He noted that this would lead to a large number of different possible combinations of maternal and paternal chromosomes in the gamete nuclei, if the chromosome number were at all large: indeed 2^n combinations, where n is the haploid chromosome number. He quoted as an example the Sea Urchin *Lytechinus variegatus* with 36 chromosomes in the somatic cells and hence 2^{18} or 262,144 possible gametic combinations of paternal and maternal chromosomes, so that the number of types of offspring from a single pair would be 2^{36} or approximately $6 \cdot 87 \times 10^{10}$! The possible number of different assortments of parental chromosomes will vary greatly with the species, because chromosome numbers show such a big range. The extremes recorded for the haploid number are 2 in a few arthropods and in the flowering plant *Haplopappus gracilis* (Jackson, 1957), and approximately 510 in the fern *Ophioglossum petiolatum* (Manton and Sledge, 1955). Sutton drew attention to the parallel between the presumed independent orientation of homologous chromosome-pairs at meiosis, and Mendel's observation of independent inheritance of different character-differences.

PLATE 1 (a)–(d) Stages of mitosis seen in acetic-orcein squash preparations of root-tip cells of *Crocus balansae* (2n = 6). Magnification ca. ×750.
(Courtesy of S. A. Henderson)

(a) *above* Mid-prophase

(b) *above* Metaphase

(c) Early anaphase

(d) Late anaphase

(e) Metaphase of mitosis in a leucocyte from peripheral blood of a human male (2n = 44 + X + Y). The material was treated with colchicine before fixation, and is a squash preparation stained with acetic-orcein. Magnification ca. ×400. X = probable X-chromosome. Y = probable Y-chromosome.
(Courtesy of D. Briggs)

(f) A squash preparation of salivary gland chromosomes from a mature larva of *Drosophila melanogaster*, stained with acetic-orcein (cf. Fig. 9.1, p. 143) Magnification ca. ×400. C = Chromocentre.
(Courtesy of D. Briggs)

PLATE 2   The course of meiosis as seen in acetic-orcein squash preparations of spermatocytes of the locust *Schistocerca gregaria* (2n = 22 + X in the male) (continued on Plate 3). Magnification ca. ×1000. X = X-chromosome. In (a) and (f), which are autoradiographs (4 days' exposure), the tissue was treated for 1 hour at 30°C with either 100 μC/ 0·2 ml of ³H-thymidine (a) or 100 μC/0·1 ml of ³H-uridine (f) before fixation. The grains reveal where uptake of the radioactive label has taken place, and show that preleptotene DNA synthesis (a) has occurred in the X-chromosome and the autosomal region of the nucleus (cf. p. 173), and that RNA synthesis at early diplotene (f) has taken place in the autosomal bivalents, but not in the X-chromosome which is evidently inactive (see p. 311).   *(Courtesy of S. A. Henderson)*

(a) Preleptotene (autoradiograph)   (b) Late leptotene

(c) Late zygotene   (d) Late pachytene

(e) Early diplotene   (f) Early diplotene (autoradiograph)

Confirmation of this random orientation of different chromosome-pairs on the first-division spindle was obtained by Carothers (1913). She examined 300 cells showing metaphase I or anaphase I of meiosis from males of *Brachystola magna* heterozygous for an inequality in the size of one of the chromosomes. She found that this size difference always segregated at the first division of meiosis. The single X-chromosome moves in its entirety to one pole at this division. In 146 of the cells, the smaller component of the unequal pair went to the same pole as the X-chromosome, and in the remaining 154 cells it was the larger component which segregated with the

FIGURE 6.4   Metaphase I (*a* and *c*) and anaphase I (*b* and *d*) of meiosis in males of *Brachystola magna* heterozygous for an inequality in the size of one of the chromosomes (from Carothers). The unequal chromosome-pair and the X-chromosome are shown black. (*a* and *b*) Smaller component orientated to move to the same pole as the X-chromosome. (*c* and *d*) Larger component so orientated.

X-chromosome (see Fig. 6.4). Similar results were obtained with another grasshopper, *Arphia simplex*. Some exceptions to this random orientation of different chromosome-pairs on the meiotic first-division spindle are discussed in §16.2.

§ 6.10   Sex chromosomes

The first definite evidence for a connection between the chromosomes and a character-difference showing Mendelian inheritance came from work on sex-determination. Henking (1891) in studies on meiosis at sperm-formation in the hemipterous insect *Pyrrhocoris apterus* observed a deeply-staining chromatin-element, which passed to one pole on each anaphase II spindle, so that half the sperms received it and half did not (see Fig. 6.5(*a*) and (*b*)). He labelled it X as he was uncertain whether it was a chromosome or not. Later workers on insect cytology established its chromosomal nature, and after observing a similar unpaired chromosome in various grasshoppers, McClung (1902) suggested that it was concerned with sex-determination. This was established by Wilson (1905) who discovered that the single X-*chromosome* (as he called it, Wilson 1909) of the male *Protenor belfragei*

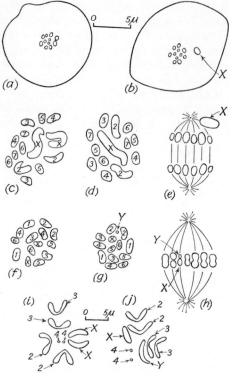

FIGURE 6.5   Sex chromosomes in various insects. $X = X$-chromosome. $Y =$ Y-chromosome. Numbers refer to the autosomes in order of diminishing size

(*a* and *b*) *Pyrrhocoris apterus*. Polar views of the two groups of chromosomes on one of the spindles at anaphase II of meiosis in the male (from Henking, 1891). The single X-chromosome moves to one pole at anaphase II.

(*c–e*) *Protenor belfragei* (from Wilson).

(*c*) Female. Late prophase of mitosis in an oogonium. Two X-chromosomes present.

(*d*) Male. Late prophase of mitosis in a spermatogonium. A single X-chromosome present.

(*e*) Male. One spindle at anaphase II of meiosis. The single X-chromosome moves to one pole.

(*f–h*) *Lygaeus turcicus* (from Wilson).

(*f*) Female. Late prophase of mitosis in an oogonium. Two X-chromosomes present.

(*g*) Male. Late prophase of mitosis in a spermatogonium. An X- and a Y-chromosome present.

(*h*) Male. One spindle at metaphase II of meiosis. The X- and Y-chromosomes separate to opposite poles at anaphase II.

(*i* and *j*) *Drosophila melanogaster* (from Stevens).

(*i*) Female. Polar view of metaphase of mitosis in an oogonium. Two X-chromosomes present.

(*j*) Male. Polar view of metaphase of mitosis in a spermatogonium. An X- and a Y-chromosome present.

has two counterparts in the female, so that the somatic chromosome numbers of male and female are 13 and 14 respectively (Fig. 6.5(c)-(e)). He argued from these observations that the sperms which receive an X-chromosome will give rise to females and those that do not to males. Similar observations were made on several other hemipterous insects, while in a second group of these insects, exemplified by *Lygaeus turcicus*, both sexes were found to have the same chromosome number ($2n = 14$ in this instance), but one chromosome in the male was much smaller than the corresponding one in the female (Fig. 6.5(f)-(h)). Again Wilson argued that there must be a causal connection between these chromosomes and sex.

Stevens (1905) independently made similar observations on other insects, for instance the beetle *Tenebrio molitor* (Meal worm) where she found that the male has 19 large and 1 small chromosome in its somatic cells, while the female has 20 large chromosomes. Later she showed (1908) that *Drosophila melanogaster* has four pairs of chromosomes in its somatic cells and that in the male the two components of one pair are of unequal size (Fig. 6.5(i) and (j)). The term *Y-chromosome* was proposed by Wilson (1909) for the odd chromosome when present, so *Lygaeus*, *Tenebrio* and *Drosophila* could be described as female *XX* and male *XY*, and *Protenor* as female *XX* and male *X*. Wilson (1909) suggested that in both these categories sex was determined by the number of X-chromosomes. He argued that since a Y-chromosome was not always present it played no part in sex-determination.

§ 6.11   The chromosome theory of sex-linkage

On the basis of Wilson's theory of sex-determination, Morgan (1911a) postulated that the gene for white eyes in *Drosophila melanogaster* is carried by the X-chromosome. This hypothesis to explain the sex-linkage which he had found (see Chapter 3) represented an important advance over his earlier theory (based on that of Punnett and Bateson for *Abraxas*), since it was no longer necessary to assume that all male Drosophilas were heterozygous for white eye-colour, for, with only one X-chromosome in the male, heterozygosity was impossible for sex-linked characters. Moreover the criss-cross inheritance of the X-chromosomes was exactly paralleled by that of white eye-colour (see Figs 6.6 and 6.7).

The sex-linkage of the pale form of *Abraxas grossulariata* was similarly explained when it was established that in Lepidoptera it is the female which has either an X- and a Y-chromosome, or an unpaired X-chromosome, while the male has 2 X-chromosomes, that is, the converse of the situation in *Drosophila*.

Red-green colour blindness in man was found to show criss-cross inheritance similar to white eye-colour in *Drosophila*. That is to say, colour-blindness is usually manifest only in males, whose daughters act as carriers of it to half their sons. The female *XX*, male *XY* sex-determining mechanism in man was confirmed subsequently (cf. Pl. 1(e)). By contrast, the dominant character barred feather-colouring of the Barred Plymouth Rock and its recessive allele the black feather-colouring of the Black Langshan variety of

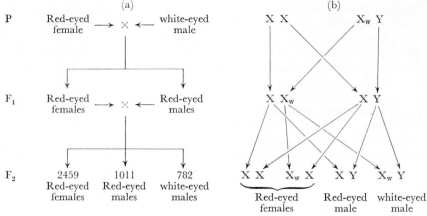

FIGURE 6.6   (a) Morgan's data (1910) for the inheritance of white eye-colour in
the normally red-eyed fly *Drosophila melanogaster*.
(b) The hypothesis which he proposed (1911*a*) to account for these
results, namely, that the gene for white eyes is carried by the
X-chromosome. Explanation of symbols:
X = *X*-chromosome with dominant normal allelomorph of
white-eye gene, and hence causing red eyes.
X_w = *X*-chromosome with recessive gene for white eyes.
Y = *Y*-chromosome (plays no part in inheritance).
Two *X*-chromosomes give a female, one *X*-chromosome a male.
The shortage of males in F_2, particularly those with white eyes,
compared with expectation, can probably be accounted for by
lowered viabilities.

Gallus domesticus were found to show sex-linkage of the *Abraxas* type, and the
cytology confirmed that birds, like Lepidoptera, have the female *XY*,
male *XX* sex-determining mechanism.

Baur (1912) obtained the first example of sex-linkage in plants. He
discovered a form of *Silene alba* (White Campion) with narrow grass-like

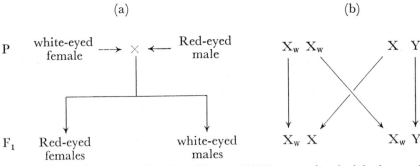

FIGURE 6.7   (a) Further data from Morgan (1910) concerning the inheritance of
white eye-colour in *Drosophila melanogaster*, and
(b) his chromosome hypothesis (1911*a*) to account for them. Symbols
as in Fig. 6.6.

leaves. It was found to be a staminate plant. Pollen from it was used to fertilize a female plant with normal broad leaves. All the progeny were normal, and when intercrossed they gave 167 plants with broad leaves and 60 with narrow leaves, in agreement with the Mendelian expectation of a 3:1 ratio (expected frequencies 170·25 and 56·75, deviations 3·25, $\chi^2 = 0·24$, $n = 1$, $P = 0·9–0·5$). When 52 of the narrow-leaved plants were grown to maturity all were found to be male, while 23 of the broad-leaved ones comprised 15 female and 8 male, in good agreement with the 2:1 ratio of the sexes expected in F_2 individuals with the dominant phenotype, if *Silene alba* is like *Drosophila* in its sex-linkage (compare Fig. 6.6), that is, female XX, male XY, with the gene for narrow leaves carried by the X-chromosome. Subsequently, cytological studies confirmed that *Silene* has this chromosome formula.

§ 6.12   XXY Drosophila

The chromosome theory of Mendelian heredity may be said to have become established with the publication of the results of combined cytological and genetical studies by Bridges (1914, 1916) with an abnormal strain of *Drosophila melanogaster* having two X-chromosomes and a Y chromosome.

Morgan (1910) had reported that a white-eyed female *Drosophila* crossed with a normal red-eyed male always gave equal numbers of the converse types in F_1, that is, red-eyed females and white-eyed males. On the hypothesis that the gene for white eyes is carried by the X-chromosome these results were readily explained (Morgan 1911a) by the criss-cross inheritance of the X-chromosomes, as indicated in Fig. 6.7. However, Morgan and Bridges discovered a strain of white-eyed females which gave some unexpected progeny from such a cross. These unexpected individuals comprised about 4·3% of the progeny, and consisted of approximately equal numbers of the two parental forms (white-eyed females and red-eyed males). The occurrence of these *matriclinous* daughters (that is, resembling their mother) and *patriclinous* sons (resembling their father) appeared to contradict the chromosome hypothesis.

Bridges studied the progeny in the succeeding generation, with the following results. The matriclinous daughters (white eyed; class (i) in Table 6.2) behaved like their mother and again gave about 4.3% of parental forms when crossed with normal red-eyed males. The patriclinous sons (red-eyed; class (ii) in Table 6.2) when crossed with unrelated females gave no abnormal progeny in the next or succeeding generations. Half of the ordinary patriclinous daughters (red-eyed; class (iii)) gave normal progeny indefinitely, and the other half (class (iv)) inherited the property of giving about 4·3% of unexpected progeny. Half of the ordinary matriclinous sons (white eyed; class (v)) gave normal progeny indefinitely and the other half (class (vi)) transmitted the property of producing exceptional progeny to some of their daughters, although not themselves having this property. These results are summarised in Table 6.2(a).

To account for these results, Bridges postulated that the original white-eyed female was abnormal in possessing a Y-chromosome in addition to two

TABLE 6.2   (a) Bridges' results from crossing an abnormal white-eyed female *Drosophila melanogaster* with a normal Red-eyed male, (b) his total data (1916) from this and similar crosses using various sex-linked mutant characters, and (c) his hypothesis to explain these results. Symbols as in Fig. 6.6.

(a) Parents		Red-eyed (normal) male	
White-eyed female from abnormal stock			2·1% of white-eyed females (i), all with some exceptional progeny.
	2·2% of Red-eyed males (ii), all with normal progeny.		
	49·0% of Red-eyed females, half (iii) with normal progeny, and half (iv) with some exceptional progeny.		46·7% of white-eyed males, half (v) with normal progeny, and half (vi) with some exceptional progeny.

(b) Parents		Normal males	
Females from abnormal stock, with various sex-linked mutant characters			1169 females of mutant appearance (i).
	1235 males of normal appearance (ii).		
	27,679 females of normal appearance (iii and iv).		26,391 males of mutant appearance (v and vi).

(c) Parents			XY (Red-eyed male) Sperm			
			X		Y	
X_wX_wY (white-eyed female from abnormal stock)	Eggs	8·2% $\begin{cases} X_wX_w \\ Y \end{cases}$	XX_wX_w Dies		(i) X_wX_wY	
			(ii) XY		YY	Dies
		91·8% $\begin{cases} X_w \\ X_wY \end{cases}$	(iii) XX_w		(v) X_wY	
			(iv) XX_wY		(vi) X_wYY	

X-chromosomes. Furthermore he postulated that at the first division of meiosis in the maturation of the eggs there was variability of behaviour such that in about 92% of meioses one X-chromosome and the Y-chromosome went to one pole and the remaining X-chromosome to the other pole, while in the other 8% the two X-chromosomes separated from the Y. This hypothesis will account perfectly for all the observations, as indicated in Table 6.2(c). Individuals with 0 or 3 X-chromosomes were thought not to survive.

Confirmation of this XXY hypothesis was obtained from cytological studies: Bridges found that the white-eyed females and half the red-eyed ones had two X-chromosomes and a Y-chromosome, exactly as the theory predicts. It is presumed that the original XXY female arose through fertilisation by a Y sperm of an abnormal egg containing two X-chromosomes. This egg might have been the consequence of a meiotic abnormality whereby both X-chromosomes passed to the same pole of the spindle. Bridges (1916) reported several instances of this failure of the X-chromosomes to separate at meiosis even in the absence of a Y-chromosome. Altogether he bred 56,474 F_1 progeny from XXY females carrying various sex-linked characters crossed to normal males, with the results shown in Table 6.2(b). The percentages in Table 6.2(a) are based on these results.

§ 6.13   Sex determination

In addition to establishing the truth of the chromosome theory of Mendelian inheritance, Bridges' experiments with XXY flies also confirmed Wilson's theory of sex-determination, for it was evident that an XXY fly was female and an XYY fly male, as expected if sex is determined by the number of X-chromosomes irrespective of the number of Y-chromosomes. Bridges (1922) later showed that sex is determined by the proportion of X-chromosomes to other chromosomes (*autosomes*). If A stands for a haploid set of autosomes and X for an X-chromosome, $\frac{X}{A}$ is $\frac{1}{2}$ in the normal male and $\frac{2}{2}$ in the normal female. With three X-chromosomes $\left(\frac{X}{A} = \frac{3}{2}\right)$ abnormal sterile females of low viability and delayed development were obtained. Bridges also obtained triploid flies with three sets of autosomes and found that $\frac{X}{A} = \frac{1}{3}$ gave an abnormal sterile male of slow development, $\frac{X}{A} = \frac{2}{3}$ gave a sterile fly of appearance intermediate between the two sexes, while $\frac{X}{A} = \frac{3}{3}$ gave a female of almost normal appearance, although sterile. Thus his results were consistent with the view that sex was determined by the proportion of X-chromosomes and autosomes, which were presumed to carry genes for female and male characters, respectively. Later work has confirmed that, irrespective of the number of Y-chromosomes, $\frac{X}{A}$ of $\frac{1}{2}$ or less gives males, 1 or more gives females, and between $\frac{1}{2}$ and 1 gives intermediates.

On the other hand, in *Silene alba, Homo sapiens* and *Mus musculus* a different mechanism appears to operate. Westergaard (1958) in reviewing his own and others' work with *Silene* showed that the presence of the *Y*-chromosome gives a male and its absence a female, irrespective of the number of *X*-chromosomes and sets of autosomes. The only exceptions are tetraploid plants with 4 *X*-chromosomes but only 1 *Y*-chromosome, which are usually hermaphrodite. It appears that the male-determining genes reside on the *Y*-chromosome and the female-determining on the *X*-chromosome, and that a ratio of 4*X*:1*Y* is required even to produce an hermaphrodite. Work with fragmented *Y*-chromosomes suggests that this chromosome contains genes which lead to the development of male characters and others which suppress the development of female characters.

In *Homo sapiens* and *Mus musculus* normal females have two *X*-chromosomes and normal males an *X*- and a *Y*-chromosome. Compared with the other human chromosomes, the *X*-chromosome is in the third class for size, while the *Y*- is in the seventh or smallest class (Pl. 1(*e*)). In both *Homo* and *Mus* an abnormal condition occurs occasionally where there is a single *X*-chromosome and no *Y*-chromosome in the somatic nuclei. Such individuals are female, and fertile in *Mus* (Welshons and Russell, 1959), but usually sterile and with impaired development in *Homo* (Turner's syndrome). Individuals with two *X*-chromosomes and a *Y*-chromosome are sterile males, both in *Mus* (Russell and Chu, 1961) and *Homo* (Jacobs and Strong, 1959). In man, such individuals have certain slight female characteristics (Klinefelter's syndrome). It thus appears that, as in *Silene*, sex in these mammals is determined by the proportion of *X*- and *Y*-chromosomes.

§ 6.14   Conclusion

Although Bridges' work on *XXY Drosophila* may be said finally to have established the truth of the chromosome theory of Mendelian heredity, nevertheless the theory still met opposition. This was primarily because it was found necessary to postulate that the homologous chromosomes regularly exchanged segments at meiosis, a notion which some biologists thought conflicted with the concept of the individuality and permanence of the chromosomes. This will be discussed in the next chapter.

7. The hypothesis of chromosomal crossing-over

§ 7.1 De Vries' theory of factor exchange

In his formulation of the chromosome theory of Mendelian heredity, Sutton (1903) pointed out that the number of distinct characters in an organism must exceed the number of chromosomes. He argued from this that the basis of an allele was only a part of a chromosome, and that if the chromosomes permanently retain their individuality all the factors represented by one chromosome must be inherited together. However, within a short time, four apparently independently-inherited character-differences were known in *Pisum sativum* in addition to the seven studied by Mendel, and yet the haploid chromosome number was known to be only seven. Similarly, the number of apparently freely-inherited character-differences in *Antirrhinum majus* was found to exceed the haploid chromosome number of 8. These findings appeared to be a fatal objection to the chromosome theory. However, De Vries (1903) had proposed a theory which offered a solution to this dilemma.

De Vries accepted Sutton's view that the chromosomes formed the material basis of Mendelian heredity, and that many factors must co-exist in each chromosome, but to account for the apparently independent inheritance of each character-difference he supposed that an exchange of material took place between the maternal and paternal homologous chromosomes while they were closely associated in pairs during prophase I of meiosis. He argued that if two like factors lay opposite each other, a simple exchange of factors could occur. He assumed that in any given instance it was a matter of chance whether particular factors were exchanged or not. He argued further that a factor could be exchanged only for a like one, that is, for one which represented the corresponding hereditary character, otherwise each chromosome would not retain the entire series of factors. He regarded it as essential that the progeny should receive from their parents the sum total of these factors, as representing all the characters of the species. He pointed out that after these hypothetical exchanges had occurred, each chromosome would contain some paternal and some maternal units. Furthermore, since the two chromosomes of a pair pass into different gamete-nuclei, this redistribution of factors between the homologous chromosome-pairs would lead to the formation of gametes with all possible combinations of the parental character-differences, just as Mendelian theory required.

§7.2   Morgan's evidence for crossing-over

De Vries' theory of exchanges between homologous chromosomes gained little support at the time. In the first place there was no evidence that such exchanges occurred, and secondly the idea of exchanges was thought by many to be contrary to the concept of the permanence and individuality of the chromosomes. For the same reasons, when Bateson, Saunders and Punnett (1905) discovered partial linkage between two different characters in *Lathyrus odoratus* (see Chapter 3), they did not favour the chromosome theory as an explanation. But when Morgan (1911*a*), working with *Drosophila*

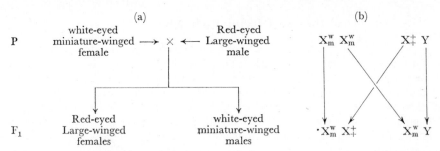

FIGURE 7.1   Morgan's results from crossing a white-eyed miniature-winged female with a normal male *Drosophila melanogaster*.
(a) F_1 results.
(b) Hypothesis to explain (*a*).
X_m^w = X-chromosome with recessive genes for white eyes (*w*) and miniature wings (*m*).
X_+^+ = X-chromosome with dominant normal allelomorphs *w* and *m*.
Y = Y-chromosome.

melanogaster, turned up a similar example of partial linkage, he had no alternative but to postulate a De Vriesian exchange of material between homologous chromosomes, because the characters concerned, white eye-colour and miniature wings, both showed sex-linkage. If the genes for each of these characters were carried by the X-chromosome, as the sex-linkage data suggested, then the only way to explain the occurrence of new combinations of them was to postulate exchanges between the two X-chromosomes (in the female insect, since the male has only one X-chromosome). Thus, when he crossed a white-eyed miniature-winged female with a normal (Red-eyed Large-winged) male, the F_1 progeny were similar except that the sexes were reversed, that is, the females were all normal and the males all white-eyed and miniature-winged (see Fig. 7.1). This result is what is expected (see Chapter 6) if the genes for white eyes and miniature wings are both carried by the X-chromosomes (see Fig. 6.7). The F_1 flies were allowed to interbreed, and 2441 progeny (F_2) obtained (Morgan 1911*b*). The numbers of each kind are shown in Table 7.1(*a*). It will be noticed that flies with the grand-parental character-combinations (white-eyed miniature-winged and Red-eyed Large-winged) are the most frequent in both sexes (classes (i) to (iv)).

The surprising discovery, however, was the occurrence of appreciable numbers of flies with the other two combinations of the eye and wing characters (classes (v) to (viii)). Altogether there were just 900 of these out of the 2441 or 36·9%. Morgan's hypothesis to explain these results is shown in

TABLE 7.1   Morgan's results from crossing a white-eyed miniature-winged female with a normal male *Drosophila melanogaster*

$\qquad\qquad\qquad$ (a) F_2 results
$\qquad\qquad\qquad$ (b) Hypothesis to explain (a).
$\qquad\qquad\qquad$ Symbols as in Fig. 7.1.

(a)

Parents(F_1)	White-eyed Miniature-winged Males				
	Eyes	Wings	Females	Males	Totals
Red-eyed Large-winged females	white	miniature	(i) 359	(ii) 391	750⎫ 1541
	Red	Large	(iii) 439	(iv) 352	791⎭
	white	Large	(v) 218	(vi) 237	455⎫ 900
	Red	miniature	(vii) 235	(viii) 210	445⎭
	Totals		1251	1190	2441

(b)

Parents (F_1) and their Gametes				$X^w_m Y$	
				Sperm	
				X^w_m	Y
$X^w_m X^+_+$	Eggs	63·1%	$\begin{cases} X^w_m \\ X^+_+ \end{cases}$	(i) $X^w_m X^w_m$ (iii) $X^+_+ X^w_m$	(ii) $X^w_m Y$ (iv) $X^+_+ Y$
		36·9%	$\begin{cases} X^w_+ \\ X^+_m \end{cases}$	(v) $X^w_+ X^w_m$ (vii) $X^+_m X^w_m$	(vi) $X^w_+ Y$ (vii) $X^+_m Y$

Table 7.1(b). He assumed that in 36·9% of the eggs an exchange of factors had occurred, just as De Vries had anticipated, between the two X-chromosomes.

Another Mendelian character in *Drosophila* which Morgan found to show sex-linkage was yellow body-colour. When he crossed a white-eyed yellow-bodied female with a normal (Red-eyed Grey-bodied) male, the F_1 progeny comprised normal females and white-eyed yellow-bodied males, as expected with sex-linkage (Fig. 7.2). When the F_1 flies were intercrossed, 2205 F_2 flies were obtained. The numbers of each kind are shown in Table 7.2. Again it is flies with the grandparental character-combinations (white-eyed yellow-bodied and Red-eyed Grey-bodied) which were most frequent, but

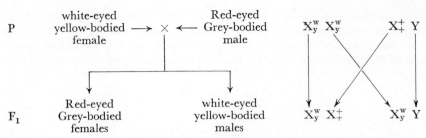

P   white-eyed yellow-bodied female → × ← Red-eyed Grey-bodied male

F₁   Red-eyed Grey-bodied females   white-eyed yellow-bodied males

FIGURE 7.2   Morgan's results from crossing a white-eyed yellow-bodied female
with a normal male *Drosophila melanogaster*.
(a) F_1 results.
(b) Hypothesis to explain (a).

X_y^w = X-chromosome with recessive genes for white eyes (w) and
yellow body (y).

X_+^+ = X-chromosome with dominant normal allelomorphs of
w and y.

Y = Y-chromosome.

TABLE 7.2   Morgan's results from crossing a white-eyed yellow-bodied female
with a normal male *Drosophila melanogaster*
(a) F_2 results
(b) Hypothesis to explain (a)
Symbols as in Fig. 7.2

(a)

Parents (F_1)	White-eyed Yellow-bodied Males				
	Eye-colour	Body-colour	Females	Males	Totals
Red-eyed Grey-bodied females	white	yellow	(i) 543	(ii) 474	1017⎫ 2176
	Red	Grey	(iii) 647	(iv) 512	1159⎭
	white	Grey	(v) 6	(vi) 11	17⎫ 29
	Red	yellow	(vii) 7	(viii) 5	12⎭
		Totals	1203	1002	2205

(b)

Parents (F_1) and their Gametes				$X_y^w Y$	
				Sperm	
				X_y^w	Y
$X_y^w X_+^+$	Eggs	98·7%	$\begin{cases} X_y^w \\ X_+^+ \end{cases}$	(i) $X_y^w X_y^w$ (iii) $X_+^+ X_y^w$	(ii) $X_y^w Y$ (iv) $X_+^+ Y$
		1·3%	$\begin{cases} X_+^w \\ X_y^+ \end{cases}$	(v) $X_+^w X_y^w$ (vii) $X_y^+ X_y^w$	(vi) $X_+^w Y$ (viii) $X_y^+ Y$

this time the other two combinations of these character-differences appeared only infrequently: 29 out of 2205, or 1·3%. Morgan concluded that the factors responsible for these character-differences tended to remain together much more often than those in the previous experiment. This principle of partial linkage he called the *third law of heredity* (Morgan 1919), the first two laws being those of Mendel (see Chapter 3).

Morgan (1911*b*) reported results for over 9000 F_2 flies from crosses involving these characters (white eyes, miniature wings and yellow body) in different combinations. It was evident that the grandparental combinations were always the most frequent. Thus, when a homozygous Red-eyed yellow-bodied female was crossed with a white-eyed Grey-bodied male, the male F_2 progeny comprised 349 with Red eyes and yellow bodies and 374 with white eyes and Grey bodies (the grandparental combinations), while there were just two of each of the other combinations. It was the latter which were so frequent in the F_2 progeny from the cross described in the last paragraph, where these were the grandparental combinations. Morgan concluded that during segregation of character-differences at meiosis certain genes tend to remain together, not because of any attraction between them but because they lie near together in the same chromosomes. Furthermore, he argued that characters remain associated together to a greater extent the nearer the corresponding genes are together in the chromosome. The following year Morgan and Cattell (1912) introduced the term *crossing-over* for the process of interchange by which new combinations of linked factors arise.

§ 7.3 Linkage maps

Sturtevant (1913) took Morgan's argument a stage further. He pointed out that the proportion of cross-overs, that is, progeny derived from gametes in which an exchange had occurred, could be used as an index of the distance between any two genes. Morgan had already shown that this proportion was approximately constant for any particular genes, irrespective of their initial combinations. Thus, he had found that white *versus* Red eyes showed about 1% of cross-overs with yellow *versus* Grey body, whether initially the factors were in *coupling* (dominants in one parent, recessives in the other) or in *repulsion* (one dominant and one recessive in each parent). Sturtevant suggested that the unit of distance between two factor-pairs should be taken to be of such length that, on the average, one cross-over will occur in it out of every 100 gametes formed. In other words, he proposed that the percentage of cross-overs should be used as the index of distance. This concept of distance led him to an important discovery, namely, that the distances between a series of linked factors were additive, implying that the factors could be represented by a linear map. Thus, Morgan's F_2 data (1911*b*) from a cross between a yellow-bodied white-eyed miniature-winged female and a normal male gave 1·3% of cross-overs for the body-colour and eye-colour characters, 32·6% for eye-colour and wing-size, and 33·8% for body-colour and wing-size (see Table 7.3). The latter percentage is very

TABLE 7.3   Data of Morgan (1911b) for the F_2 progeny of a cross between a yellow-bodied white-eyed miniature-winged female and a normal male *Drosophila*. The shortage of yellow-bodied flies compared with the normal Grey in each complementary pair is probably due to a lower viability.

Characters			Number	Cross-overs		
Body colour	Eye colour	Wing size		Body colour and eye colour	Eye colour and wing size	Body colour and wing size
Grey	Red	Large	758	—	—	—
yellow	white	miniature	700	—	—	—
Grey	Red	miniature	401	—	401	401
yellow	white	Large	317	—	317	317
Grey	white	miniature	16	16	—	16
yellow	Red	Large	12	12	—	12
Grey	white	Large	1	1	1	—
yellow	Red	miniature	0	0	0	—
		Totals	2205	29	719	746
		Percentage	100	1·3	32·6	33·8

close to the sum of the other two and implies that the eye-colour factors lie between the others. The linkage map, using the percentages as distances, is shown in Fig. 7.3(*a*). Sturtevant pointed out that there was no means of knowing whether or not the distances as drawn represent the actual spatial distances, because some parts of the chromosome might be more liable to exchange than others. However, the ability to represent the factors by a linear map provided a new argument in support of the chromosome theory, since the chromosome was itself of thread-like proportions. The principle of the linear order of genes was called by Morgan (1919) the *fourth law of heredity*.

FIGURE 7.3   (*a*) Linkage map of the factors for yellow body (y), white eyes (w), and miniature wings (m) in *Drosophila melanogaster* derived from Morgan's data (1911*b*). (*b*) Summary of the data in Table 7.3 on the basis of the linkage map in (*a*). The lines indicate the position of the exchanges.

§ 7.4   Double crossing-over

Sturtevant found that the additive property of cross-over frequencies did not hold if all three frequencies were large. He attributed this discrepancy to double cross-overs. The data in Table 7.3 illustrate the effect of such double exchanges. There were 29 exchanges between the factors for body-colour and eye-colour and 719 between those for eye-colour and wing-size, making a total of 748, but between body-colour and wing-size there appeared to be only 746. The discrepancy is due to the single Grey-bodied white-eyed Large-winged fly. In the production of the egg from which this fly developed two exchanges must have occurred between the X-chromosomes, with the result that the body-colour and wing-size factors ('Grey' and 'Large', respectively) appeared together as in the grandparent, although the intervening factor (white eyes) was derived from the other grandparent (see Fig. 7.3(*b*)). It is evident that large cross-over frequencies give an inaccurate map, since, unless intervening factors are available, there will be no means of detecting double cross-overs. Various empirical formulae have been devised to allow for the effects of double crossing-over by 'correcting' recombination frequencies to give 'map units'.

In the light of these findings by Morgan and Sturtevant, earlier observations by others took on a new significance. Thus, characters due to factors placed far apart in a chromosome would evidently assort almost at random in the gametes, owing to the frequent occurrence of crossing-over between them. Here was evidently the explanation of how the number of apparently freely-inherited character-differences could exceed the haploid chromosome number.

§ 7.5   Test-crosses

The characters in *Lathyrus odoratus* found by Bateson, Saunders and Punnett (1905) to show 12% of cross-over gametes (Purple *versus* red flower colour and Long *versus* round pollen-shape) (see Chapter 3) could now be interpreted as due to factors at a distance apart of 12 units (or slightly more allowing for double cross-overs) on one of the chromosomes. Although *L. odoratus* was thus the first plant (or indeed organism of any kind) for which linkage map data became available, it is not a particularly favourable organism for linkage studies. This is because self-fertilisation (F_2) data are not easily interpreted (see Table 3.2). In studying linkage it is preferable to cross the heterozygous F_1 individuals with the homozygous recessive, since the relative frequencies of the different kinds of gametes from the F_1 heterozygote are then reflected directly in the frequencies of different kinds of progeny. Such a cross is called a *test-cross*. In *L. odoratus*, cross-fertilisation is tedious and gives few seeds per pollination. An ideal plant for linkage studies was found in *Zea mays*. In this grass the male and female flowers are widely separated at the apex and near the base of the plant, respectively, with the result that controlled cross-pollinations are readily made and moreover, several hundred seeds are normally obtained from a single pollination.

The first example of linkage in *Zea* was found by Collins (1912) between two endosperm characters: the colour of the aleurone layer and the horny (= starchy) or waxy texture of the endosperm tissue. An aleurone layer with a purplish pigment was found to be dominant to a colourless aleurone, and

TABLE 7.4   Data of Bregger (1918) for coupling and repulsion test-crosses with Coloured *versus* colourless aleurone (C/c) and Starchy *versus* waxy endosperm (*Wx/wx*) in *Zea mays*.
　　　　　　　(*a*) Primary data.
　　　　　　　(*b*) Totals for contingency χ^2 test (see text).

(*a*)

Testcross	Coloured Starchy	Colourless Waxy	Coloured Waxy	Colourless Starchy	Total
Coupling	147	133	65	58	403
Repulsion	46	32	103	111	292

(*b*)

Testcross	Parental	Recombinant	Total
Coupling	280	123	403
Repulsion	214	78	292
Total	494	201	695

the normal horny (starchy) endosperm giving a translucent grain was dominant to the opaque waxy endosperm, which had been found to occur in a maize variety from China. Several genes affect the aleurone pigmentation, and the first straightforward test-cross data for the waxy character and the colour factor showing linkage to it were obtained by Bregger (1918). He crossed a pure-breeding strain having Coloured aleurone and Starchy endosperm (*C C Wx Wx*) with one having colourless aleurone and waxy endosperm (*c c wx wx*). The doubly heterozygous F_1 plant so obtained had the factors in coupling $\left(\dfrac{C\ Wx}{c\ wx}\right)$. It was test-crossed with the strain having colourless aleurone and waxy endosperm (*c c wx wx*), and gave an ear with 403 grains, details of which are given in Table 7.4(*a*). There were 280 grains with the grandparental character combinations but only 123 with the other two combinations. The cross-over frequency is therefore 30·5%.

Bregger also crossed a pure-breeding strain having Coloured aleurone and waxy endosperm (*C C wx wx*) with one having colourless aleurone and Starchy endosperm (*c c Wx Wx*), and test-crossed the doubly heterozygous

PLATE 3   Meiosis in acetic-orcein squash preparations of male *Schistocerca gregaria* ($2n = 22 + X$) (continued from Plate 2). Magnification ca. ×1000. $X = X$-chromosome. In (*a*) and (*b*) the autosomal bivalents (but not the X-chromosome) have a lampbrush appearance (see p. 297 and p. 311).

(Courtesy of S. A. Henderson)

(*a*) Diplotene   (*b*) Diakinesis

(*c*) Metaphase I   (*e*) One cell at metaphase II (polar view)

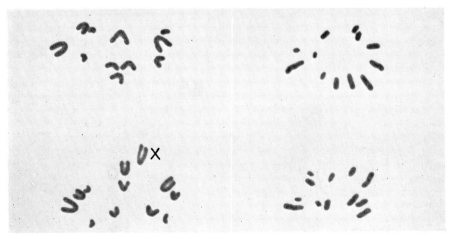

(*d*) Anaphase I   (*f*) One cell at anaphase II (side view)

PLATE 4

(*a*) Electron micrograph of a thin section of an oocyte nucleus of the Dipteran insect *Chironomus tentans* at pachytene of meiosis, showing cores (see p. 131). Slightly hypotonic fixation has been used to bring out the structural components of the cores. Magnification ×35,000. *Ch* = chromosomal fibrils of bivalents. *Co* = cores, consisting of 2 lateral elements, 2 much finer central longitudinal elements, and numerous exceedingly fine fibres crossing the pairing space between the longitudinal elements. *NM* = nuclear membrane. (*Courtesy of G. Meyer*)

(*b*)–(*e*) Asci of the fungus *Sordaria brevicollis* from a cross between a mutant with buff-coloured ascospores and another with yellow ascospores. The wild-type spores are black and the double-mutant spores are white (colourless). The buff and yellow mutants show linkage with about 9% recombination. Magnification ca. ×350.
(*Courtesy of M. H. V. Cooray*)

(*b*) Ascus with 4 buff (to left) and 4 yellow spores, implying no crossing-over between the gene loci.

(*c*) Ascus with 2 buff, 2 white, 2 black and 2 yellow spores (1 crossover between the loci).

(*d*) Ascus with 4 white and 4 black spores (a four-strand double crossover between the loci: see Fig. 8.12, p. 110).

(*e*) Ascus with the spore sequence: 3 buff, 1 white, 1 yellow, 1 black, 2 yellow; indicating postmeiotic segregation (see p. 264) at either the buff or the yellow mutant site.

F_1 progeny, which had the factors in repulsion $\left(\dfrac{C\ wx}{c\ Wx}\right)$, with the homozygous recessive strain $(c\ c\ wx\ wx)$. From this cross he obtained an ear with 292 grains, the details of which are also given in Table 7.4(a). Again the grand-parental forms were recovered with higher frequency than the others, and the cross-over frequency is 26·7%. The results of the two test-crosses are set out in Table 7.4(b). Application of the contingency χ^2 test (see Chapter 4) gives

$$\chi^2 = \frac{695[(280 \times 78) - (214 \times 123)]^2}{403 \times 292 \times 494 \times 201} = 1\cdot2, \qquad n = 1,$$

and from Table 4.2 (p. 27), $P = 0\cdot5$–$0\cdot1$. Hence, the two estimates of the cross-over frequency do not differ significantly. It might be thought that the best estimate of the recombination frequency would be obtained simply from the total data, that is, $\dfrac{201}{695}$ or 28·92%. However, Muller (1916) pointed out that when coupling and repulsion linkage data are available, the effects of differential viabilities can be minimised by calculating the geometric mean of the ratios of recombinant to parental progeny from each cross. In the present instance, these ratios are $\dfrac{123}{280}$ and $\dfrac{78}{214}$, and their geometric mean is

$$\sqrt{\frac{123}{280} \times \frac{78}{214}} = 0\cdot4001.$$

If there are 40·01 recombinants to every 100 parental genotypes, the recombination frequency is $\dfrac{40\cdot01}{140\cdot01} = 28\cdot58\%$.

A third character of the endosperm of *Zea mays*, namely, a shrunken condition such as gives a concave surface to the apex or side of the mature grain, instead of the normal convex surface, was found to be determined by a recessive gene, *sh*, which showed linkage to C/c and Wx/wx. Stadler (1926) made extensive studies using these three linked character-differences. In one of these experiments the triple heterozygote (with all three factors in coupling) was crossed as female parent with a homozygous recessive plant as male parent, thereby forming a 'three-point test cross', The 45,832 grains on 63 progeny plants were classified in respect of the three pairs of characters and the results are given in Fig. 7.4(a). From the data, the frequency (p) of recombination between C/c and Sh/sh is $\dfrac{1033 + 32}{45832} = 2\cdot32\%$. Similarly, the frequency (q) of recombination between Sh/sh and Wx/wx is $\dfrac{9109 + 32}{45832} = 19\cdot94\%$, and the frequency ($r$) of recombination between C/c and Wx/wx is $\dfrac{1033 + 9109}{45832} = 22\cdot13\%$. On the basis of these frequencies, it is evident that the locus of the gene for shrunken endosperm lies between the other two. The linkage map is shown in Fig. 7.4(b). As in the *Drosophila*

FIGURE 7.4   (a) Numbers of progeny of various genotypes from a *Zea* test-cross
(Stadler 1926).

 C = Dominant gene for Coloured aleurone layer of the endo-
  sperm.
 c = Recessive allele for colourless aleurone.
 Sh = Dominant gene for normal Non-shrunked endosperm.
 sh = Recessive allele for shrunken endosperm.
 Wx = Dominant gene for Starchy (translucent) endosperm.
 wx = Recessive allele for waxy (opaque) endosperm.

(b) Linkage map based on the data in (a).

example discussed in § 7.4, the slight discrepancy in the figures is due to
double cross-overs, since

$$p + q = r + \frac{64}{45832}.$$

If another gene X/x, were available between Sh/sh and Wx/wx, the recombination frequency of Sh/sh and X/x plus the recombination frequency of
X/x and Wx/wx would no doubt exceed 19·94%.

The frequency of recombination between C/c and Wx/wx in Stadler's
experiment (22·1%) was significantly less than that found by Bregger
(28·6%). Such variation in recombination frequencies is of frequent occurrence, and may be due to genetic or to environmental factors affecting the
frequency of crossing-over. It is evident that distances on linkage maps
have no absolute values, but are likely to differ in different experiments.

§ 7.6   Evidence that crossing-over is associated with chromosomal exchange

Creighton and McClintock (1931) were the first to obtain convincing
evidence that genetic crossing-over of linked characters is associated with
exchange of parts between homologous chromosomes. They bred a strain

of *Zea mays* heterozygous for two peculiarities of chromosome 9 and for two hereditary characters known to be carried by this chromosome. The chromosomal characters were the presence or absence of a knob at the end of the short arm, and the presence or absence of a part of chromosome 8 in place of part of the long arm. The genetic characters were two of those referred to in § 7.5, namely, a Coloured (C) or colourless (c) aleurone layer to the endosperm of the maize grain, known to be due to a gene difference located near the knob, and Starchy (Wx) or waxy (wx) endosperm, due to a factor difference located near the point of attachment of the portion of chromosome 8. The combinations of these characters in the heterozygote were as follows:

FIGURE 7.5   The pair of no. 9 chromosomes in Creighton and McClintock's strain of *Zea mays* heterozygous for two structural characters of the chromosome and for two endosperm characters. The structural characters were the presence and absence at one end of the chromosome of a knob, and at the other end of an interchange of a segment with a segment (shown black) of chromosome no. 8. C = Gene for Coloured, *c* = allele for colourless aleurone layer to the endosperm. *Wx* = Gene for Normal Starchy endosperm, *wx* = allele for waxy endosperm.

On one edition of chromosome 9 there was the knob, the dominant gene *C* for Coloured aleurone, the recessive gene *wx* for waxy endosperm, and the portion of chromosome 8. On the other edition of chromosome 9, the other alternative of each of these characters was present (Fig. 7.5). This quadruple heterozygote was crossed with a plant having no knobs and no parts of chromosome 8 on either of its 9th chromosomes, and also homozygous for the recessive gene *c* for colourless aleurone, but heterozygous for the Starchy-waxy character-difference. There were 27 progeny, of which 13 could be fully scored and interpreted (see Table 7.5). Since both parents were heterozygous for the Starchy-waxy character-difference, any progeny similarly heterozygous have been omitted from the table since it cannot be established from which parent the *Wx* and *wx* factors were derived. (As indicated in Chapter 5, the *Wx Wx* and *Wx wx* genotypes can be distinguished by examination of the pollen after staining with iodine.) All 13 progeny showed complete linkage between the aleurone colour factors and the knobbed or knobless condition, and 11 of them also showed complete linkage between the quality of the endosperm and presence or absence of the interchange. When the genetical characters crossed-over, so did the cytological ones. In two of the progeny there was evidently a cross-over between the *Wx/wx* locus and that of the point of attachment of the part of chromosome 8. The data form striking evidence that genetical crossing-over is associated with exchange of parts between homologous chromosomes. Whether this comes about by breakage and rejoining, or in the process of replication of the hereditary material, is discussed in Chapter 15.

TABLE 7.5 Numbers of progeny found by Creighton and McClintock (1931) from a *Zea* cross, using as one parent a plant heterozygous both for two abnormalities in chromosome 9 and for two characters of the endosperm (aleurone colour and food reserve) known to be due to genes borne by this chromosome. A normal chromosome 9 was present in addition to the one described in the table. Individuals heterozygous for the food reserve characters have been omitted.

Chromosome 9 Characters \ Endosperm Characters		Coloured	Colourless	Coloured	Colourless
		Waxy	Starchy	Starchy	Waxy
Knob present	Interchange with chromosome 8 present	3	0	0	0
No knob	No interchange	0	5	0	0
Knob present	No interchange	0	0	1	0
No knob	Interchange with chromosome 8 present	0	2	0	2

A few weeks later Stern (1931) reported similar results for *Drosophila melanogaster*. He had obtained four different strains of female flies, each heterozygous for two abnormalities in the *X*-chromosome and for two sex-linked characters. Over 27,000 progeny from these females were scored for the latter characters, and 364 of them were also examined cytologically and scored for the chromosomal characters. All four experiments gave similar results, but only one will be described.

The female parents in this experiment carried the factor for the recessive character carnation-coloured eyes on one of their *X*-chromosomes, which was structurally normal. On the other *X*-chromosome was the normal allele of carnation eye and the dominant gene for Bar eye. This chromosome was also structurally abnormal in two respects: firstly, it had part of a *Y*-chromosome attached at one end just beyond the carnation locus; secondly, it was broken into two parts, the break being just beyond the Bar locus. This means that the proximal part carried both the Bar gene and the normal allele of carnation. The distal part was attached to the small fourth chromosome (Fig. 7.6). The male parent was structurally normal, but carried the gene for carnation eyes on its *X*-chromosome. Details of the 8231 progeny of this cross are given in Table 7.6. Out of this number 107 were examined cytologically, including 54 in which crossing-over had occurred between the loci for carnation and Bar. Without exception, these 54 flies also showed crossing-over for the chromosomal characters. Bar eye-shape was always associated

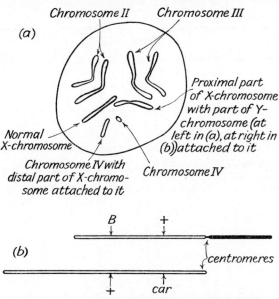

FIGURE 7.6   The chromosomes of the female parents in one of Stern's experiments with *Drosophila melanogaster* which demonstrate that genetical crossing-over is associated with physical exchange between the corresponding homologous chromosomes.

(*a*) Polar view of mitotic metaphase.

(*b*) The *X*-chromosomes. B = Dominant gene for Bar eye-shape, and the plus sign ($+$) at the corresponding position = recessive normal allele; *car* = recessive gene for carnation eye-colour, and the plus sign at the corresponding position = dominant normal allele. The attached part of the *Y*-chromosome is shown black.

with the broken *X*-chromosome to which it was closely linked, and normal Red eye-colour was associated with the attached piece of *Y*-chromosome. Indeed, as indicated in the table, there was only one fly out of the 107 which showed breakdown of these linkages: a cross-over had apparently occurred between the carnation locus and the point of attachment of the *Y*-chromosome segment.

TABLE 7.6   Numbers of progeny found by Stern (1931) from a *Drosophila* cross, using females heterozygous both for two abnormalities in the X-chromosome and for two sex-linked characters, carnation eye-colour and Bar eye-shape. A normal X-chromosome (in females) or Y-chromosome (in males) was present in addition to the X-chromosome described in the table. The shortage of normal progeny (Red round eyes) is thought to be due to their failure to survive owing to loss of one of their small fourth chromosomes.

X-chromosome characters / Sex-linked characters		Normal Red / Bar	Carnation / Normal round	Carnation / Bar	Normal Red / Normal round
Part of Y-chromosome attached	Broken	26	0	0	0
Without Y-chromosome	Unbroken	0	26	0	0
Without Y-chromosome	Broken	1	0	45	0
Part of Y-chromosome attached	Unbroken	0	0	0	9
Total progeny (including those in which chromosomes were not examined)		4001	4157	61	12

Stern's data constitute further evidence that genetical crossing-over involves exchange of material between the appropriate homologous chromosomes. Thus, just 20 years after Morgan's crucial discovery of new combinations of two sex-linked character-differences in the progeny of a *Drosophila* cross, which led him to postulate interchange of parts between homologous chromosomes, Stern, using both genetical and cytological characters in the identical chromosome, obtained overwhelming evidence of the truth of Morgan's postulate. The mechanism of crossing-over is discussed in Chapter 15.

8. The chiasmatype theory

§ 8.1 Chiasmata

As indicated in Chapter 6, the chromosome pairs seen at late prophase I of meiosis usually present the appearance either of a cross or of one or more loops. Janssens (1909) gave the name *chiasma* (meaning a cross) to the nodes between the arms or loops in these diplotene or diakinetic configurations. He also adopted in the same publication a particular hypothesis (described below) to account for the origin of these nodes. The use of the term chiasma was at first intimately bound up with this particular interpretation of them. However it is customary nowadays to use the term for these nodes, irrespective of the theory adopted to account for them. It is highly inconvenient to have a name for an observed structure the use of which is dependent on a theory to explain it. Hence, throughout this book chiasma will be used as Janssens first defined it, for a node in the paired chromosomes at the first division of meiosis. It should not be taken to imply any particular interpretation of its origin.

§ 8.2 Janssens' theory

At the diplotene stage the chromosomes have already divided into two daughter-chromatids, with the result that four threads are present in each chromosome-pair. Janssens had studied meiosis in several organisms, but particularly at sperm-formation in the amphibian *Batrachoseps attenuatus*. At the chiasmata at the diplotene stage, whenever the fixation and staining had been particularly good, he observed that of the four filaments, two cross each other and two do not (Fig. 8.1(a) and Pl. 3(a)). At anaphase I, when the chiasmata break down, the two chromatids which pass to one pole of the spindle were seen to lie together on one side of each chiasma and to lie apart on the other side (Fig. 8.1(c) and (d)). It was evident that two of the four chromatids crossed at each chiasma. These observations have been amply confirmed in many organisms.

Janssens believed that prior to the formation of the chiasmata, the paternal and maternal chromosomes in the early diplotene stage were loosely coiled round each other, as in Fig. 8.2(b). In order to derive chiasmata from such a loose coil, Janssens postulated that the paternal and maternal chromatids made contact at intervals, and that one of each penetrated the other until they broke, whereupon they rejoined in new ways paternal to maternal, and *vice versa*. The other two chromatids (one paternal and one maternal) were considered to remain intact, so giving rise to the typical chiasma with two

FIGURE 8.1   Chromosome-pairs showing chiasmata
at meiosis in males of *Batrachoseps
attenuatus* (from Janssens, 1909). The
number and position of the chiasmata
varies from cell to cell. (*a*) Diplotene
stage (2 chiasmata). (*b*) Diakinesis
(3 chiasmata). (*c*) Metaphase I (1
chiasma). (*d*) Anashase I.

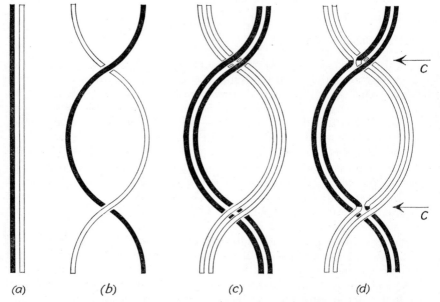

FIGURE 8.2   Diagrams to show the structure of a pair of homologous chromosomes at (*a*) the pachytene stage and (*b–d*) successives early diplotene
stages, according to Janssens' hypothesis of the origin of chiasmata
C = Chiasma. Black = paternal and white = maternal origin.

chromatids crossing each other and two not (Fig. 8.2(*d*)). This remarkable hypothesis has been a centre of controversy ever since it was first put forward.

Janssens also used the teleological argument that the occurrence of his hypothetical exchanges between one paternal and one maternal chromatid at each chiasma would ensure that the four nuclei, to which the four chromatids of each diplotene chromsome-pair were distributed, had different combinations of paternal and maternal segments of each chromosome, and hence would account for the universal existence of two nuclear divisions in meiosis and four products. He argued that meiosis was a mechanism for the production of four haploid nuclei all of different genotypes. He pointed out that there would then be segregation of some factor differences at each division of meiosis (Fig. 8.3(*b*)) in contrast to the widely held view that segregation of paternal from maternal chromosomes occurred at the heterotype or first division of meiosis (Fig. 8.3(*a*)), with the identical daughter-chromosomes

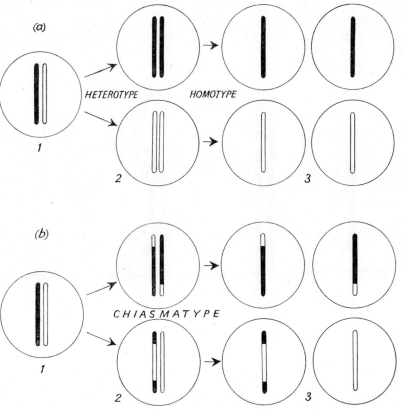

FIGURE 8.3   Diagrams of (1) the pachytene stage of prophase I, (2) telophase I, and (3) telophase II, according to (*a*) the hypothesis that meiotic segregation occurs only at the first division, and (*b*) Janssens' hypothesis that it occurs partly at each division. Black = paternal and white = maternal origin.

composing each of them separating from one another at the homotype or second division (Fig. 8.3(*a*)). To emphasise this difference from the heterotype-homotype theory of meiotic segregation, he called his idea the *chiasmatype* theory.

Janssens also pointed out that his theory provided an escape from the dilemma of the existence of a larger number of freely assorting allelomorphic characters than there are pairs of chromosomes.

§ 8.3 The classical theory

The weak link in Janssens' argument was his postulation that loose coils preceded the formation of chiasmata. Since he was observing fixed and stained material, it was difficult to test this postulate by observation. It was based on the assumption that division of each chromosome into two chromatids did not occur until after the paternal and maternal chromosomes had begun to separate in the early diplotene stage (Fig. 8.2(*b*) and (*c*)). It is true that at the preceding pachytene stage the chromosomes appear to be single threads (Fig. 8.2(*a*)). However, the possibility remained that division of the chromosomes into daughter-chromatids occurs before the early diplotene separation is initiated (Fig. 8.4(*b*)). An alternative explanation of the origin

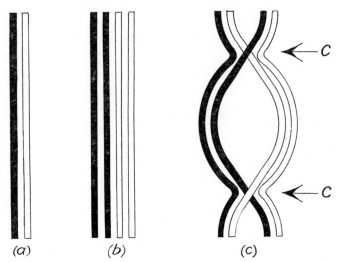

(a)   *(b)*   *(c)*

FIGURE 8.4   Diagrams to show (*a*) early pachytene, (*b*) late pachytene, and (*c*) diplotene chromosomes according to the classical hypothesis of the origin of chiasmata.   C = Chiasma.   Black = paternal and white = maternal origin.

of chiasmata is then possible, namely that at a chiasma there is a change of pairing partner. At one region of the chromosome two paternal chromatids would be associated and likewise the two maternal ones, but on the other side of a chiasma each pair of chromatids would consist of one paternal and one

maternal thread (Fig. 8.4(*c*)). This *classical hypothesis* to explain chiasmata
was preferred by most cytologists becaust it did not require breakage and
rejoining of chromosomes, with consequent threat to their permanence and
individuality.

§ 8.4 Genetic evidence in support of Janssens' theory

When Morgan (1911*a*) first discovered that new combinations of sex-
linked characters were appearing in the F_2 generation of a *Drosophila* cross,
he favoured De Vries' theory of factor exchange. However, shortly afterwards
he realised that the sex-linked factors were not assorting at random, as De
Vries' theory demanded, but (as indicated in the last chapter) were showing
partial linkage of various intensities. He then favoured Janssens' chiasmatype
theory as an explanation.

§ 8.5 An objection to Janssens' theory

Muller (1916) pointed out a difficulty of Janssens' theory, namely that the
exchanges were supposed to occur at the diplotene stage when the chromosomes are relatively short and thick, and yet crossing-over must be between
precisely homologous points of paternal and maternal threads if the cross-over
chromosomes were not to have duplications or deficiencies of the linearly-
arranged genes. Muller argued that factors must be set very close together in
the chromosomes, and hence that crossing-over required a high degree of
precision, because in *Drosophila* mutations in new 'loci' (positions in the
chromosomes) were still turning up regularly. He therefore suggested that the
exchanges perhaps took place earlier in meiosis when the chromosomes
were still in the form of slender threads, as for example at the zygotene stage.
This suggestion raised a fundamental question.

§ 8.6 Crossing-over in relation to chromosome duplication

An essential feature of Janssens' theory was that crossing-over should
occur between only two of the four chromatids, otherwise the presence of two
threads crossing one another and two not at each chiasma would not be
explained. But at the zygotene stage the chromosomes were thought to be
undivided. Hence crossing-over at this stage, as postulated by Muller, would
presumably involve whole chromosomes and so would be contrary to the
chiasmatype theory. To test the truth of Janssens' theory it was therefore
essential to know whether crossing-over occurred before or after the chromosomes had duplicated. If exchange involved only two of the four chromatids,
as Janssens supposed, this would be conclusive evidence that crossing-over
did not occur before chromosome duplication (Fig. 8.5(*a*)). On the other
hand, if crossing-over involved all four chromatids at the same locus, there
were two possible explanations: either exchange occurred while the chromosomes were still single threads and the subsequent duplication produced
two editions of each (Fig. 8.5(*b*)); or all four chromatids were broken at
corresponding positions and were subsequently joined paternal to maternal,

and *vice versa* (Fig. 8.5(*c*)). Janssens himself thought he had cytological evidence that the latter alternative occurred occasionally.

Bridges (1916) was the first to obtain information on this fundamental question of whether crossing-over takes place before or after chromosome duplication. During the course of his work with the *XXY* strain of *Drosophila*

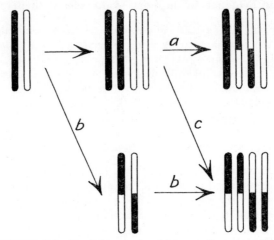

FIGURE 8.5   Possible ways in which crossing-over might occur.

(*a*) Janssens' chiasmatype hypothesis: crossing-over after chromosome duplication and involving only two of the four chromatids.

(*b*) Crossing-over at the two-strand stage before chromosome duplication.

(*c*) Crossing-over after chromosome duplication but involving all four chromatids at the same locus (thought by Janssens to occur occasionally).

Black = paternal and white = maternal origin.

melanogaster (see Chapter 6), he obtained *XXY* females which were heterozygous for the sex-linked characters vermilion eye-colour and eosin eye-colour. These characters are both recessive to the normal Red eyes and are due to genes showing about 30% recombination with one another. The doubly-heterozygous *XXY* females, some with vermilion and eosin in coupling and some with them in repulsion, were crossed with Bar-eyed but otherwise normal males. The dominant gene Bar is sex-linked and leads to the production of a narrow eye instead of the normal round eye. Any progeny from this cross which receive an *X*-chromosome from their father will have Bar eyes. Hence any female progeny with eyes of the normal round shape must have received both their *X*-chromosomes from their mother. They will correspond to the flies in class (i) of Table 6.2, which represent about 2% of the progeny. From the coupling crosses, 422 non-Bar females were obtained, of which 414 had Red eyes like their mother and 8 had vermilion, eosin or vermilion-eosin eyes. Similarly, from the repulsion crosses there were 168 non-Bar females with Red eyes and 5 with vermilion or eosin eyes. The genotypes of the vemilion- and eosin-eyed females were established by further breeding and the results are given in Table 8.1. All those that were homozygous for eosin were found to be heterozygous for vermilion, and *vice versa*. To obtain flies of these constitutions requires crossing-over between the two X-chromosomes of the mother during maturation of her eggs, and furthermore such crossing-over must take place between individual chromatids and involve only two of them (one derived from each X-chromosome) (see Fig. 8.6). With no crossing-over, or with crossing-over before chromosome duplication, any two of the four chromatids will always be either identical or complementary, that is of genotypes (i) to (vi) in Fig. 8.6. The occurrence of genotypes (viii) to (x) was proof of crossing-over after chromosome duplication. Altogether, Bridges obtained information about 11 cross-overs between the loci of vermilion and eosin and every one of them was between two chromatids.

Anderson (1925) obtained more evidence that crossing-over occurred only at the four-strand stage. A female *Drosophila* was discovered after treatment with X-rays, in which the two X-chromosomes were joined together at one end. This union was demonstrated cytologically, for a single V-shaped chromosome replaced the two rod-shaped X-chromosomes. It was also shown by the fact that on crossing with a normal male, sex-linked characters which she possessed were manifest in her daughters and not in her sons. This was in direct contrast to the usual behaviour of sex-linked characters, which show criss-cross inheritance (see Chapter 6). The daughters of the attached-X female will inherit her two joined X-chromosomes, and moreover there will be opportunity at meiosis during maturation of her eggs for crossing-over to occur between them. The parent attached-X female was heterozygous for the recessive sex-linked characters forked bristles, garnet eye-colour, tan body-colour, and cut wing-tips. If no crossing-over occurred the daughters would have a double X-chromosome identical with that of their mother. On the other hand, crossing-over in certain intervals of the chromosome could lead to one or more of the recessive characters becoming homozygous and hence manifest, just as in Bridges' earlier work.

Out of 4344 daughters of attached-X females heterozygous for these genes, Anderson found totals of 226 (5·2%) with forked bristles, 414 (9·5%) with garnet-coloured eyes, 698 (16·1%) with tan-coloured bodies and 672 (15·5%) with cut wings. The occurrence of these individuals, homozygous for one or more recessive characters for which the mother was heterozygous, was evidence of crossing-over between the joined X-chromosomes, and in order to obtain more information, a random sample of 188 of the daughters was subjected to detailed study. The genetic constitution of each X-chromosome of each individual was established from the frequencies of different phenotypes in their progeny from suitable crosses. The results are set out in Table 8.1 with the four pairs of alleles taken two at a time. In each instance, of the

TABLE 8.1   Numbers of different genotypes of female *Drosophila melanogaster* when the two *X*-chromosomes of each individual have both been derived from their mother. Bridges' (1916) data refer to *XXY* flies, Anderson's (1925) to attached *XX*, and Bridges & Anderson (1925) to triploid *XXX*. A dash (—) as distinct from zero (0) indicates flies of normal phenotype, the genotype of which was not determined. There were 414 of these in the coupling crosses (column 2) and 168 in the repulsion crosses (column 3).

The Ten Possible Genotypes (Female Parent $\frac{AB}{ab}$)	XXY Bridges (1916)		Attached XX Anderson (1925)			Triploid XXX Bridges & Anderson (1925)			
	Vermilion (a) and eosin (b)	Vermilion (a) and eosin (B)	Forked (a) and garnet (B)	Garnet (A) & tan (b)	Tan (a) and cut (B)	Bar or forked and dusky or miniature	Dusky or miniature and lozenge or tan	Lozenge or tan and ruby or bifid	Ruby or bifid and scute or yellow
(i) $\frac{AB}{AB}$	—	0	8	15	21	2	3	3	5
(ii) $\frac{ab}{ab}$	2	0	11	25	36				
(iii) $\frac{AB}{ab}$	—	—	126	103	104	153	167	140	126
(iv) $\frac{Ab}{aB}$	—	—	11	9	8	3	1	2	0
(v) $\frac{Ab}{Ab}$	0	—	0	0	0	0	0	0	0
(vi) $\frac{aB}{aB}$	0	0	0	0	0	0	0	0	0
(vii) $\frac{AB}{Ab}$	—	—	2	3	7	0	0	2	5
(viii) $\frac{aB}{ab}$	3	1	1	5	4				
(ix) $\frac{AB}{aB}$	—	4	10	13	3	1	2	7	16
(x) $\frac{Ab}{ab}$	3	—	19	15	5				

10 genotypes theoretically possible, 8 were represented. The missing ones were always those with two identical cross-over chromosomes (genotypes (v) and (vi)) and they can only be obtained by postulating that crossing-over occurs at the two-strand stage (unless double cross-overs are invoked) (see Fig. 8.6). Conversely there were present all the genotypes with one

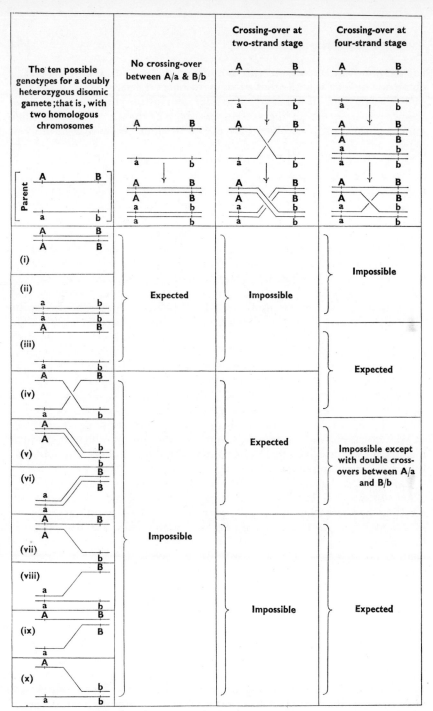

FIGURE 8.6 The genotypes expected for the gametes from a double heterozygote $\frac{AB}{ab}$ if two of the four meiotic chromatids pass into each gamete. The expectations with no crossing-over, with crossing-over at the two-strand stage, and with crossing-over at the four-strand stage, are shown in separate columns.

parental and one cross-over chromosome (nos. (vii) to (x)) which can be obtained only by assuming that crossing-over occurs between two chromatids, that is, at the four-strand stage. The data demonstrate that every one of 87 cross-overs, about which information was obtained, took place after chromosome replication and involved only two of the four chromatids at any one place.

Bridges and Anderson (1925) obtained further evidence that crossing-over occurs at the four-strand stage from studies of triploid *Drosophila* with sex-linked characters. The evidence was obtained from 182 diploid female progeny with 2 *X*-chromosomes both derived from the mother and between which crossing-over had occurred. The 3 *X*-chromosomes in the triploid flies were each uniquely identified at five different positions by the genes they carried, and this enabled the source of the 2 *X*-chromosomes in the daughters to be determined. The results are given in Table 8.1 for the four consecutive regions of the chromosome delimited by the genes. The totals in each column are less than 182 because progeny containing genes derived from all three maternal *X*-chromosomes have been omitted. The results are in complete agreement with those of Bridges (1916) and Anderson (1925). The total data from the three publications indicate no cross-overs at the two-strand stage (classes (v) and (vi)) and 131 at the four-strand stage and involving only two of the four strands (classes (vii) to (x)).

These experiments which demonstrate that crossing-over occurs exclusively at the four-strand stage are open to the criticism that they are concerned with crossing-over under abnormal conditions: *XXY*, attached *XX* or triploid *Drosophila*. The ideal way in which to obtain information about the stage at which crossing-over occurs is to recover the four products of a single meiosis, in isolation from those of neighbouring meioses. This tetrad analysis is possible in many plants.

Pascher (1918) crossed two species of the haploid unicellular green alga *Chlamydomonas* differing in several characters and isolated a number of the resulting zygotes. Meiosis in *Chlamydomonas* occurs on germination of the zygote and leads to the production of four motile cells. Pascher examined the characters of these cells and found that in each tetrad the parental characters always segregated two and two. Thus one parent had pear-shaped cells and a laterally-placed chloroplast, while the other had spherical cells and a basal chloroplast. The four cells from each tetrad always comprised two with pear-shaped and two with spherical cells, and similarly two had lateral and two basal chloroplasts. Pascher found that in some tetrads there were two cells like one parent and two like the other, while in others all four cells differed from one another, the tetrad having, for example, one cell with each of the four combinations of the shape and chloroplast characters. The existence of such 'tetratype' tetrads showed that segregation of character-differences could occur at either division of meiosis and was in agreement with the hypothesis that crossing-over occurred at the four-strand stage, although convincing evidence of this would require linked factors.

Soon afterwards tetrad analysis was achieved in bryophytes and in basidiomycete and phycomycete fungi, but it was not until Lindegren (1933)

found linked characters in the ascomycete fungus *Neurospora crassa* that
direct evidence was obtained by tetrad analysis that crossing-over occurs
at the four-strand stage and involves only two of the four strands at any one
place. *Neurospora crassa* is a haploid fungus existing in two mating-types.
Meiosis occurs immediately after fusion of the nuclei of opposite mating-type.
Wilcox (1928) had shown that in the closely allied species *N. sitophila* the
four haploid nuclei resulting from meiosis are linearly arranged within an
elongated tube-like cell, the ascus, such that the two second-division spindles
do not overlap (see Fig. 8.7). Subsequently mitosis takes place in each

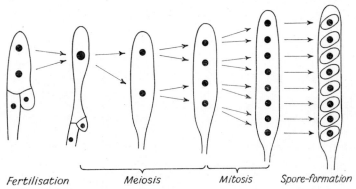

Fertilisation   *Meiosis*   *Mitosis*   *Spore-formation*

FIGURE 8.7   Stages in the development of the ascospores of
             Neurospora sitophila.

nucleus, and again the spindles do not overlap. Spore walls are then laid
down round each nucleus, and the mature ascus, which is about 150 μ long
and 15 μ wide, contains a linear sequence of 8 black elliptical spores, each
measuring about 25 μ in length and 15 μ in width. She dissected a number of
asci using a fine needle and isolated the spores in sequence. When the resulting cultures were tested for mating-type four were always of one mating-type
and four of the other. Moreover, spores 1 and 2 numbering from the top of
the ascus were always alike, and so were 3 and 4, and so on. In other words,
the spores were in identical pairs, as would be expected if the third nuclear
division in the young ascus was mitotic (cf. Pl. 4(*b*)–(*d*)).

Dodge (1929) made similar ascus dissections and found evidence that the
mating-type factors sometimes segregate at the first division of meiosis and
sometimes at the second division. This was confirmed by Lindegren (1932)
who dissected numerous asci of *N. crassa* and tested the spores for mating-
type. His results are shown in Table 8.2. Eleven out of 273 asci showed one
or more pairs of non-identical spores, numbering from the end of the ascus,
in contrast to what was expected if the cytology was similar to that of
N. sitophila. However in every instance exchanging the position of two
adjacent spores would suffice to explain these anomalies, and he presumed
that either third-division spindle overlap or spore displacement during
dissection was responsible. The 273 asci can then be classified into six
classes numbered I to VI in the table. Classes I and II correspond to

8

segregation of A from a at the first division of meiosis, if the nuclear behaviour is like *N. sitophila*. The numbers of asci in these two classes were not significantly different (observed frequencies 105 and 129, expected 117, deviations 12, $\chi^2 = 2\cdot5$, which with 1 degree of freedom, is associated with a probability of just over $0\cdot1$ of obtaining a deviation as large or larger by chance). Classes III to VI correspond to segregation of A from a at the second division

TABLE 8.2   Lindegren's data (1932) for the segregation of the mating-type factors in asci of *Neurospora crassa*. The letters A and a denote the two mating-types.

Class	Position of spore in ascus								Number
	1	2	3	4	5	6	7	8	
I	A	A	A	A	a	a	a	a	102⎤ 105
	A	A	A	a	A	a	a	a	3⎦
II	a	a	a	a	A	A	A	A	123⎤ 129
	a	a	a	A	a	A	A	A	6⎦
III	A	A	a	a	A	A	a	a	8⎤ 9
	A	a	A	a	A	A	a	a	1⎦
IV	a	a	A	A	a	a	A	A	5
V	A	A	a	a	a	a	A	A	10⎤ 11
	A	a	A	a	a	a	A	A	1⎦
VI	a	a	A	A	A	A	a	a	14
								Total	273

of meiosis, and again the numbers in the classes do not differ significantly (observed frequencies 9, 5, 11 and 14, expected 9·75, deviations 0·75, 4·75, 1·25 and 4·25, $\chi^2 = 4\cdot5$, which for three degrees of freedom implies a probability of between 0·5 and 0·1 of by chance getting a deviation as large or larger than that observed). However the frequencies of classes I and II clearly differ significantly from those of the other four.

Lindegren (1933) reported further data from ascus dissection in *N. crassa*. He crossed a strain of the fungus with pale aerial filaments and conidia (asexual spores) with one lacking conidia, which he described as fluffy from the appearance of the aerial growth. The normal fungus has orange-coloured conidia. Each of the characters (pale and fluffy) appeared to differ from normal by a single gene, for the spores from each ascus produced four pale and four orange cultures, and they could also be classified for the presence or absence of conidia and again there were four progeny per ascus in each class. Lindegren dissected 109 asci showing segregation for these characters. The numbers of asci with first- and second-division segregation which he obtained are shown in Table 8.3. The frequency of second-division segregation for mating-type in this set of data (11·0%) is slightly lower than that found previously (14·3%), but the difference is not significant. (Contingency $\chi^2 = \dfrac{382[(234 \times 12) - (39 \times 97)]^2}{273 \times 109 \times 331 \times 51} = 0 \cdot 74$, which, with one degree of freedom means that P is just under 0·5, or in other words, a

TABLE 8.3   Lindegren's data (1933) for first- and second-division segregation frequencies for various character-differences in *Neurospora crassa*.

Character difference		Numbers of asci showing segregation			Percentage of asci showing 2nd division segregation	Distance of gene from centromere
		First division	Second division	Total		
Mating-type	Data of Table 8.2	234	39	273	14·3	7·1
	New data	97	12	109	11·0	5·5
	Total	331	51	382	13·4	6·7
Pale/normal orange conidial colour		73	36	109	33·0	16·5
Fluffy/normal growth-form		42	67	109	61·4	30·7

difference as large or larger than that found may be expected to occur by chance nearly every other time on the average.) On the other hand the second-division segregation frequencies of the pale and fluffy characters (33·0% and 61·4% respectively) clearly differ significantly from each other and from that for mating-type.

Lindegren's hypothesis to explain these results was that crossing-over occurred at the four-strand stage and involved only two of the four chromatids, and furthermore that the paternal and maternal centromeres of the chromosome pair segregated from one another at the first division of meiosis. Second-division segregation of a pair of alleles would then be the consequence of crossing-over between their locus and the centromere of the chromosome, while first-division segregation would mean that the factors had separated along with the centromeres, without crossing-over in between (Fig. 8.8). Owing to the variability in the position of cross-overs a given pair of alleles would sometimes separate at the first division of meiosis and sometimes at the second division. Lindegren pointed out that it followed from this that the frequency of second-division segregation for a particular character-difference was a measure of the frequency of crossing-over between the gene concerned and its centromere, and hence was a measure of their distance apart on the linkage map.

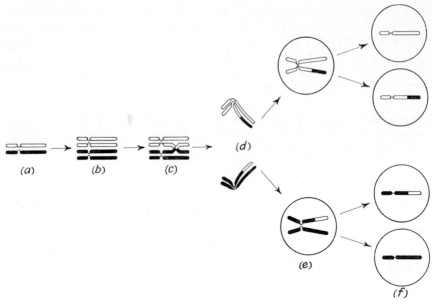

FIGURE 8.8   Diagrams of a pair of homologous chromosomes at various stages of
meiosis to illustrate Lindegren's hypothesis of centromere segregation
at the first division of meiosis, and crossing-over at the four-strand
stage. This hypothesis was put forward to account for the characteristic frequency of second-division segregation for each gene.
(*a*) Pachytene stage. (*b*) End of pachytene stage. (*c*) Diplotene stage.
(*d*) Anaphase I. (*e*) Telophase I. (*f*) Telophase II.
The constrictions indicate the centromeres, and the shading the
parental origin.

It will be recalled that Sturtevant (1913) had proposed that the unit of
distance between two gene loci on a linkage map should be such as to give rise
to 1% of cross-over gametes (see §7.3). In a haploid organism such as
Neurospora meiosis leads directly to the next generation, so the percentage
frequency of progeny with non-parental combinations of two character-
differences is the measure of the distance apart on the linkage map of the
factors concerned. However, if crossing-over occurs at the four-strand
stage, one exchange will lead to two cross-over and two non-cross-over
progeny (compare Fig. 8.8). Hence every time a pair of allelomorphs
segregate from one another at the second division of meiosis, the four products of meiosis will comprise two cross-overs and two non-cross-overs for
the interval between the locus of the alleles and the centromere. Thus 1% of
cross-over progeny, which is the unit on the map, will be produced by
second-division segregation in 2% of meioses, or in other words frequencies of
second-division segregation expressed as percentages can be converted into
gene-centromere map distances simply by halving them. The centromere
distances obtained in this way for the factors studied by Lindegren are given
in the right-hand column of Table 8.3.

TABLE 8.4 Lindegren's data (1933) for the numbers of parental and non-parental combinations of character-differences in the 436 pairs of spores from 109 asci of *Neurospora crassa*.

Pair of Character-differences	Parental	Non-parental	Percentage Recombination
Mating-type and pale/normal (orange) conidial colour	338	98	22·5
Mating-type and fluffy/normal growth form	222	214	49·0
Pale/normal (orange) conidial colour and fluffy/normal growth-form	224	212	48·6

Lindegren's theory of first-division segregation of centromeres was supported by the recombination data from his 109 asci (see Table 8.4). The numbers of parental and non-parental associations of mating-type and fluffy growth-form (222 parental and 214 non-parental) do not differ significantly, and nor do those for the pale and fluffy characters (224 parental and 212 non-parental). On the other hand, the mating-type and pale characters showed partial linkage, with 22·5% recombination. It follows that the genes responsible for these character-differences are located 22·5 units apart on the same linkage map. This figure agrees well with the sum of their centromere distances (22·0) (see Fig. 8.9). Lindegren concluded that the genes for mating-type and pale conidia are located in opposite arms of the chromosome, and that his hypothesis of first-division segregation of centromeres, together with crossing-over at the four-strand stage and involving only two of the four strands, was correct (cf. Pl. 4(*c*)).

The hypothesis of first-division segregation of the centromeres, which is required by the chiasmatype theory, had been proposed earlier by Bridges and Anderson (1925), but their evidence was indirect and less convincing. An examination of their data and those of Anderson (1925) in Table 8.1 shows that there are progressive changes in the frequencies of the various

FIGURE 8.9   Linkage map of the mating-type chromosome of *Neurospora crassa*, showing the similarity between the distance apart of the mating-type and 'pale' gene loci based on second-division segregation frequencies (figures above the line) and that based on recombination frequency (figure below the line). The data are from the analysis of 109 asci by Lindegren (1933).

genotypes as one proceeds from column to column across the table, or in other words, as one proceeds along the chromosome from region to region (see Fig. 8.10). By extrapolation, it appeared that at a point beyond the gene

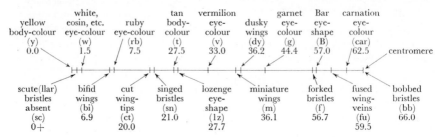

FIGURE 8.10   Linkage map of the *X*-chromosome of *Drosophila melanogaster* to show the relative positions of genes mentioned in the text. The figures show the distance from the distal end in map units. (Data chiefly from Morgan, 1926.)

for forked bristles, which in both experiments marked one end of the part of the chromosome under study, the genotypes homozygous for the *A* or the *a* allele (that is, classes (i), (ii), (vii) and (viii)) would diminish to zero. It was suggested that at this hypothetical point alleles (such as *A* and *a*) always segregated from one another at the first division of meiosis and sister genes (such as *A* and *A*) always passed to opposite poles at the second meiotic division. Since the *X*-chromosome in *Drosophila melanogaster* is rod-shaped, the centromere must lie at or near one end, and it was natural to suggest that this corresponded with the hypothetical point of first-division segregation.

With the attached-*X* flies this point of zero frequency of homozygotes would be the place where the two *X*-chromosomes joined, but this was thought to coincide with the centromere since, as already indicated, the chromosome when fixed and stained appeared V-shaped with two equal arms. Anderson's data allowed this point of junction to be mapped. From Table 8.1, out of the 188 flies studied, 22 (11·7%) were homozygous at the 'forked' locus (classes (i), (ii), (vii) and (viii) in the 'forked and garnet' column) and 48 (25·5%) were homozygous at the 'garnet' locus (classes (i), (ii), (ix) and (x) in the same column). Since homozygosis is thought to be due to crossing-over between gene and attachment-point, these frequencies are a measure of the distances of the gene loci from this point on the linkage map. The two *X*-chromosomes in an attached-*X* fly are the equivalent of two spores from opposite ends of a *Neurospora* ascus. Homozygous flies (*A/A* or *a/a*) are equivalent to second-division segregation asci, but only half the occurrences of second-division segregation are detected. This is evident from examination of Table 8.2: there are 25 asci (classes V and VI) in which spores 1 and 8 are identical, compared with a total of 39 in which second-division segregation has occurred. Since frequencies of second-division segregation must be halved for use as map distances, homozygosis frequencies, which are equivalent to the half values, can be used directly as map distances between gene loci and the point of junction of the two *X*-chromosomes. This has been done in Fig. 8.11.

Out of the 376 *X*-chromosomes in Anderson's 188 flies, 54 (14·4%) were cross-overs between 'forked' and garnet' (classes (vii) to (x), plus twice class (iv) in Table 8.1). This frequency is close to the difference between the other two (see Fig. 8.11). Thus the recombination and homozygosis data agree,

FIGURE 8.11   Linkage map of part of the *X*-chromosome of *Drosophila melanogaster* showing the similarity between the distance apart of the 'forked' and 'garnet' gene loci based on homozygosis frequencies (figures above the line) and that based on recombination frequency (figure below the line). The data are from the analysis of 188 attached-*X* females by Anderson (1925).

and suggest that the point of junction of the two *X*-chromosomes is about 12 units beyond the 'forked' locus. This corresponds well with the position of the terminal gene known (bobbed bristles) in the linkage group (see Fig. 8.10).

Support for the hypothesis of first-division segregation of centromeres could also be obtained from the observations of Carothers (1913) at spermatogenesis in the grasshopper *Brachystola magna*. As mentioned in §6.9, she found an unequal chromosome-pair, and the inequality always segregated at the first division of meiosis. Carothers concluded that the spindle-fibres became attached at the unequal end at metaphase I (see Fig. 6.4).

The discovery that crossing-over takes place, not between paternal and maternal chromosomes, but between individual daughter chromatids, one of paternal and one of maternal origin, constituted strong evidence in support of Janssens' chiasmatype theory. However, the data which led to this discovery provided no information about crossing-over in relation to chiasmata. The next important question, therefore, in testing the truth of Janssens' theory, was to establish whether or not the frequencies and distribution of cross-overs in groups of linked genes were in agreement with the frequencies and distributions of chiasmata in the corresponding chromosomes.

§ 8.7   Genetical interference

Muller (1916) pointed out that the occurrence of one crossing-over in *Drosophila* interferes with the coincident occurrence of another in the same pair of chromosomes, and termed the phenomenon *interference*. For example, Morgan's data for 2205 flies in Table 7.3 indicate 29 cross-overs (1·3%) between the loci for yellow body-colour and white eyes, and 719 (32·6%) between the loci for white eyes and miniature wings. The expected frequency of double cross-overs, if crossing-over occurs at random, is given by the product of these frequencies, or $\dfrac{29}{2205} \times \dfrac{719}{2205} = 0.43\%$. The observed frequency of double cross-overs was $\dfrac{1}{2205}$ or 0.045%. Muller suggested that the most useful way to measure the intensity of interference was to divide the observed double cross-over frequency by the expected value (assuming no interference), and so obtain a fraction showing what proportion of the coincidences which would have happened on pure chance really took place. In the present example this ratio is

$$\frac{2205 \times 1}{29 \times 719} = 0.106.$$

He called this quantity the *coincidence*, pointing out that a low value such as this means much interference. He showed that in the X-chromosome of *Drosophila* the intensity of interference is very great over short intervals, but falls off with distance, such that for regions 40 units or more apart in the linkage group the coincidence has risen to near 1. Morgan (1919) called the phenomenon of interference the *fifth law of heredity*. Genetical interference has since been found to occur in most organisms that have been investigated. Thus, in *Zea*, from Stadler's data in Fig. 7.4(*a*), the frequency of double cross-overs expected if there is no interference is

$$pq = \frac{1065}{45,832} \times \frac{9141}{45,832},$$

or 212·4 out of the 45,832 progeny. The observed frequency was only 32. Hence, the coincidence is $\dfrac{32}{212\cdot4} = 0.150$.

Stevens (1936) pointed out that for non-adjacent regions of a chromosome, the coincidence had frequently been wrongly estimated. He showed that the best estimate, whether the regions under study were adjacent or not, was given by the standard expression

$$\frac{n \times n_{pq}}{n_p \times n_q}$$

where n is the total number of individuals, and n_p, n_q, and n_{pq} are, respectively, the numbers of individuals showing a recombination in segment p, in segment q, and simultaneously in segments p and q, but with the important corollary that these numbers must be irrespective of the occurrence of recombination elsewhere. Stevens calculated coincidence values from published recombination data for *Drosophila melanogaster*. Some of his results are given Table 8.5. It is evident that within the one arm of the X-chromosome there is strong interference over short intervals, declining to no interference (coincidence 1) at about 40 units separation, as Muller had found. On the other hand, between the two arms of chromosome II he found there was no interference.

TABLE 8.5 Coincidence values obtained by Stevens (1936) from published recombination data for two linkage groups in *Drosophila melanogaster*. The six intervals between gene loci in linkage-group I averaged 9.4 units in length. The interval spanning the centromere in linkage-group II was 3 units long and the other six averaged 17·3 units. The coincidence values in the lower part of the table, and for three and four intervening segments in the upper part, do not differ significantly from unity.

Region	Number of Intervening Segments					
	0	1	2	3	4	5
Within one arm of link-age-group I (*X*-chromosome)	0·03	0·13	0·55	1·00	1·01	—
	0·06	0·37	0·87	1·06	—	—
	0·12	0·64	0·82	—	—	—
	0·24	0·71	—	—	—	—
	0·19	—	—	—	—	—
Across the centromere of linkage-group II	—	1·01	1·05	0·97	1·11	0·89
	—	—	1·00	0·97	0·97	—
	—	—	—	0·98	—	—

§ 8.8   Chromatid interference

With the discovery that crossing-over is between daughter chromatids and not parent chromosomes, ideas about interference had to be revised. It could no longer be implicitly assumed that interference meant that the position of one exchange between homologous chromosomes affected the position of a neighbouring exchange. Haldane (1931) pointed out that if adjacent cross-overs were usually between different pairs of chromatids, forming a four-strand double cross-over as in Fig. 8.12, a moderate degree of genetical interference was compatible with a random distribution of the points of exchange. This is possible because four-strand double cross-overs lead only to single cross-over progeny, since no chromatid is broken more than once. Mather (1933*a*) gave the name of *chromatid interference* to the phenom-enon of non-random distribution between the chromatids involved in successive cross-overs. There are four possible relationships between the strands concerned in two cross-overs, and they are illustrated in Fig. 8.12. There are two kinds of three-strand double cross-overs, depending on which parent contributes the unbroken strand. If crossing-over is at random as regards the strands involved, the four types will occur with equal frequency, or in other words, the ratio of two-strand:three-strand:four-strand double cross-overs will be as 1:2:1.

Emerson and Beadle (1933) were the first to obtain appreciable data concerning the strand-relationship of adjacent cross-overs. They used attached-*X Drosophila melanogaster* heterozygous for several sex-linked characters, and like Anderson (1925) determined the frequencies of the various genotypes in the progeny of a cross. With three or more pairs of alleles segregating simultaneously, it is possible to distinguish between two classes of double cross-overs: (*A*) two-strand and one kind of three-strand, and (*B*) four-strand and the other kind of three-strand. Anderson (1925) found 3 progeny of type *A* and 4 of type *B*. Emerson and Beadle, from their

FIGURE 8.12   The four kinds of double cross-overs and the corresponding tetrad genotypes from the cross *ABC* × *abc*. (i) Two-strand, (ii) and (iii) three-strand, and (iv) four-strand relationship (cf. Pl. 4(*d*)).

own data together with unpublished data of Sturtevant, brought these totals to 73 *A*, 62 *B*. The frequencies of the two types do not differ significantly, and the inference was that, as far as the evidence went, there was no chromatid interference in this chromosome.

Tetrad analysis with three or more linked factors provides full information on the strand-relationship of cross-overs. This is evident from the fact that the four tetrad genotypes in Fig. 8.12 are all different. The first data of this kind were obtained by Lindegren with *Neurospora crassa*. Extensive results have been obtained subsequently with this organism by a number of authors, and Bole-Gowda, Perkins and Strickland (1962) quote totals of 423 two-strand, 759 three-strand and 329 four-strand double cross-overs as the pooled results of a number of recent studies. This represents a significant excess of two-strand double cross-overs over four-strand. Data obtained by Knapp and Möller (1955) with *Sphaerocarpos donnellii*, Strickland (1958) with *Aspergillus nidulans*, and Ebersold and Levine (1959) with *Chlamydomonas reinhardi* indicate no chromatid interference, but in some instances there was an excess of two-strand double cross-overs, which, in view of the *Neurospora* results, might be found to be significant with more extensive data.

The strands involved in adjacent cross-overs can sometimes be determined cytologically. Some of the most extensive information of this kind was obtained by Brown and Zohary (1955) with *Lilium formosanum*, and is described in §8.15. It indicated no chromatid interference within a chromosome arm.

§ 8.9   Cross-over position interference

If, as would thus appear, chromatid interference is commonly absent, it follows that genetical interference between cross-overs must often be wholly attributed to the position of one point of exchange interfering with the position of a neighbouring exchange, as indeed was originally supposed. To this phenomenon, Mather (1933a) gave the name 'chiasma interference'. Carter and Robertson (1952) suggested that a more explicit title would be 'chiasma position interference'. Both these names are open to the objection that they use a cytological term, chiasma, to describe a genetical phenomenon. In other words, by using these terms one assumes that the chiasmatype theory is true. A more appropriate title would be 'cross-over position interference' or simply *position interference*.

§ 8.10   Chiasma position interference

If chiasmata correspond to cross-overs, as the chiasmatype theory demands, and if cross-overs show position interference, then it is to be expected that chiasmata will also show position interference. Haldane (1931) demonstrated this, using data of Maeda (1930) for chiasma frequencies in the pollen-mother-cells of *Vicia faba*. The 12 somatic chromosomes of this plant comprise five pairs of about equal size and with sub-terminal centromeres, and one pair about twice as long and with the centromere near the middle. Maeda recorded the numbers of chiasmata at metaphase I in 1100 of the five smaller chromosome-pairs (which were not individually distinguishable) and in 1057 of the large one. The mean chiasma frequencies were 3·5 in the short chromosomes and 8·1 in the long one. Haldane drew attention to the distribution of chiasma frequencies about these mean values. In the short chromosomes, a majority had three or four chiasmata and the range was from 1 to 6, while in the long one there was a great concentration at 7 to 9 chiasmata and the total range was from 3 to 13. He pointed out that if the distribution of chiasmata was at random along the chromosomes, the frequencies of chromosomes with different numbers of chiasmata would fit a Poisson distribution, in which the variance is equal to the mean. Analysis of Maeda's data showed that for both the short chromosomes and the long one there was much less variation in chiasma frequency than would be expected on the Poisson distribution. Thus, for the short chromosomes the variance was only about one-quarter of the mean and for the long one about one-third. These differences from random chiasma distribution were highly significant and indicated that the occurrence of one chiasma was greatly reducing the likelihood of another in its vicinity. Haldane obtained similar results from the analysis of less extensive data for several other flowering plants.

Mather (1933*a*) made the converse analysis. He took published recombination data for linkage groups II and III of *Drosophila melanogaster*, assumed there was no chromatid interference and that chiasmata corresponded to points of crossing-over between two chromatids, and determined the chiasma distribution that would result. He found that the *Drosophila* genetical data would lead to a chiasma distribution in which the variance was $\frac{1}{6}$ to $\frac{1}{4}$ of the mean, in good agreement with the cytological data from Angiosperms.

8.11   Chiasma frequencies and cross-over frequencies

The pattern of distribution of chiasmata in chromosomes thus appears to be in agreement with the hypothesis that chiasmata correspond to the points of crossing-over. However, if the chiasmatype theory is true, one would also expect to find correspondence between chiasma frequencies and cross-over frequencies in individual chromosomes. Morgan, Sturtevant, Muller and Bridges (1915) reported that mutant genes in *Drosophila melanogaster* fell into four linkage groups. Within groups there were various intensities of partial linkage, while between groups parental and non-parental combinations were statistically equal in frequency. These findings agreed with the observation that the haploid chromosome number was 4. Morgan (1919) called this equality between numbers of linkage groups and of chromosomes the *sixth law of heredity*. Although at the time established only for *Drosophila*, later work has confirmed the truth of this law for many organisms including for example *Zea mays* with 10 linkage groups and chromosomes, and *Neurospora crassa* with seven of each. Morgan *et al.* (1915) also found that the number of mutants in each *Drosophila* linkage group was roughly proportional to the physical size of the corresponding chromosome.

Darlington (1934*b*) showed that there was agreement between chiasma and cross-over frequencies for each chromosome of *Zea mays*. He obtained a mean total chiasma frequency of 27·1 for the ten chromosome-pairs in the pollen-mother-cells. Distributing these chiasmata amongst the chromosomes in proportion to their lengths, using more recent estimates of the latter from Rhoades (1950), has given the figures in the third column of Table 8.6. However, Darlington found evidence that the shorter chromosomes had relatively more chiasmata in relation to their length, as indicated in the caption to the table. He compared the estimated chiasma frequencies with the cross-over frequencies derived from published linkage data. More extensive data from Rhoades (1950) are now available and are given in the fourth column of the table. With crossing-over occurring between only two of the four chromatids, one exchange will produce 50% of cross-over gametes and 50% with the parental gene combinations. Hence 50 units on the linkage map is equivalent to an average of one exchange per meiosis in that interval of the chromosome. The figures in column 4 have therefore been obtained by taking the total length of each linkage map and dividing it by 50. In every instance the frequencies of crossing-over are slightly less than the

TABLE 8.6   Comparison of chiasma and cross-over frequencies in *Zea mays*. The data in columns 2 and 4 are from Rhoades (1950), and the total chiasma frequency is from Darlington (1934*b*), who found evidence that the short chromosomes have slightly more chiasmata in relation to their length. His estimates of the chiasma frequencies of chromosomes 1, 2, 9 and 10 would approximate to 3·8, 3·2, 2·2 and 2·0, respectively.

Chromosome Number	Length in μ at Mid-Pachytene	Estimated Mean Chiasma Frequency if Proportional to Length	Mean Cross-over Frequency of Mapped Portion
1	82	4·0	3·1
2	67	3·3	2·6
3	62	3·0	2·4
4	59	2·9	2·2
5	60	2·9	1·4
6	49	2·4	1·3
7	47	2·3	1·9
8	47	2·3	0·6
9	43	2·1	1·4
10	37	1·8	1·1
Totals	553	27·0	18·0

chiasma frequencies (on average two-thirds of them), but this is to be expected since it is unlikely that genes have been mapped at the extreme ends of the chromosomes. This agreement with expectation gives further support to the view that chiasmata correspond to the points of crossing-over, and hence supports the chiasmatype hypothesis.

The probability that a newly-obtained mutant will show linkage to a previously known mutant will depend on the chromosome number and the cross-over frequency for that organism. Carter (1955) has shown how total cross-over frequencies per meiosis can be estimated from such linkage data, and has applied the method to data for *Mus musculus* (Mouse). Of 33 mutants, 9 were due to genes situated within 25 units of a previously discovered mutant, from which the total cross-over frequency per meiosis was estimated to be approximately 34. This estimate did not differ significantly from the observed total chiasma frequency for the 20 chromosome pairs, which was approximately 38.

The evidence presented so far in this chapter has established that crossing-over occurs between two of the four chromatids; that these chromatids appear to be chosen more or less at random at each cross-over; that paternal and maternal centromeres segregate from one another at the first division of meiosis; and that chiasmata and points of crossing-over show similar frequencies of occurrence and corresponding intensities of interference. All these findings are in agreement with Janssens' chiasmatype theory, but nevertheless do not constitute convincing evidence of the truth of the theory.

§ 8.12   Belling's modification of Janssens' theory

Janssens' theory, although favoured almost at once by geneticists, received no support from other cytologists for nearly 20 years. They criticised it on the grounds that they could find no evidence for the breakage and rejoining of

FIGURE 8.13   Diagrams to illustrate Belling's modification of Janssens' hypothesis of exchange between homologous chromosomes. Chromatid segments derived from one parent are shown with a broken line and those derived from the other parent by an unbroken line. (*a*) Pachytene stage. (*b*) Diplotene stage.

threads at the early diplotene stage, such as he had claimed to have seen. However, Belling (1928*a*), after studying the meiotic chromosomes in various flowering plants, proposed a modification of Janssens' theory which removed this criticism. He suggested that the exchange between chromatids took place at the preceding pachytene stage, while the homologous chromosomes were closely associated. Exchange at this stage could not be directly observed, but the chiasmata seen subsequently would be the consequence of these exchanges, if one accepted, as Janssens had done, that throughout the length of each chromosome of the bivalent association, the pairing at the diplotene stage was always between daughter-chromatids derived from the same parent chromosome (Fig. 8.13). Belling (1929) gave two primary reasons for believing that the diplotene pairing was of this kind.

§ 8.13   Unequal chromosome pairs

Firstly, whenever homologous chromosomes differed in appearance at one end, as had been observed by Carothers (1913), Wenrich (1916) and others in various Orthoptera, and by Belling himself in *Aloe purpurascens*, the two short chromatid-ends were always associated with one another at the diplotene stage and similarly with the two long ones (Fig. 8.14(a)). This was true whether or not the centromere was close to the end where the difference occurred. Darlington (1932, pp. 274–277) took this argument a stage further. He pointed out that since on the chiasmatype hypothesis sister-chromatids are always associated at the diplotene stage, the loop or pair of arms containing the centromeres will have two paternal chromatids associated at one centromere region and two maternal at the other. Since these centromere regions move to opposite poles at anaphase I, paternal and maternal centromeres will always show first-division segregation, just as Bridges & Anderson (1925) had postulated on genetic evidence. If there is no chiasma between the centromere and a region of the chromosome where the homologues differ, then this difference will segregate at the first division of meiosis, as found by Carothers (1913) with *Brachystola magna*. On the other hand, a single chiasma between centromere and inequality would lead to second-division segregation for the region of difference.

An example of regular second-division segregation for an inequality was found by Wenrich (1916) at spermatogenesis in the grasshopper *Phrynotettix tschivavensis*. Chromosome-pair B was found in 11 individuals to show heterozygosity for the presence and absence of a large terminal granule. Wenrich observed a single medially-placed chiasma in each B chromosome-pair. Since the two chromatid-ends with the granule were always associated with one another, and similarly with the two without the granule, and since Wenrich states that he found no indication of breaking or recombining of the parts of chromatids, he must have assumed that one paternal and one maternal centromere went to each pole at the first division. On the other hand, Darlington suggested there was first-division segregation of centromeres and that crossing-over had occurred at the position of the chiasma.

In two individuals of *Phrynotettix*, Wenrich found a similar inequality in chromosome-pair C, but here it was variable in behaviour (Fig. 8.14(b) and (c)). Out of 928 cells which he examined at metaphase I, 472 showed first-division segregation for the inequality and the remaining 456 (49·2%) showed second-division segregation. As with chromosome-pair B, the metaphase configuration was cross-shaped, implying a single medially-placed chiasma. Wenrich suggested that the centromeres were situated at the end of the chromosome showing the inequality when this segregated at the first-division of meiosis, and that they moved to the other end with second-division segregation. Darlington put forward the suggestion that the centromere was fixed in position, that it was medially placed, that the chiasma might occur in either arm, and that crossing-over preceded its appearance. If crossing-over occurred in the opposite arm to the inequality, first-division segregation of the latter would occur, and if in the same arm there would be second-division segregation. However, the centromere appeared to be subterminal and not median in position.

Nur (1961) has offered a solution to this dilemma. He discovered in another short-horned grasshopper, *Calliptamus palaestinensis*, that an inequality in a chromosome-pair, although often appearing terminal, was really interstitially placed (Fig. 8.14(d) and (e)). The centromere was sub-terminal

FIGURE 8.14   Unequal chromosome-pairs at stages of the first division of meiosis.

(*a*)   *Aloe purpurascens* (from Belling, 1928c).

(*b*) and (*c*)   *Phrynotettix tschivavensis* chromosome-pair *C* (from Wenrich, 1916).

(*d*) and (*e*)   *Calliptamus palaestinensis* (from Nur, 1961).

(*b*) and (*d*)   First-division segregation for the inequality.

(*c*) and (*e*)   Second-division segregation for the inequality. The diagrams to the right of the drawings in (*a*), (*d*) and (*e*) show the interpretation of the observed structures according to the chiasmatype hypothesis, with the black and white segments indicating the parental origin.

in position and at meiosis in the male a single chiasma occurred regularly and appeared always to be in the long arm, just as in chromosome-pair *C* of *Phrynotettix* studied by Wenrich. Out of 410 cells in *Calliptamus* at the diplotene or diakinetic stage, Nur found that the chiasma appeared to be proximal to the inequality in 379 (92·4%) and distal to it in the remaining 31. Examination of 69 cells at anaphase I showed 63 (91·3%) with second-division segregation for the inequality and 6 with first-division segregation, in agreement with the observations at the earlier stage. It is presumed that the inequality in chromosome-pair *C* of *Phrynotettix*, studied by Wenrich (1916), was also interstitially placed although appearing terminal, and that chiasmata occurred proximal and distal to it equally often.

Several authors have made quantitative studies with unequal chromosome-pairs showing variability of behaviour like Wenrich's pair *C*. Their results are given in the upper part of Table 8.7. In each study the interval between centromere and region of inequality was short and never showed more than a single chiasma. With the exception of Haga's data for *Paris verticillata*, there was no significant difference (contingency χ^2 value, for one degree of freedom, less than 4—see last column of Table 8.7) between the chiasma frequency observed at diakinesis or metaphase I, and the second-division segregation frequency observed at anaphase I or II. A remarkable feature of meiosis in *P. verticillata* is the regular occurrence of chiasmata close to the centromere in either or both arms of each chromosome. It is therefore exceptionally difficult material in which to record the frequency of cells with a chiasma between the centromere and the inequality. In Haga's data, 667 cells had a chiasma in the unequal arm and 333 were thought to show chiasmata only in the other arm, but owing to the close proximity of the centromere to these chiasmata it is probable that some of them were in fact in the unequal arm. Hence the excess of second-division segregations (82·25%) over chiasmata (66·7%) is expected.

The data in the lower part of Table 8.7 refer to individuals heterozygous for the presence and absence of an exchange of part of an arm between two different (that is, non-homologous) chromosomes. Such individuals will have two chromosome-pairs each with an unequal arm. If the two chromosomes and their exchanged portions are similar in appearance, it may not be possible to recognise them individually, as was found by Kayano (1960*a*) with *Disporum sessile* and by Noda (1961) with *Scilla scilloides*. In any event, in such interchange heterozygotes the recognition of the unequal pairs at diakinesis or metaphase I requires skill, since the two pairs will commonly be held together by chiasmata to form a quadrivalent association. As with the simple inequalities discussed in the last paragraph, the intervals between centromere and inequality were short and except in chromosome I of *Acrida lata* (see table) never showed more than one chiasma. Without exception, no significant differences were found between the chiasma frequencies and the corresponding second-division segregation frequencies.

On the chiasmatype hypothesis, paternal and maternal centromeres segregate at the first division of meiosis, and the segregation of a chromosomal inequality at the second division can only be accounted for by

9

TABLE 8.7   Frequencies of cells with and without a chiasma between the centromere and an inequality in a chromosome-pair, and frequencies of first- and second-division segregation for the inequality. In the right-hand column the contingency χ^2 values are given from a comparison of the chiasma and segregation frequencies. χ^2 values of less than about 4 indicate no significant difference between chiasma frequencies and second-division segregation frequencies.

Type of Structural Heterozygote	Organism and Reference	Chromosome Pair	Diakinesis or Metaphase I				Anaphase I or II				χ^2 $n=1$
			Without Chiasma	With Chiasma	Total	Percentage with Chiasma	1st Division Segregation	2nd Division Segregation	Total	Percentage 2nd Division Segregation	
	Mesocricetus auratus Koller, 1938	X & Y	206	47	253	18·6	87	24	111	21·6	0·46
	Paris verticillata Haga, 1944	D	333	667	1000	66·7	355	1645	2000	82·25	91·3
Simple inequality	*Lilium formosanum* Brown & Zohary, 1955	A* {	183	425	608	70·0	69	172	241	71·4	0·18
			114	120	234	51·3	67	81	148	54·7	0·43
		I* {	21	150	171	87·7	15	123	138	89·1	0·15
			72	273	345	79·1	43	149	192	77·6	0·17
	Allium fistulosum Zen, 1961	S	151	618	769	80·4	61	237	298	79·5	0·087

Lilium maximowiczii Noda, 1960	J_1	490	110	600	18·3	981	219	1200	18·25	0·0019
	J_2	600	0	600	0	1200	0	1200	0	0
Disporum sessile Kayano, 1960a	A	1549	651	{ 1100	Mean 29·6	1987	853	{ 1420	Mean 30·0	0·12
	B			1100 }				1420 }		
Non-homologous interchange										
Acrida lata Kayano & Nakamura, 1960	I	0	50†	50	97·0†	2	28	30	93·3	0·60
	II	9	41	50	82·0	3	27	30	90·0	0.94
Allium fistulosum Zen, 1961	S	59	208	267	77·9	17	50	67	74·6	0·33
	F	138	129	267	48·3	29	25	54	46·3	0·073
Scilla scilloides Noda, 1961	a	1128	2820	{ 1974	Mean 71·4	278	678	{ 478	Mean 70·9	0·097
	b			1974 }				478 }		

*The two sets of data for chromosome A of *Lilium formosanum* refer to different individuals heterozygous for the same chromosomal deficiency, while those for chromosome I refer to the same individual in different years.

†In chromosome I of *Acrida lata* there were 47 cells with single and 3 with double chiasmata. Assuming there was no chromatid interference, only half the double chiasmata would lead to second-division segregation.

postulating crossing-over between the centromere and the region of difference. Hence the finding that second-division segregation frequencies are statistically equal to chiasma frequencies is equivalent to finding that crossing-over and chiasma frequencies are equal, and so provides strong support for the chiasmatype theory. Furthermore, the invariable occurrence of pairing at late prophase and metaphase I between the two long segments, and similarly with the two short segments making up the inequality, even when a single chiasma has occurred between the inequality and the centromere, shows that these chiasmata are not merely points where the four threads have changed partners, but that breakage and crossing-over have occurred.

Inequalities in diplotene chromosome-pairs in oocytes of *Triturus cristatus* (Crested Newt) observed by Callan and Lloyd (1956) have provided direct evidence in support of the chiasmatype theory. The chromosomes at this stage are greatly elongated and have a remarkable 'lampbrush' structure (see Chapter 16), in which the two chromatids of which they are composed extend individually into lateral loops. The four chromatids in a chromosome-pair usually showed loops of similar appearance at corresponding positions, but in each meiotic cell in certain individuals a particular loop was absent from two of them. It was evident that these individuals were heterozygous for a difference at this point in the chromosome. The significant observation was that the two chromatids which possessed this particular loop were paired, and similarly with the two without the loop. A number of such differences between homologues were observed, and in each instance it was evident that sister-chromatids were paired at the diplotene stage, as expected on the chiasmatype theory.

§ 8.14 Polyploids

Belling's second main reason for believing that the diplotene pairing was between sister-chromatids was to account for configurations of three homologous chromosomes which he had observed at meiosis in triploid horticultural varieties of *Hyacinthus orientalis*. Belling (1929) and Darlington (1929*b*) discovered with triploid *Hyacinthus* and Newton and Darlington (1929) with triploid *Tulipa* that although for each chromosome all three homologues came together at the zygotene stage of meiosis, only two showed close pairing in any one region of the chromosome (cf. §6.4). However, at intervals there were changes of partner. Thus a typical pachytene trivalent association is like that shown diagrammatically in Fig. 8.15(*a*) with two changes of pairing partner. Belling thought that the chiasmata seen at the diplotene stage in a trivalent chromosomal association could not have arisen by an exchange of pairing partner, but required crossing-over to explain their origin.

Here also the argument was taken further by Darlington (1930) who demonstrated with polyploid *Hyacinthus* that a chiasma was the consequence of previous crossing-over. This demonstration was based on the observation that a chromosome may show two chiasmata *A* and *B* (see Fig. 8.15(*b*)–(*d*)) with one homologue, and a third chiasma *C* with another homologue at a

point between A and B. To account for such a configuration it is necessary
to assume that at the earlier pachytene stage there were changes of pairing
partner as in Fig. 8.15(a). On this assumption, chiasmata A and B must
involve the same four chromatids, and therefore chiasma C must involve

FIGURE 8.15   Diagrams of a trivalent chromosomal association to illustrate Darlington's demonstration that crossing-over must
precede chiasma-formation.
(a) Pachytene stage.
(b–d) Alternative explanations of diplotene configuration
with three chiasmata.
(b) With all chiasmata due to changes of pairing partner
without breakage (classical hypothesis).
(c) With chiasmata A and B classical, but C due to
breakage and crossing-over (chiasmatype hypothesis).
(d) With all chiasmata due to crossing-over (chiasmatype
hypothesis).

breakage and crossing-over (see Fig. 8.15(b) and (c)). Critical evidence is not
available for chiasmata A and B but there is no reason to suppose they differ
from C. Such intermediate chiasmata with a third homologue are of frequent
occurrence at meiosis in polyploid organisms. Since the pachytene association in all polyploids appears to be strictly confined to pairs over any given
region of a chromosome, it follows that all such intermediate chiasmata with
a third homologue must be the consequence of previous crossing-over.

§ 8.15   Chromosomal inversions

A third important source of critical information about chiasmata in
relation to crossing-over followed from the discovery by McClintock (1931)
that if a segment of a chromosome has become relatively inverted, individuals
heterozygous for such an inversion show reversed pairing at the pachytene
stage. Following X-irradiation of pollen, she obtained a plant of *Zea mays*
heterozygous for a long inversion in chromosome 2. It occupied parts of
both arms and included about two-thirds of the total length of the chromosome. Characteristic loops were formed at the pachytene stage in the

pollen-mother-cells, with the two homologous chromosomes passing along the loop in opposite directions, such that homologous parts were in association (see Fig. 8.16(i) and (ii)). Later (McClintock, 1933) in untreated *Zea* she found a plant heterozygous for an inversion within the short arm of chromosome 8 and she showed that crossing-over within the inversion led to the production of a chromatid with two centromeres (dicentric) and another with none (acentric) (see Fig. 8.16(v)). This is true, provided, as in this instance, the inversion is paracentric, that is, the centromere does not lie within it. The dicentric chromatid formed a bridge joining the two chromosomes of the pair as they began to move apart at anaphase I and prevented their separation until it broke. The acentric chromatid appeared as a chromosomal fragment at the side of the spindle, where it lagged behind at anaphase I. In this plant heterozygous for the inversion in chromosome 8, she observed 25 cells with bridge and fragment at anaphase I out of 281 examined, whereas 123 cells from a control plant without an inversion had none.

These observations opened up the possibility of a direct comparison between chiasma frequencies within an inversion and cross-over frequencies in the same inversion, manifest as bridge and fragment at anaphase I. In making such a comparison it is necessary to take into account the consequences of double crossing-over. In her *Zea* plant heterozygous for the chromosome 8 inversion, McClintock (1933) found one instance of the chromosome-pair at anaphase I joined by two dicentric bridges and with two acentric fragments alongside. She explained this as due to a four-strand double cross-over within the inversion. Smith (1935) found a wild plant of *Trillium erectum* which was heterozygous for a short inversion near the middle of the long arm of chromosome *D*. In about 9·5% of the pollen-mother-cells at metaphase I or anaphase I, a dicentric bridge and an acentric fragment about 6 μ long were present. In a further 2·5% of the mother-cells the fragment was present without the bridge, but then a dicentric loop could be seen at metaphase I, which gave a bridge at anaphase II. He explained the first-division loop by postulating one cross-over within the inversion and a second cross-over between the inversion and the centromere, such that one chromatid was involved in both cross-overs, that is, there was a three-strand double cross-over (see Fig. 8.16(vi)–(viii)). The proximal cross-over, that is, the one between inversion and centromere, then has the effect of converting the first-division bridge into a loop.

Smith's observations form the basis of a cytological method, referred to earlier in this chapter, of testing for chromatid interference. With no chromatid interference, a cross-over in a paracentric inversion and another proximal to it will give rise to equal frequencies of bridges at anaphase I (two- or four-strand relationships) and anaphase II (three-strand relationships between the two cross-overs). The marked excess of first-division bridges (9·5%) over loops (2·5%) in Smith's data for *Trillium erectum* may be due to the occurrence of cross-overs within the inversion without a proximal cross-over, rather than to an excess of two- and four-strand relationships over three-strand. On the other hand, Brown and Zohary (1955) following *X*-irradiation of pollen, obtained plants of *Lilium formosanum* heterozygous

FIGURE 8.16   Diagrams to show stages of meiosis in a chromosome-pair heterozygous for an inversion in the middle of one arm. *A B C D E* represent different regions of the chromosome arm. The normal sequence
is alphabetical, but in the inversion the regions *B, C* and *D* are
reversed to give the sequence *A D C B E*. A hollow circle represents a
centromere derived from one parent and a solid circle from the other.
(i)   Leptotene stage.
(ii) Pachytene stage with pairing in a loop such that homologous
      regions are associated.
(iii) and (iv) Diplotene stage with chiasmata at *A, C* and *E*. The
      chiasma at *C* is in the inversion and is of characteristic
      appearance, best seen in (iv). The cross-over at *C*
      involves the same two strands (or the other two) as
      that at *A*.
(v)   Anaphase I, with dicentric bridge and acentric fragment, such
      as would result from the configurations shown in (iii) and (iv).
(vi) and (vii) As (iii) and (iv), but the chiasma in the inversion is
      at *B* instead of *C*, giving an asymmetrical configura-
      tion, and the cross-overs at *A* and *B* involve three
      strands altogether instead of two or four.
(viii) Anaphase I, with dicentric loop and acentric fragment, such
      as would result from the configurations shown in (vi) and (vii).
The dicentric and acentric chromatids are shown interlocked at the
reversed chiasma in (vii), but not in (iv). Whether or not they will
be interlocked is thought to be a matter of chance.

123

for a long inversion in one arm of chromosome H, where chiasmata in the inversion were regularly associated with proximal chiasmata in the same arm. Thus, 278 pollen-mother-cells from two individuals were examined at diakinesis and every one of the 252 cells containing chiasmata within the inversion also had a single proximal chiasma. The same number of anaphase I cells was counted and showed 131 cells with a dicentric bridge and 121 with a dicentric loop, in excellent agreement with the 1:1 ratio of two-strand plus four-strand: three-strand double cross-overs expected in the absence of chromatid interference (deviations 5, $\chi^2 = 0.40$, $n = 1$, P is just over 0.5).

Crossing-over within a paracentric inversion in heterozygous form leads to other peculiarities in addition to the anaphase bridge or loop and fragment. Darlington (1936b), from studies of the chromosomes at spermatogenesis in the grasshoppers *Chorthippus parallelus* and *Stauroderus bicolor* showed that a cross-over near either end of the inversion gives an asymmetrical configuration at the diplotene and diakinetic stages (Fig. 8.16(vi) and (viii)), and Brown and Zohary (1955) drew attention to the characteristic morphology of the *reversed chiasmata* following crossing-over within an inversion. These chiasmata may or may not have the dicentric and acentric chromatids interlocked, depending on how the diplotene loops open out (see Fig. 8.16 (iv) and (vii)). In *Lilium formosanum* they could rarely distinguish a reversed chiasma with interlocked chromatids from a normal chiasma, but numerous examples were seen of reversed chiasmata where the chromatids were not interlocked, and also of asymmetrical configurations. The observation of reversed chiasmata and of the chiasmata responsible for asymmetrical configurations provide direct support for the chiasmatype theory, since, like the intermediate chiasmata in trivalent associations discussed earlier, crossing-over must have preceded their formation.

The direct comparison between chiasma frequencies in a paracentric inversion, observed at diakinesis, and bridge (or loop) and fragment frequencies, observed at anaphase I, has been made by Brown and Zohary (1955) with *Lilium formosanum*. Their data show an excellent agreement between chiasma and cross-over frequencies. In one plant of *L. formosanum* heterozygous for the chromosome H inversion 145 cells were examined at diakinesis. There were 17 without chiasmata in the inversion, 67 with one chiasma and 61 with two chiasmata. On the chiasmatype hypothesis and assuming there was no chromatid interference, two chiasmata within the inversion would be the consequence of two-strand, three-strand and four-strand double cross-overs in the ratio 1:2:1. The two-strand double cross-overs would give no bridges and fragments, as though without crossing-over in the inversion, since the two cross-overs would in effect cancel out. The three-strand double cross-overs would give one bridge and fragment, and the four-strand double cross-overs would give two bridges and fragments. Hence, the expected frequencies of cells with 0, 1 and 2 fragments at anaphase I can be calculated (see Table 8.8(a)). It was found that there was agreement between observed and expected numbers of fragments at anaphase I. A second plant also showed agreement: see Table 8.8(b). Thus Brown and Zohary's data provide strong support for the chiasmatype theory.

TABLE 8.8 Comparison of chiasma frequencies at diakinesis in an inversion in chromosome *H* of *Lilium formosanum* and fragment frequencies at anaphase *I*, from the data of Brown and Zohary (1955). The data in (*a*) and (*b*) relate to two different plants.

(*a*)

	Diakinesis		Expected Percentages of Cells with 0, 1 and 2 Fragments at Anaphase *I*		
No. of Chiasmata	Observed Nos. of Cells (Total 145)	Percentage Cells	0	1	2
0	17	11·7	11·7	—	—
1	67	46·2	—	46·2	—
2	61	42·1	10·5	21·0	10·5
Anaphase I {	Expected percentages		22·2	67·2	10·5
	Expected numbers of cells (total 121)		26·9	81·3	12·8
	Observed numbers of cells (total 121)		21	80	20
			$\chi^2 = 5·5$, $n = 2$, $P = 0·1–0·05$		

(*b*)

	Diakinesis		Expected Percentages of Cells with 0, 1 and 2 Fragments at Anaphase I		
No. of Chiasmata	Observed Nos. of Cells (Total 133)	Percentage Cells	0	1	2
0	9	6·8	6·8	—	—
1	55	41·3	—	41·3	—
2	69	51·9	13·0	25·9	13·0
Anaphase I {	Expected percentages		19·8	67·2	13·0
	Expected numbers of cells (total 197)		38·8	132·6	25·6
	Observed numbers of cells (total 197)		45	123	29
			$\chi^2 = 2·1$, $n = 2$, $P = 0·1–0·5$		

§ 8.16 Additional cytological evidence for the chiasmatype theory

Critical cytological evidence for the occurrence of chiasmata as a consequence of previous crossing-over is available from several additional sources, but unlike the three main lines of evidence discussed above, these others have only rarely been observed, or have not been subjected to sufficient quantitative analysis. Darlington (1931*c*) reported figure-of-eight

shaped chromosomal configurations at meiosis in *Oenothera* species, in which
the chiasma at the centre of the '8' could only be interpreted as due to
previous crossing-over between a pair of chromosomes which were heterozygous at both ends for interchanges of segments with non-homologous
chromosomes. Mather (1933*b*) described an instance where two of the 12
chromosome-pairs at meiosis in a pollen-mother-cell of *Lilium regale* were
interlocked such that a medianly placed chiasma could only have arisen as a
consequence of previous crossing-over, and in *L. henryi* and *L. japonicum* he
several times observed (Mather 1935) a chiasma between a chromosome
fragment and a normal chromosome, again implying previous crossing-over.
Darlington (1935) observed coiling of chromosomes round one another on
each side of a chiasma at the diplotene stage of meiosis in a species of
Fritillaria, and deduced that the chiasma must have been the consequence of
crossing-over, but this argument is valid only on the assumption that the
coiling of the chromosomes round each other had arisen before they divided
into chromatids.

Kayano (1960*b*) obtained an individual of *Disporum sessile* heterozygous for
structural differences at both ends of the long arm of chromosome *A*: the
presence or absence of an interchange with chromosome *B* at one end, and
the presence or absence of a terminal knob (satellite) at the other. Study of
this chromosome in 1100 pollen-mother-cells at metaphase I of meiosis
showed 537 (48·8%) without chiasmata, 381 with 1 chiasma, 163 with 2
chiasmata, and 19 with 3 chiasmata. Assuming the chiasmatype hypothesis is
true, and that there was no chromatid interference, the expected frequencies

TABLE 8.9 Comparison of chiasma frequencies at metaphase I in the long arm of
chromosome *A* of *Disporum sessile* with the frequencies of different combinations at
anaphase II of structural features at each end of the arm, from the data of Kayano
(1960b).

Metaphase I			Expected Percentages of Cells with Different Combinations at Anaphase II of the 4 Copies of Chromosome *A*		
No. of Chiasmata	Observed Nos. of Cells (Total 1100)	Percentage Cells	All 4 Parental	2 Parental 2 Recombined	All 4 Recombined
0	537	48·8	48·8	—	—
1	381	34·6	—	34·6	—
2	163	14·8	3·7	7·4	3·7
3	19	1·8	0·2	1·4	0·2
Anaphase II { Expected percentages			52·7	43·4	3·9
Expected numbers of cells (total 80)			42·2	34·7	3·1
Observed numbers of cells (total 80)			43	34	3

$$\chi^2 = 0·034, n = 2, P = 0·99-0·98$$

can be calculated of anaphase II cells in which the 4 chromosome A's resembled those of the parent, or in which 2 of them showed recombination of the characters by which their ends differed and 2 did not, or in which all 4 showed recombination (see Table 8.9). The observed numbers of these 3 classes of anaphase II cells were in close agreement—indeed alarmingly close agreement—with the expected values (see table). The expected frequency of recombinant chromosome A's is $\frac{1}{2}(100 - 48\cdot8)\% = 25\cdot6\%$, and the observed number in 1671 chromosome A's examined at anaphase II was 419 or $25\cdot1\%$, again in very close agreement ($\chi^2 = 0\cdot23, n = 1, P = 0\cdot9\text{–}0\cdot5$).

§ 8.17 The hypothesis of crossing-over by breakage of classical chiasmata

The observations discussed above provide overwhelming evidence for a connection between chiasmata and crossing-over, but before drawing the conclusion that crossing-over is the cause of a chiasma, it is necessary to consider another hypothesis which relates chiasmata to crossing-over. Wenrich (1916), although not favouring breakage of chromosomes, thought that at the point where two chromatids cross each other in a chiasma, which he regarded merely as a point where chromatids change partners, a weakness of the strands might cause them to break and then recombine to give cross-over chromatids. This hypothesis of crossing-over through breakage of classical chiasmata has been revived on many occasions. It is open to the objection advanced by Muller (1916) against Janssens' theory, namely, that the precision needed in crossing-over is difficult to account for if the breakage and rejoining occur when the chromosomes are relatively short and thick, as at the diplotene stage. Indeed this difficulty is still more serious if the breakage occurs even later, as Wenrich's theory would suppose, since at diakinesis the chromosomes reach their maximum state of contraction. However, the theory appeared to find support from a reduction in the number of chiasmata between the diplotene stage and metaphase I in many organisms.

§ 8.18 Terminalisation of chiasmata

This support was removed when Darlington (1931*a*), following a study of meiosis in *Primula sinensis*, showed that the reduction in numbers could be accounted for by postulating that the chiasmata moved to the ends of the chromosomes and replaced one another there, without breakage (see Fig. 8.17). This process of *terminalisation*, as he called it, is found in some organisms, particularly those with small chromosomes, but not in others. In *P. sinensis* Darlington found from 2 to 5 interstitial chiasmata in each diplotene chromosome-pair, but at diakinesis and metaphase I all the chiasmata had terminalised and hence there were only two per bivalent association (or only one if no chiasmata had occurred in one arm). On the chiasmatype theory, terminalisation implies that the position of the chiasmata will no longer coincide with the points of crossing-over (Fig. 8.18).

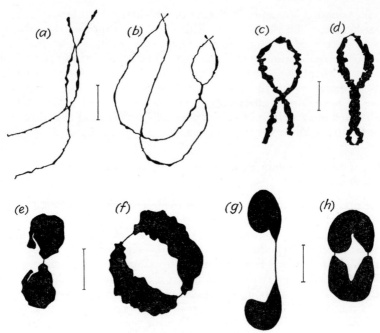

FIGURE 8.17   Drawings of chromosomes of *Primula sinensis* to show
terminalisation of chiasmata (from Darlington, 1931a).
The vertical lines represent 1 μ.
(*a*) and (*b*) Early diplotene stage.
(*c*) and (*d*) Late diplotene stage.
(*e*) and (*f*) Diakinesis.
(*g*) and (*h*) Metaphase I.

The acceptance of the notion of chiasma movement led to the final dis-
crediting of the idea that the chromosomes associate end to end instead of
side by side in early prophase I of meiosis. This idea had been maintained,
at least for some organisms, for nearly half a century. The end-to-end
pairing had never been observed but was inferred from the end-to-end
association seen at diakinesis and metaphase I in, for example, *Oenothera*.*
Darlington's theory of terminalisation of chiasmata explained these late
prophase I terminal associations as of secondary origin from an earlier
lateral association (Darlington 1929*a*, 1931*c*). The recognition of the
terminal chiasma led Darlington to two further hypotheses: firstly (1929*b*)
that it is chiasmata, either interstitial or terminal in position, that are
responsible for maintaining the chromosomes in pairs between the end of the
pachytene stage and the end of metaphase I; and secondly (1931*b*) that
meiosis can be looked upon as a precocious mitosis, with the force which
keeps the daughter-chromatids together in pairs during the prophase of

* The multiple associations of chromosomes seen at meiosis in many species of *Oenothera*
are due to heterozygosity for interchanges of chromosome arms between non-homologous
chromosomes (cf. § 9.2).

(a)

(b)

(c)

(d)

FIGURE 8.18   Diagram to show terminalisation of
chiasmata. The constrictions indicate
the centromeres, and the shading the
parental origin.

(*a*)–(*d*) Successive stages from early
diplotene to diakinesis, show-
ing how three interstitial chiasmata become two terminal
chiasmata. The points where
crossing-over has taken place
remain unchanged.

mitosis also responsible for the zygotene and pachytene pairing of whole
undivided chromosomes and for their diplotene separation again when the
chromosomes divide into chromatids. This precocity hypothesis of meiosis
now appears improbable (see § 11.5).

§ 8.19   Objections to the chiasma breakage hypothesis

Darlington (1931*a*) pointed out that crossing-over takes place both in
organisms such as *Primula sinensis*, where the number of chiasmata diminishes
between the diplotene stage and metaphase I, and in organisms such as

Zea mays where it does not diminish. Moreover, the evidence presented earlier of agreement between chiasma and cross-over frequencies in *Zea mays* is inexplicable on the chiasma breakage hypothesis. Likewise, the critical evidence from various cytological sources, notably unequal chromosome-pairs, polyploids and inversions, that crossing-over precedes chiasma-formation, is clearly at variance with the chiasma breakage theory. However, Sax (1930) pointed out that the classical theory could be reconciled with such observations if one postulated a broken classical chiasma alongside each observed (classical) chiasma. This hypothesis is effectively the same as the chiasmatype theory as regards its consequences, since every observed chiasma is associated with crossing-over. However, whereas on the chiasmatype theory crossing-over is the cause of the chiasma, on Sax's suggestion crossing-over is the result of the disappearance of a classical chiasma near the observed one. There was no direct evidence for the latter suggestion, and with the accumulation of evidence that crossing-over precedes chiasma-formation, it became absurd to postulate a broken classical chiasma near every critical chiasma, and Sax (1936) accepted the chiasmatype theory.

§ 8.20   Male *Drosophila*

An objection to the chiasmatype theory which has frequently been raised is based on cytological and genetical observations with male *Drosophila*. Early in the genetic work with *D. melanogaster* it was discovered that there was no crossing-over in the male (see Morgan, Sturtevant, Muller and Bridges 1915). This was expected for sex-linked characters, since the male has only one *X*-chromosome, but was wholly unexpected for autosomal characters. Unfortunately, *Drosophila* is exceptionally unfavourable material for study of chiasmata. Darlington (1934a) found no chiasmata in the autosomes of male *D. pseudo-obscura*, the homologous chromosomes merely lying parallel to one another at diakinesis and metaphase I. In *Drosophila*, unlike most organisms, homologous chromosomes show pairing in the somatic cells as well as at meiosis, and the pairing of the autosomes at meiosis in the male was similar to this somatic association. On the other hand, Darlington found chiasmata between the *X*- and *Y*-chromosomes in the region near the centromeres where pairing takes place. In order to reconcile these observations with first-division segregation of the *X*- and *Y*-chromosomes, which is known to occur in *Drosophila*, Darlington had to postulate the regular occurrence of two chiasmata in close proximity and both in the same chromosome arm, and with a two- or four-strand relationship between their associated cross-overs. Such an elaborate explanation could hardly be said to support the chiasmatype theory. Cooper (1949) claimed to have seen chiasmata in the autosomes at meiosis in male *D. melanogaster*, and also in the somatic cells. Such chiasmata could not be associated with crossing-over, since none normally occurs in the male. Cooper concluded that these were classical chiasmata, without chromosome breakage and crossing-over. However, Slizynski (1964) has also examined the chromosomes of *D. melanogaster* males at meiosis and has found evidence that what appear to be chiasmata in the autosomes are merely places of superficial contact. Similar chiasma-like associations were also observed between non-homologous chromosomes. It thus appears that there are no chiasmata in male *Drosophila*, not even classical ones.

Electron microscopy has confirmed that in male *Drosophila* the association between homologous chromosomes at meiosis is abnormal. Moses (1956) observed chromosomal 'cores' consisting of alternating bands of light and dark lines on electron micrographs of thin sections of spermatocytes of the crayfish *Procambarus clarkii* at prophase I of meiosis. These cores appear to be of general occurrence in chromosomes at the time of meiotic pairing, except when chiasmata and crossing-over are lacking. The cores consist of 2 dark electron-dense bands lying in one plane and 120–150 mμ apart, with a third dark band, of variable appearance depending on the species, placed midway between the other two (Moses & Coleman 1964) (Pl. 4(*a*)). Fine threads cross the spaces between the dark bands. The cores apparently lie between the paired chromosomes and extend throughout their length. Meyer (1961) found no pairing cores at meiosis in male *D. melanogaster*, and they were also lacking (Meyer 1964) in unpaired chromosomes of triploid females, and in a mutant in which chromosome pairing and crossing-over were suppressed. Moreover, in several other Diptera the presence of cores was associated with the occurrence of chiasmata, and lack of cores with their absence.

§ 8.21   Conclusion

The data presented in this chapter have provided a substantial body of evidence that chiasmata are invariably the consequence of previous crossing-over between two of the four chromatids, and hence that Janssens' chiasma-type theory, in the modified form proposed by Belling, is true.

9. *The classical theory of the gene*

§ 9.1 Multiple alleles

A discovery of great importance for the theory of the gene was made by Cuénot (1904). He found that the number of alternatives for a particular character which showed Mendelian inheritance was not limited to two. From the breeding of different strains of albino mice (*Mus musculus*), he obtained individuals with a black coat-colour, and others with a yellow coat. On crossing each of these with the normal grey he found that the black coat-colour was inherited as a Mendelian recessive and the yellow as a Mendelian dominant (with the complication that the homozygous yellow mice were apparently inviable). Furthermore, from crosses involving both the genes for black and for yellow fur, he found that these behaved as alleles towards one another, with yellow dominant to black. In other words, the genes for yellow, grey and black fur formed a series of alleles. There are six possible genotypes with respect to 3 alleles (the 3 homozygotes and the 3 heterozygotes), since a normal diploid individual necessarily cannot contain more than 2 alleles. Subsequently, the coat-colours grey with a light belly, and black with a light belly were found to belong to the same series of alleles. Normal mice are grey on the belly as well as on the back. Light belly-colour was found to be dominant to dark and grey back-colour dominant to black, so in order of descending dominance, the alleles are: Yellow; Grey with Light belly; Grey with grey belly, and black with Light belly (heterozygote Grey with Light belly); black.

Many other examples of multiple alleles were soon found. One of the first to be established in plants was through the work of Emerson (1911) with *Zea mays*. He had self-pollinated, and also inter-crossed, a number of strains of maize differing in the colour of the reproductive organs. He found that when he crossed pure-breeding strains having different colours in the axis (*cob*) of the fertilised female inflorescence, and in the ovary tissue (*pericarp*) surrounding the seed, only two classes appeared in F_2. Since the pericarp, like the cob, is parental tissue, all the grains on a maize ear will be alike as regards the pericarp colour, although there may be variation on the ear in the colour of the underlying tissues of the seed. The numbers of individuals in the two classes approximated to a 3:1 ratio, with the more frequent class having the same appearance as the F_1 generation. The deduction was clear: each pair of strains differed by one gene. Moreover, since different combinations were tested and all gave 3:1 ratios in F_2, it was evident that, in respect of the colour of these structures, the genes by which the strains differed were allelic. For example, he found that an F_1 plant with

132

red cob and pericarp gave an F_2 family consisting of 17 plants with red and 4 plants with white (colourless) cob and pericarp. Another red F_1 plant, from a different cross, gave in F_2 45 plants with red and 12 with variegated (red and white) cob and pericarp. A third F_1 plant, with the latter characters, gave in F_2 23 plants with variegated and 6 with colourless cob and pericarp. Evidently, red, variegated, and colourless cob and pericarp are determined by a series of 3 alleles, with red dominant to both the others, and with variegated dominant to colourless.

Over a dozen alleles are now known at this gene locus, giving different shades of red pigment (anthocyanin) and different distributions of it: for example, white cob and red pericarp; red cob and colourless pericarp; white cob and half-red pericarp (red at base, colourless at top of each grain); red cob and half-red pericarp. In every instance, the deeper shades of red were found to be dominant to the lighter ones, and the presence of colour to be dominant to its absence. Thus the heterozygote of the allele giving white cob and red pericarp with the allele giving red cob and colourless pericarp had red cob and pericarp. Moreover, dominance was found to be incomplete, a red-white heterozygote being paler than the red homozygote.

One of the best-known examples of multiple alleles was discovered by Morgan (1912) in *Drosophila melanogaster*. The white-eyed mutant of this normally red-eyed fly was found in 1910. The next year a male fly with yellowish-pink eyes described as eosin-coloured, occurred in an otherwise white-eyed family. On crossing eosin-eyed with normal red-eyed flies, the eosin character was found to show sex-linkage and to behave as a simple recessive to red. On crossing an eosin-eyed female with a white-eyed male the F_1 flies were all eosin-eyed, and in F_2 1147 eosin-eyed and 344 white-eyed flies were obtained, in agreement with a 3:1 ratio (expected frequencies 1118·25 and 372·75, deviations 28·75, $\chi^2 = 2·95$, $n = 1$, $P = 0·1$–$0·05$). It was evident that the white and eosin eye-colours were inherited as a pair of alleles, with eosin dominant to white.* It was significant that in both F_1 and F_2 there were no wild-type (red-eyed) flies.

This result was in striking contrast to the results obtained when non-allelic mutants were crossed. For example, Morgan (1911*b*) had crossed a pink-eyed female with a male with bright red eyes which he described as vermilion-coloured. Both these eye-colours had been found to be inherited as recessive characters to the normal dull red eyes. All the F_1 generation flies from this cross had normal red eyes, and out of 1884 F_2 individuals, 1090 had normal red eyes, 397 had vermilion eyes, 313 had pink eyes and 84 had orange (= vermilion-pink) eyes. These figures approach a 9:3:3:1 ratio (1060:353:353:118) such as would be expected with two independently-inherited pairs of character-differences, but there is a significant shortage of flies carrying the gene for pink eyes, presumably due to a lowered viability of such individuals.

----

* There was a dosage effect for the intensity of the eosin colouring. Eosin-eyed males, and females heterozygous for eosin and white, both of which would evidently have only one eosin gene per nucleus, were found to have paler eyes than homozygous eosin females with two doses of the eosin gene per nucleus.

Further alleles at the 'white eye' locus were soon found and over a dozen are now known. They are all recessive to red and dominant to white, and include the colours described as 'cherry,' 'apricot' and 'ivory'.

The examples just described illustrate the two outstanding characteristics of a series of allelic mutants. First, all the alleles affect the same character and are non-complementary, that is to say, on crossing two of them, the F_1 generation is either intermediate in appearance between the two, or like one of them. On the other hand, non-allelic mutants, although they may affect the same character, can usually complement each other: each carries the dominant normal allele of the other's mutation (assuming the mutants are recessive), and on crossing them, the F_1 progeny are unlike either but have the normal (wild-type) phenotype of the organism.

Secondly, recombination studies indicate that allelic mutants appear to be due to genes located at the same positions in the linkage group. Thus, not only do they fail to show recombination with one another when crossed, but they each give the same recombination frequencies with other mutants. Thus, Morgan *et al.* (1915) found that the white/Red and eosin/Red eye-colour differences in *Drosophila melanogaster* both gave 1% of recombination with yellow/Grey body-colour, 33% with miniature/Normal wing-size, and 44% with Bar/normal eye-shape. On the other hand, non-allelic mutants show recombination with one another when crossed, giving in F_2 some wild-type and some double-mutant individuals, as well as the parental single-mutant types. Non-allelic mutants also differ from one another in their recombination frequencies with other mutants. The logical conclusion is that allelic mutants occupy the same gene locus in one of the chromosomes, whereas non-allelic mutants occupy different loci, either in the same or a different chromosome.

One of the best-known examples of multiple alleles concerns the four human blood-groups, O, A, B and AB. These correspond to the presence or absence of two antigens, A and B, in the erythrocytes (A—A only; B—B only; AB—both; O—neither). There is a reciprocal relationship between the presence of antigens in the red cells, and of antibodies in the serum; in other words, group O serum has antibodies against both A and B antigens, group A serum has antibodies against B, group B against A, and group AB against neither. Agglutination of cells occurs when a cell suspension and a serum are mixed, if they have an antigen and an antibody in common. Bernstein (1925) showed that the four blood-groups were inherited as Mendelian characters determined by three alleles A, B and O. Of the 6 genotypes (OO, AA, AO, BB, BO, AB), AA and AO are indistinguishable in phenotype and constitute blood group A, and similarly BB and BO are indistinguishable as group B. In Britain, the mean frequencies of the four blood-groups are approximately 46·7% for O, 41·7% for A, 8·6% for B and 3·0% for AB. Weinberg (1909) extended the Hardy-Weinberg theorem (see § 2.6) to include three alleles in a population. He showed that under the same conditions as for two alleles (that is, a large population, random mating, and no selection, migration or mutation), the frequencies of the 6 possible genotypes for three alleles are given by the terms of $(p + q + r)^2$, where p, q and r denote the frequencies of the three alleles. If p, q and r correspond to A, B and O, respectively, applying the British frequencies given above, $r^2 = 0\cdot467$, $p^2 + 2pr = 0\cdot417$, $q^2 + 2qr = 0\cdot086$, and $2pq = 0\cdot030$, from which good estimates for p, q and r are $p = 0\cdot257$, $q = 0\cdot060$ and $r = 0\cdot683$. Thus, 68·3% of British ABO chromosomes carry allele O, 25·7% carry allele A, and 6·0% allele B. Further alleles (subgroups of A) have since been recognised (see Race and Sanger, 1962).

§ 9.2 Mutation

The nature of the process of mutation whereby the various alleles at a gene locus are evidently derived from one another is clearly of fundamental importance to the theory of the gene. The term mutation was introduced into biological literature by De Vries (1901). He had made extensive studies of *Oenothera lamarckiana* (Evening Primrose) and found that new forms, differing appreciably in appearance from the original, apparently arose abruptly in small numbers in each generation. On the basis of these observations, he proposed a general theory of species formation by means of sudden discontinuous changes, to which he gave the name *mutation*. Study of the cytological and genetical behaviour of this and other species of *Oenothera* by many scientists during the succeeding 30 years established that these plants have an abnormal hereditary mechanism. It appears that successive exchanges of arms between non-homologous chromosomes have taken place during the course of their evolution, until all or nearly all the chromosomes have become involved. The plants are maintained heterozygous for these interchanges of chromosome segments by adaptations which prevent the survival, or in some instances even the formation, of the homozygotes. However, these adaptations occasionally break down, and this leads to the formation of small numbers of individuals homozygous, or at least partially so, for the chromosomal interchanges present in the parent. Owing to the presence of recessive genes which thereby become manifest, these homozygotes differ in appearance from the original plant, and moreover breed true for these characters. Thus it became evident that the 'mutations' in *Oenothera* described by De Vries were really the revealing of hereditary variation already present in the parent but normally hidden, rather than changes in the genes themselves. However, De Vries' idea of abrupt changes, even if unacceptable as a general hypothesis for the evolution of new species, was required to account for the origin of the character-differences which showed Mendelian inheritance. It was natural therefore that the term should have been transferred from the species to the gene.

The existence of multiple alleles implied that a gene could mutate in more than one way. This is illustrated by the behaviour of the white-eye alleles in *Drosophila melanogaster*, first studied by Morgan. As already mentioned, the original white-eyed fly arose from the normal red, and the original eosin-eyed fly from the white. But subsequently several instances were discovered of eosin eye-colour arising directly from red. Moreover, these steps were reversible, eosin occasionally mutating back to red, and also to white. An important feature of gene mutation was that the mutated gene was evidently replicated and passed to the progeny in the mutated form, since the altered phenotype was inherited. However, the rate at which mutations occurred was so low that it was exceedingly difficult to make detailed or quantitative studies of the process.

§ 9.3   Muller's grandsonless-lineage technique

Muller (1928*a*) described two ingenious techniques which he had devised for measuring the mutation rate in *Drosophila melanogaster*. Some 10 years previously he had come to the conclusion, on theoretical grounds, that lethal mutations might be sufficiently frequent to be studied quantitatively, since they were likely to occur considerably more often than those causing a visible change in the appearance of the organism. However, the detection of lethal mutations is more difficult than the detection of non-lethal ones. A mutation will in general not be manifest in a diploid organism such as a fly until the F_3 generation has been bred from the individual in which it occurred, since most mutations are recessive to their normal alleles. However, mutations occurring in the X-chromosomes of *Drosophila* are more favourably placed for detection, because they will become evident a generation sooner, causing, if lethal, the death of a fraction of the F_2 males. But even so, such mutations are not easily found, since the deaths will probably occur shortly after fertilisation, and it will be necessary to try and distinguish a real shortage of males from a chance fluctuation from the normal 1:1 ratio of the sexes. With often fewer than 30 progeny per female, such a distinction may not be possible.

Muller's technique was to use a known recessive lethal gene in one of the X-chromosomes of a female in order to discover whether another recessive lethal gene was present in the other X-chromosome. The known lethal gene would necessarily be in the maternally-derived X-chromosome since the gene would have been lethal to the male parent with its single X-chromosome. A new lethal mutation, if present in the other X-chromosome, would presumably have arisen in the sperm which fertilised the egg from which the female developed. Such a mutation would cause the female to produce no sons, since, unless a cross-over occurred between the loci of the two lethal factors, the single X-chromosome in the male progeny would necessarily carry one or other of the two lethal genes. Crossing-over could be prevented, since strains of *Drosophila* were available in which it was largely suppressed in particular chromosomes. (This cross-over suppression was later shown to be due to the presence of inversions in heterozygous form occupying the greater part of the length of the chromosome. As shown in § 8.15, crossing-over within an inversion leads to the production of chromosomes with extensive duplications and deficiencies of chromosomal segments, and consequently to inviable gametes.) Thus, Muller was able to detect the occurrence of lethal mutations in the X-chromosomes of the reproductive cells of male *Drosophila* by the failure of these flies to produce any grandsons when their daughters carried a known lethal factor and a cross-over suppressor in the other X-chromosome.

§ 9.4   Muller's accumulation technique

Muller also devised a method for counting lethal mutations which allowed them to accumulate over a number of generations until significant numbers were present. With the low mutation rates usually encountered, this method was likely to be preferable to the grandsonless-lineage method. A strain of flies was used in which there were two different recessive lethal (or sterility) genes, one in each chromosome of one of the pairs other than the X-chromosome. One of the pair also carried a cross-over suppressor: the other was the test-chromosome. In such a strain the known lethal (or sterility) genes would automatically be maintained in heterozygous condition, since the homozygotes would not survive (or would not leave any progeny). Any additional recessive lethal mutations which appeared would be similarly maintained and could be allowed to accumulate. Their existence in the test-chromosome could be revealed when desired by crossing one fly from each test lineage to another stock, and then interbreeding the progeny. Genes for several recessive characters were present in the test-chromosome, and consequently, in the absence of lethal mutations, each of these characters would be expected to be shown by one quarter of the F_2 generation following the outcross. However, if a lethal mutation was present, recessive characters linked to it would be absent.

Muller's first success with his lethal mutation counting techniques was the demonstration that a rise of temperature of 8°C produced a significant increase in the mutation rate. Using the accumulation method just described, 381 independent families kept at 19°C acquired a total of 12 lethal mutations in the test-chromosome in 16–17 generations occupying 11 months, and 359 lines kept at 27°C accumulated 31 lethals in the same chromosome in 18 generations during a period of 12 months. The mutation rates were therefore $\dfrac{12}{381 \times 16 \cdot 5} = 0 \cdot 19\%$ per chromosome per generation at 19°C, and $\dfrac{31}{359 \times 18}$ $= 0 \cdot 48\%$ at 27°C. The difference was significant.

This demonstration represented a considerable achievement, because numerous previous attempts by many experimenters to bring about a significant alteration in mutation rate by changing the external conditions in various ways had met with failure. Muller had found mutation rates varying up to 10 times greater in some experiments than others from unknown causes but presumably primarily due either to differences in physiological condition or genotype. Unless the conditions were carefully controlled, as in Muller's experiment, such variation would obscure the effects of particular environmental factors.

A 2·5-fold increase of rate with an 8°C rise in temperature such as Muller found, pointed tentatively to mutation as a multimolecular chemical change, since such reactions give increases of this order ($Q_{10} = 2$–3).

§ 9.5   Mutations induced by radiations

Muller's second success with his techniques for studying mutation quantitatively was an outstanding one. Using the grandsonless-lineage method, he showed (Muller 1927, 1928b) that X-rays enormously increased the rate of mutation. Males were irradiated and then crossed with females carrying the known lethal gene and the crossover suppressor in one of their X-chromosomes. Any daughters from this cross who failed to produce any sons must have had another recessive lethal gene in their other X-chromosome, the one derived from their irradiated father (see Table 9.1). To reduce the labour of searching for these grandsonless lineages, the dominant gene for Bar eye-shape was incorporated in the chromosome carrying the known lethal gene and the crossover suppressor. Only daughters with Bar

TABLE 9.1   Basis of Muller's grandsonless-lineage technique for detecting lethal mutations in the X-chromosome of *Drosophila melanogaster*.

Female Parent		Male Parent $X\,Y$ Sperm	
		X^l	Y
$X_{ClB}X$ Eggs $\Big\{$	X_{ClB}	$X_{ClB}X^l$ Bar female	$X_{ClB}Y$ Dies
	X	$X\,X^l$ Normal female	$X\,Y$ Normal male

(*a*) Progeny of a female carrying in one of her X-chromosomes a crossover suppressor (C), a recessive lethal mutation (l), and the dominant gene for Bar eye-shape (B), crossed with a male in which a lethal mutation has occurred in the X-chromosome of the sperm. X = normal X-chromosome. X_{ClB} = X-chromosome with crossover suppressor (C), known lethal gene (l), and Bar mutant (B). X^l = X-chromosome with new recessive lethal mutation.

Female Parent		Male Parent $X\,Y$ Sperm	
		X	Y
$X_{ClB}X^l$ Eggs $\Big\{$	X_{ClB}	$X_{ClB}X$ Bar female	$X_{ClB}Y$ Dies
	X^l	$X^l\,X$ Normal female	$X^l\,Y$ Dies

(*b*) Progeny of Bar female from (*a*) crossed with normal male. None of the sons survives.

eyes (and hence with the known lethal gene) were tested for their ability to produce sons. Non-lethal mutations in the X-chromosome can be detected at the same time as lethal ones, since the change of phenotype which they produce becomes evident in the grandsons of the irradiated males.

Muller found that male flies kept for 24 minutes at 16 cm from an X-ray tube (50 kV, 5 mA, 1 mm aluminium) gave 49 grandsonless lineages out of 676 tested, and others given the same irradiation for 48 minutes gave 89 such lineages out of 772 tested. The frequencies of lethal mutations in the X-chromosomes were therefore 7·2% and 11·5% respectively. Out of 198 control cultures, none were grandsonless, or, if a larger series of controls from other experiments is included, there were 5 lethal mutations in the X-chromosome of 6016 lineages tested, or 0·083%. The larger dose of X-rays thus gave a 140-fold increase in the mutation rate. As Muller had expected, the lethal mutations greatly outnumbered the non-lethal ones. Later work showed that, with both spontaneous and radiation-induced mutations, the proportion of lethal: non-lethal was about 10:1. Moreover, semi-lethal mutations giving much reduced viability (0·5—10% of normal) were rare: there were 4 with the 24-minute dose, and 12 with the 48-minute dose, or less than $\frac{1}{8}$ of the number of fully lethal mutations. Thus, the number of lethal mutations was reasonably clearly defined and likely to be a reliable guide to the total mutation-rate.

The visible mutations induced by X-rays included some at gene loci not previously known to have mutated, but othere were allelic to, or apparently identical with, previously known spontaneous mutations such as white eye-colour. Some of the lethal mutations were allelic to visible ones, suggesting that the lethal ones did not differ in any fundamental way from non-lethal. There was great variety among the visible mutations and no suggestion whatever that X-rays were causing specific genes to mutate. All the indications were that X-ray induced mutations were essentially like spontaneous ones.

Muller's data suggested a direct proportionality between X-ray dose and number of mutations induced and this was later confirmed. Irrespective of the intensity at which the irradiation was administered, and also apparently of the wavelength, a dose of 1000 r gave about 2·5% of lethal mutations in the X-chromosome, 2000 r about 5%, and so on. There appeared to be no threshold dose, numerous small doses producing as many mutations as one large one of the same total size. The linear relationship between induced mutation rate and dosage pointed to a direct action of the radiation quanta or the released electrons upon the gene. However, different genes were found to mutate with significantly different frequencies, and this applied also to alleles. Thus, Timoféëf-Ressovsky (1934), in reviewing experimental work on mutation, summarised his own extensive studies with the white-eye alleles in *Drosophila*, in which he had found that many of the various allelic changes possible, including reciprocal changes, occurred with significantly different frequencies under standard X-ray treatment. These findings again paralleled the observations on spontaneous mutation, where different genes, including different alleles, showed diverse rates of change.

Almost simultaneously with Muller's discovery of the mutagenic action of X-rays on *Drosophila*, Stadler (1928) discovered that X-rays, and also the gamma-rays from radium, caused mutation in *Hordeum vulgare* (Barley). Germinating grains were irradiated, and following self-pollination of the resulting plants, the grains from each ear were isolated. On sowing these grains, it was found that a number of those derived from one ear showed an abnormality, while other ears produced only normal progeny. It was evident that following the irradiation, one or more shoots (tillers) were heterozygous for a recessive mutation, while the remaining shoots on the same plant did not carry the mutation. Altogether 48 different mutations for seedling characters, such as white, virescent, and yellow leaf-colour, were found in the progeny of the irradiated grains, and none in the progeny of untreated plants.

Within a short time after Muller's initial discovery, mutation had been induced by radiation in a wide range of plants and animals, and it was clear that the phenomenon was a general one. It was found that all ionizing radiations, and also ultraviolet light, caused mutation. In every instance, a whole range of kinds of mutations were produced, and there was no suggestion of specific action. The findings with X-rays appeared to be typical in most respects of the results also found with the other mutagenic radiations.

An important discovery about the process of mutation was made by Stadler (1930) with *Hordeum*, and by Muller (1930*b*) with *Drosophila*. Stadler X-rayed germinating barley grains at 10°C, 20°C, 30°C, 40°C and 50°C and found no significant differences in the mutation rate. Muller X-rayed *Drosophila* males at 8°C and 34°C, and using his grandsonless-lineage technique, found 22 lethal or semi-lethal mutations in 67 lineages (33%) in the former, and 32 out of 120 (27%) in the latter. A repetition of this experiment using a smaller X-ray dose but larger samples gave 33 mutations out of 403 (8·2%) for those treated at 8°C, and 13 mutations out of 208 (6·2%) for the 34°C irradiation. It was evident that in both *Hordeum* and *Drosophila* over a large range of temperature, the mutation-rate was approximately constant.

The deduction from these experiments was that X-ray-induced mutation could not be an ordinary multimolecular chemical reaction, because such reactions have a large temperature coefficient. Rather it appeared that a unimolecular reaction was involved. The appreciable effect of temperature on the spontaneous mutation rate in *Drosophila*, which Muller had earlier found (see § 9.4) could be reconciled with the X-ray temperature data if it were supposed that whatever caused the spontaneous mutations acted indirectly through the medium of a multimolecular, and hence temperature-sensitive, chemical reaction. Calculations showed that natural radioactivity was insufficient to account for more than about one five-hundredth to one thousandth of the spontaneous mutations occurring in *Drosophila*. Moreover, if the frequency of spontaneous mutations in a given time was essentially the same in all organisms, as dependence on natural radioactivity would presumably demand, long-lived organisms such as *Homo* would of course accumulate much larger numbers of mutations per generation than would short-lived organisms such as *Drosophila*. For example, a lethal mutation in one X-chromosome out of every 1000 every 2–3 weeks (the *Drosophila* rate of 0·1% per generation) would imply that in 25 years about 1 in every 2 human X-chromosomes would acquire such a mutation. A consequence of this would be that the ratio of the sexes at birth would approximate to 2 girls : 1 boy instead of the equality (or slight preponderance of boys) that is found. It was evident that the spontaneous mutation rate was likely to be determined by the genotype and physiological condition of the organism, rather than by natural radioactivity, and that natural selection had probably acted to favour greater stability of the gene in long-lived organisms than in short. This conclusion implied that mutation rates could be influenced by chemical means.

§ 9.6   Mutations induced by chemicals

Despite the availability of Muller's highly efficient grandsonless-lineage technique for studying mutation quantitatively, it was 14 years after his discovery by this means of the mutagenic action of X-rays before clear evidence was obtained that mutations could be induced chemically. A variety of substances was tested by numerous experimenters, but the results were hardly statistically significant, until in 1941 Auerbach and Robson (1947) discovered that β-β'-dichloro-diethyl-sulphide (mustard-gas) was highly mutagenic.

A solution of mustard gas in cyclohexane was sprayed at 10-second intervals for a period up to 15 minutes into a stream of air passing over the flies. In the first experiment 1231 X-chromosomes were tested, that is to say, this number of daughters of treated males crossed to females carrying the known lethal gene was tested for their ability to produce sons. There were 90, or 7·3%, of these grandsonless lineages compared with 3 out of 1216, or 0·25%, in the untreated control. The treatment also gave rise to 11 semi-lethal mutations, whereas there was none in the control. A frequency of 7·3% of recessive sex-linked lethal mutations was comparable to that produced by 3000 r of X-rays, and was clearly highly significant.

Chemical mutagenesis was discovered independently by Rapoport (1946), who found that a solution of formaldehyde when mixed with the food of *Drosophila* in sublethal concentrations, gave 5·9% of sex-linked lethal mutations.

Following these initial discoveries with mustard-gas and formaldehyde, a wide range of chemicals was soon found to cause mutation, for example, urethane (ethyl carbamate), nitrogen mustard, manganous chloride and hydrogen peroxide. Numerous organisms were found to show mutations when treated with these substances, and their mutagenic action appeared to apply generally. The effect of these chemicals was similar to the effects of mutagenic radiations, that is to say, each produced a wide range of kinds of mutations and there was no evidence for specific action on particular genes.

§ 9.7   Structural changes in chromosomes

Before considering the significance of knowledge about mutation for the theory of the gene, another feature of mutagens must be considered. Muller (1927) discovered not only that X-rays caused mutation but also that they caused structural changes in linkage groups. This was revealed when linkage studies were made following irradiation. The recombination frequencies of genes were frequently less or more than had been found previously, suggesting that portions of hereditary material had been removed or added. Moreover, the sequence of genes was sometimes reversed, implying that a section had been turned round. In still other instances, genes showed linkage in inheritance where hitherto they had belonged to different linkage groups, and conversely, genes previously linked now showed independent inheritance. It was evident that part of one linkage group had become attached to another. Changes of all these kinds had been known previously, but they had appeared only very rarely. It seemed as if, as with mutation, X-rays were increasing the frequency of occurrence of phenomena which also occurred in their absence. It had been anticipated for some years that X-rays would be likely to cause chromosome breakage, but a remarkable feature of Muller's discovery was the frequency with which the hereditary material appeared to be joined up in new ways. Thus, Muller and Altenburg (1930) found no less than 117 instances of transfer of part of one linkage group to another in 883 lineages tested following a heavy dose of X-rays applied to *Drosophila* males.

Muller and Painter (1929) and Dobzhansky (1929) confirmed that structural changes in *Drosophila* linkage groups, following X-irradiation, were associated with corresponding changes in the chromosomes. Their work finally established that the order of the genes on the linkage map is the same as their actual physical order in the chromosome, although the relative distances often did not correspond. A large section of linkage map removed or transferred might correspond to only a small section of the chromosome, or the converse might be true. It was evident that the scale of the linkage maps varied greatly from region to region, when compared with the physical chromosome, crossing-over being more frequent in some regions than others.

Further confirmation that structural changes in *Drosophila* linkage groups involved rearrangement of the material of the chromosomes was obtained from study of the giant chromosomes in the nuclei of the salivary glands of the mature larvae. These chromosomes had been known in some other Diptera for over 50 years, before Painter (1934) discovered their value in genetics when he showed that structural changes in *Drosophila* linkage groups can be correlated with changes in the sequence of transverse discs or bands in these chromosomes. Corresponding parts of homologous chromosomes are closely paired in these salivary gland nuclei, and all the chromosomes are held together at their centromeres, the paired chromosome arms, of which there are five in *D. melanogaster* (the very short fourth chromosome apart), being cylindrical in shape, about 5 μ in diameter, and radiating for a distance of about 250 μ if straightened (Fig. 9.1 and Pl. 1(f)). By contrast, in the

FIGURE 9.1   Drawings of the giant chromosomes found in the cell nuclei of the
salivary glands of Diptera.

(a) The complete set of salivary gland chromosomes of
Drosophila melanogaster (from Painter, 1934). The two
homologous chromosomes of each kind are fused
together throughout their length, and all the chromosomes are held together in the region of their
centromeres, forming the chromocentre.

(b) The no. 4 chromosome-pair of *Chironomus tentans*
(from Beermann, 1961). The arrows show the position of the gene concerned with the secretion of
granules in particular cells of the salivary glands.
In *C. tentans* this gene occurs in a mutant form such
that no granules are produced.

(c) The left-hand end of the no. 4 chromosome-pair
of *C. pallidivittatus* showing a puff formed at the position of the gene for granule-secretion.

reproductive cells at meiosis the chromosome arms measure about 2 μ in length. Over 1000 transverse bands occur in the salivary X-chromosome, and there are similar numbers in the other four major chromosome arms. These bands differ in thickness and spacing and have all been mapped. In individuals heterozygous for a structural change, the band sequences will differ in the appropriate parts of the two halves of each chromosome pair involved. From study of these differences, the precise nature of numerous structural changes has been established.

When the salivary gland chromosomes of *Drosophila* individuals heterozygous for recessive lethal mutations were examined, an important discovery was made. It was found that the lethal mutations were often associated with minute deficiencies, a small number of adjacent transverse bands being missing. Thus, Slizynska and Slizynski (1947) reported that in the X-chromosome approximately one lethal mutation in five, by whatever means it had arisen, was associated with a small chromosomal deficiency. They had studied a total of 159 sex-linked lethal mutations and found 33, or 20·7%, showed minute deficiencies. These mutations comprised 27 of spontaneous origin (6 deficient), 24 X-ray induced (5 deficient), 4 following neutron treatment (1 deficient), 21 from ultraviolet light irradiation (5 deficient) and the remaining 83 from mustard-gas treatment, of which 16 were deficient. The most frequent size of deficiency was the loss of 2 transverse bands.

These findings raised the question of what proportion of the remaining lethal mutations were associated with deficiencies too small to be detected. Were all lethal mutations really minute losses of chromosomal material? Since lethal mutations, as indicated in § 9.5, do not appear to differ in any significant way from viable mutations, the same questions could be asked of mutations generally. These questions will be discussed in Chapters 13 and 14.

Since mutagenic radiations also caused structural changes, it was not surprising to find that mutagenic chemicals behaved similarly. Auerbach and Robson (1947) from study of genetic linkage in *Drosophila* following treatment of the flies with mustard-gas, and Oehlkers (1943) from study of *Oenothera* chromosomes at meiosis after keeping cut inflorescences in a solution of urethane (ethyl carbamate), were the first to demonstrate the induction of structural changes by chemical means. A wide range of chemicals has since been found to have this property of causing chromosome aberrations.

§ 9.8   The mechanism of induction of structural changes

Thoday and Read (1947) found that the effect of X-rays in causing structural changes in chromosomes was much influenced by the oxygen concentration at the time of irradiation. Root-tips of *Vicia faba* irradiated in the absence of oxygen gave only about one third of the aberration frequency that the same dose gave in oxygen. Kihlman (1961), in reviewing biochemical knowledge concerning the induction of structural changes, classified agents causing aberrations into three main categories.

First, some agents induce structural changes with a frequency which does not depend on the oxygen concentration, for example, alpha particles and ultraviolet light, where the effect is immediate, and alkylating agents such as nitrogen mustard and diepoxides, where the effect is delayed for some hours. These are highly reactive chemicals which presumably act more or less directly on the chromosomes, as the radiations are also presumed to do.

Secondly, there are agents which cause aberrations with a frequency which is much reduced in the absence of oxygen, but is unaffected by inhibitors of respiration. Examples of such agents are X-rays, with an immediate effect, and visible light in the presence of acridine orange, where the effect is delayed for some hours. Kihlman suggested that the oxygen reacts with free radicals produced by the radiations.

Thirdly, certain chemicals have been found to cause structural changes with a frequency which is much reduced, either by the removal of oxygen, or by the presence of respiratory inhibitors such as sodium azide. Examples are methylated oxypurines such as caffeine, where the effect is immediate, and maleic hydrazide where it is delayed for some hours. Evidently aerobic respiration is necessary for these agents to produce their effects.

It is evident that the mechanisms of induction of chromosome aberrations by radiations and chemicals are complex and diverse. Nevertheless, the end-results, in the shape of the range of different kinds of structural changes that are produced, are relatively uniform. Just as with mutation, mutagenic agents appear to produce the whole range of kinds of structural changes, although ultraviolet light has usually been found to produce relatively few interchanges between different chromosomes.

Second only to *Drosophila* as an organism for the study of structural changes has been *Zea mays*. Anderson (1936), in reviewing his own and others' work on such aberrations induced by irradiation in *Zea* chromosomes and linkage groups, drew attention to two peculiarities about these changes. First, all alterations involving two chromosomes or linkage groups were reciprocal, that is to say, if a piece of one chromosome was transferred to another, then a piece of the latter was also transferred to the former, and furthermore the rejoining was always at the points of breakage, never at the normal ends of the transferred segments. Secondly, all changes involving only one chromosome, such as inversions, duplications, deficiencies, and the production of ring-shaped chromosomes, involved interstitial segments. Deficiencies which appeared to be terminally placed, that is, loss of the end of a chromosome, were found on careful study to be in fact interstitial in position, the end segment being attached to the broken end of the main part of the chromosome.* It was evident that all these changes involved two points of breakage, followed by rejoining in new ways, and moreover, the normal ends of the chromosomes did not take part in this rejoining. These observations resembled those made with *Drosophila* referred to in § 9.7.

In order to account for these discoveries two hypotheses have been put forward. According to one, the initial event is chromosome breakage. On this

---

* Some exceptions to this are now known: see for example § 9.11.

hypothesis, it is necessary, in addition, to postulate that broken ends can rejoin, either in the original way or in new ways, but that normal chromosome ends cannot do so. According to the alternative hypothesis, the mechanism of induction of structural changes is by a process of non-homologous crossing-over or exchange, which is postulated as occurring either between different chromosomes, or between different parts of the same chromosome. This idea was first proposed by Belling (1927) with reference to an interchange of segments between non-homologous chromosomes, which he and Blakeslee had discovered in *Datura stramonium*. On this theory, the failure of normal chromosome ends to take part in rejoining is accounted for, without the necessity of postulating that these ends have special properties which prevent them from doing so.

Studies on the relation between the frequency of interchanges between different chromosomes and the dose of X- or gamma-rays showed that the frequency increased approximately as the square of the dose. A square law would be expected if two independent events were required to bring about the interchanges. These results were at first taken as evidence in support of the breakage-and-reunion theory. It was assumed that the two independent events which the square law demanded were the breaking of the two chromosomes by separate ionisation tracks. Furthermore, it was assumed that, on the other hypothesis, the first step in non-homologous crossing-over would be the making contact between two chromosome segments, and that a single ionisation-event in the vicinity of the paired segments would cause the process of exchange to occur. On this assumption, non-homologous crossing-over would give rise to a linear relationship between radiation dose and interchange frequency. Since the relationship was non-linear it was argued that the theory of non-homologous crossing-over was untenable. However, Revell (1955) pointed out that the square law does not necessarily invalidate the hypothesis of non-homologous crossing-over if one assumes that the two separate primary events are the triggering off, independently in each chromosome, of a series of changes leading to mutual crossing-over.

If the effect of radiations (and of mutagenic chemicals also, since their effects are similar) is to set in train a series of changes leading to non-homologous crossing-over, it is reasonable to suppose that this process will have features in common with normal crossing-over between homologous chromosomes at meiosis, and in particular that it will occur after the chromosomes have divided into chromatids, and that it will involve only one chromatid from each chromosome (or from each of the two participating segments of the same chromosome). Anderson (1936) made these assumptions for, having established that normal crossing-over occurs at the four-strand stage (see § 8.6), he favoured a similar situation for the hypothetical non-homologous process. The consequences of crossing-over between different parts of the same chromosome depend (a) on whether the bending back of the chromosome to bring non-homologous parts together is in the form of a letter U, or of a coil, and (b) on whether the chromatids involved are identical or sisters (see Fig. 9.2). Anderson pointed out that crossing-over between different parts of the same chromatid would give rise either to an interstitial

	U bend	Coil
Chromatids involved in cross-over		
Identical		
Sister		

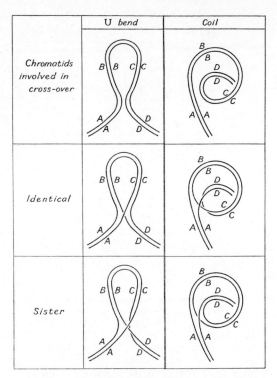

FIGURE 9.2   The four ways in which non-homologous crossing-over at the four-strand stage may occur between different parts of the same chromosome. The lines represent chromatids and the letters *A–D* denote different regions of the chromosome segment.

inversion (Fig. 9.3(*a*)) or to an interstitial deficiency, the missing segment forming a separate ring-shaped chromatid (Fig. 9.3(*b*)). The other chromatid would be normal, since it would not have taken part in the exchange. If the crossing-over was between different parts of sister chromatids, either a pair of hairpin-shaped segments, each with a duplication and a deficiency, would be formed (Fig. 9.3 (*c*)), or there would be a duplication of a segment in one chromatid and a corresponding deficiency in the other one (Fig. 9.3(*d*)).

On the alternative breakage-and-reunion theory, the configurations just described are also possible, but a simple union of sister chromatids would be expected much more frequently, following breakage of both chromatids at approximately corresponding positions. This would give rise to a pair of hairpin-shaped segments (Fig. 9.4(*a*)) similar to those derived from non-homologous crossing-over (Fig. 9.3(*c*)) but differing from them in certain

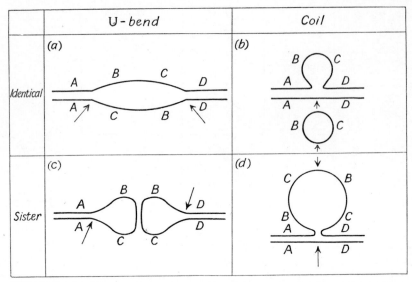

FIGURE 9.3   The configurations at metaphase of mitosis resulting from
non-homologous crossing-over between different parts of a
chromosome. The letters *A–D* correspond to those in Fig. 9.2.
It is assumed that the interval *BC* is relatively short, with the
result that the prophase pairing between the two *B* segments
has been lost, and similarly with the two *C* segments. Arrows
show the points where union has occurred.

respects. The differences are indicated by the lettering in the diagrams and
by the arrows which show the points of reunion.

In *Vicia faba* root-tip cells at metaphase, following *X*-irradiation in the
preceding resting-stage, Revell found that many of the pairs of hairpin-
shaped segments resulting from the irradiation showed constrictions at the
positions of the arrows in Fig. 9.3(*c*), but not at the positions in Fig. 9.4(*a*).
The constrictions were interpreted as showing the points of crossing-over,
since similar constrictions were often seen at the position where rejoining had

FIGURE 9.4   The types of chromosomal aberration expected on the breakage-
and-reunion hypothesis (*a*) if all broken ends show union, and
(*b–d*) if two broken ends fail to show union. Arrows indicate the
points where union has occurred.

FIGURE 9.5　The types of aberration expected following non-homologous
crossing-over between two different chromosomes (*a*) following
a complete exchange, and (*b*) if the free ends of one crossover
chromatid failed to unite. Arrows show the points where
union has occurred.

evidently occurred when different chromosomes had undergone interchange,
that is, at the positions of the arrows in Fig. 9.5(*a*).

Furthermore, Revell found that the two hairpin segments of a pair were
usually in close proximity to one another at metaphase. This would be
expected if their construction was as in Fig. 9.3(*c*) where the two homologous
segments labelled *B* would be expected to remain associated until metaphase,
and similarly with those labelled *C*. If the construction of the hairpin
segments was as in Fig. 9.4(*a*), they would be expected to have drifted apart
by metaphase.

Anderson considered the genetic consequences of these structural changes,
supposedly resulting from non-homologous crossing-over at the four-strand
stage between different parts of the same chromosome, and pointed out that
quantitative predictions capable of experimental testing would be compli-
cated by viability phenomena, since chromosome segments lacking a centromere are soon lost from a cell, and such deficiencies often cause inviability,
particularly to pollen-grains. Revell, on the other hand, has been concerned
with the immediate cytological consequences, before differential viabilities
take effect. Accurate quantitative predictions can then be made. Thus,
Revell (1959) assumed that the two kinds of bending (U-shaped and coil)
occurred with equal frequency, and that the exchanges involved either
identical or sister strands equally often. The four configurations shown in
Fig. 9.3 are then expected with equal frequency, and theoretically, by
examining chromosomes fixed a few hours after irradiation, it should be
possible to observe and count these aberrations. This should allow a direct
test of the exchange hypothesis, since on the alternative breakage-and-
reunion theory the pair of hairpin segments (Fig. 9.4(*a*), but resembling
Fig. 9.3(*c*)) would be expected with greater frequency than the configurations shown in Fig. 9.3, for the reasons given above.

11

FIGURE 9.6   The configurations expected at metaphase of mitosis as a result of
'half crossing-over' between non-homologous segments of a chromosome. The letters *A–D* correspond to those in Figs. 9.2 and 9.3.
Arrows show the points where union has occurred.

In practice, if the segment BC between the points of supposed non-
homologous exchange is short, as appears usual, the configurations in Fig.
9.3(*a*), (*b*) and (*d*), often cannot be identified with certainty, and even the
ring-chromosome (Fig. 9.3(*b*)) may be overlooked if it is small. Only the
pair of hairpin segments (Fig. 9.3(*c*)) is readily recognised. Revell thus
found that, at least in *Vicia faba* root-tips, a straightforward quantitative test
of the hypothesis of non-homologous crossing-over could not be made.
However, he suggested that in a minority of instances (7–10% in his experiments described below) the induced process of crossing-over was not completed, with the result that, although one cross-over chromatid was formed,
the free ends of the reciprocal one failed to unite. Such a 'half cross-over'
would be directly recognisable as a 'half-chiasma' when different chromosomes were involved (Fig. 9.5(*b*)), but the consequences when different
regions of the same chromosome were concerned are diverse and are shown
in Fig. 9.6. There are 8 alternatives depending on which way the chromosome bends (U or coil), which strands undergo exchange (identical or
sister), and which fail to unite. The configurations shown in Fig. 9.6(*a*),
(*b*), (*d*), (*g*) and (*h*) will appear as a break in one chromatid, those in Fig.
9.6(*e*) and (*f*) will appear as single hairpin-shaped segments, while that in
Fig. 9.6(*c*) will appear more or less normal. Hence, on the assumption that
the 8 alternatives occur with equal frequency, the occurrence of a break in
one chromatid is expected to be 2·5 times as frequent as the occurrence of
single hairpin segments. On the other hand, on the breakage-and-reunion
theory, configurations with free ends would be the direct result of a failure

to join after breakage. Simple chromatid breaks, as a result of a single ionization track and a subsequent failure to rejoin, as illustrated in Fig. 9.4(*b*), would be expected more frequently than any configurations involving two breakage events such as those illustrated in Fig. 9.4(*c*) and (*d*) and Fig. 9.6. Hence, single chromatid breaks would be expected much more than 2·5 times as often as single hairpin segments.

Revell (1959) examined 1513 cells at metaphase from *Vicia faba* root-tips treated with 50 r X-rays 5 hours before fixation, and found 32 examples of a break in one chromatid and 10 examples of single hairpin-shaped segments, in good agreement with a 2·5:1 ratio (expected frequencies 30 and 12, $\chi^2 = 0\cdot47$, $n = 1$, $P = 0\cdot5$). In a more extensive experiment, 5000 meta-phases were examined following 65 r X-rays 5 hours before fixation, and the corresponding frequencies were 169 and 67 (expected values 168·6 and 67·4, $\chi^2 = 0\cdot0038$, $n = 1$, $P = 0\cdot95$). Revell found no less than 4155 non-staining gaps or 'false chromatid breaks' in the 5000 metaphases, many or all of which would formerly have been scored as breaks, before it was recognised that a thread so fine as to be beyond the resolution of the micro-scope may join chromatid segments.

These results, taken in conjunction with the qualitative evidence given above, provide strong support for the hypothesis of non-homologous crossing-over as an explanation of the origin of structural changes induced by radiations. Furthermore, Revell has found that hairpin-shaped segments and chromatid breaks increase in frequency in proportion to the X-ray dose raised to power 1·5. This conflicts with the predictions of the breakage-and-reunion hypothesis, where chromatid breaks would be expected to show a linear relation with dose, but is in agreement with the exchange hypothesis, assuming that non-homologous crossing-over between different regions of the same chromosome is sometimes due to a single ionization track and some-times to two.

According to a recent hypothesis, the initial event in crossing-over is breakage of one of two longitudinally arranged sub-units of each partici-pating chromatid, followed by association between these sub-units (see Chapter 15). There are several points of agreement between this postulated mechanism and the requirements of the Anderson-Revell chromatid-exchange hypothesis for the origin of structural changes.

§ 9.9   The hypothesis of the chromosome as a string of beads

The classical concept of the gene, which grew up as soon as the chromo-some theory was accepted, was to liken the chromosome to a string of beads, each bead representing a different gene. This idea incorporated all the salient features about genes, namely, that they behaved in inheritance as discrete particles which appeared not to influence one another, that they were linearly arranged in the chromosome, and that crossing-over between homologous chromosomes at meiosis apparently occurred between them.

The three primary ways of defining the gene, that is, in terms of its specific effect on a particular character or group of characters, in terms of its recombination with neighbouring genes as a result of crossing-over, and in terms of its change to a different allele as a result of mutation, were thought to represent different aspects of the same structure. Thus, the gene was considered to be a specific molecule or aggregate of molecules making up the bead, which in some way controlled the development of a particular character in the organism. Crossing-over was imagined as a process of mechanical exchange which could cause breakage between corresponding beads in homologous chromosomes followed by rejoining in new ways, but which necessarily left the beads themselves intact. Mutation was thought of as an abrupt change in the molecular structure of the gene of a kind which was stable and was copied when the molecule was duplicated, and thereby inherited, and which led to a change in the appropriate character of the organism.

Multiple alleles could also be incorporated into the bead hypothesis, since it was only to be expected that the molecular structure of a gene could be changed in many different ways. Structural changes would represent abnormal rearrangements of bead sequence, or the duplication or omission of some of them. Two other observations appeared to reinforce the bead concept. Firstly, the sequence of the genes in the chromosome seemed to be a random, fortuitous one, such that neighbouring genes were presumed to be concerned with totally unrelated characters in the organism. This heterogeneity supported the idea that neighbouring genes in no way influenced one another, and that their proximity was merely a consequence of the favouring by natural selection of a stringing together of the hereditary units as a more efficient means of distributing them with precision between daughter-cells at cell-division. Secondly, the structure of a chromosome as seen at the leptotene stage of meiosis had itself been likened to a string of beads. Belling (1928b) went so far as to postulate that each chromomere represented a specific gene, and others made a similar suggestion about the discs or bands in salivary gland chromosomes. Without going as far as this, many saw in the visible heterogeneity of the chromosome support for the bead hypothesis.

On the other hand, Raffel and Muller (1940) pointed out that although it was often assumed that the lines of demarcation between genes, as defined by crossing-over, breakage, mutation, function, and reproduction, would coincide with one another, there was no evidence for this, and the assumption had only a doubtful theoretical basis. Moreover, it was only an assumption that the lines of demarcation of the units defined by each of these criteria were necessarily invariable, non-overlapping or even well-defined. In other words, there was no evidence that the hereditary material was really subdivided into intra- and inter-genic components, such as the bead idea implied. The gene was recognised at the functional level by its effect on the development of the organism, but it was not a necessary consequence of this that genes were differentiated from one another physically: the beads and the thread connecting them might both be made of the same material. Goldschmidt (1938) had taken this idea to its logical conclusion when he suggested that it was the chromosome, which he thought of as a large chain molecule, which was the hereditary unit, that mutations were changes in this molecule at specific points, and that these changes disturbed the normal interplay of catalysed reactions. He considered that each point in the chain had a definite meaning in the chemical properties of the whole, as with all molecules, but that the unmutated (or wild-type) gene was merely a theoretical concept. That is to say, he regarded the normal (wild-type) condition as controlled by the whole chain as a unit, without the separate existence of individual genes.

Few geneticists were willing to go as far as Goldschmidt, with whom the string-of-beads idea had become a string without beads. Nevertheless, it was recognised that there was no evidence that the units of function, of recombination, and of mutation were co-extensive, such as the bead hypothesis assumed. Indeed, evidence against this hypothesis was accumulating.

§ 9.10   Evidence against the bead hypothesis: the position effect

The bead hypothesis suffered its first setback when Sturtevant (1925) made a most unexpected discovery. The dominant sex-linked gene called Bar, which causes a narrow eye in *Drosophila melanogaster* instead of the normal round eye, was unusual in that it appeared to mutate with comparatively high frequency. Zeleny (1921) found that, out of 85,008 progeny of homozygous Bar-eyed females crossed with normal males, 52 (or approximately 1 in every 1600) showed reversion to the normal round eye, and 3 (or approximately 1 in every 28,400) showed mutation to a more extreme form dominant to Bar, which he called Ultra-bar. Ultra-bar itself showed similar changes.

Sturtevant and Morgan (1923) found that these changes were confined to the female, and moreover were not true mutations but were due to crossing-over. They studied the progeny of homozygous Bar-eyed females which were heterozygous for the recessive genes for *forked* bristles and for *fused* wing-veins. These genes are placed 0·2 and 2·5 units, respectively, away from Bar on either side. It was found that, whenever a reversion from Bar to normal eye-shape occurred there was crossing-over between the loci of the 'marker' genes *forked* and *fused*. Sturtevant (1925) found that this also applied to the origin of Ultra-bar from Bar. Some of his data are given in Table 9.2. He concluded that the normal round and the more extreme Ultra-bar eye characters arose from Bar (B) through crossing-over occurring obliquely so as to give two Bar alleles (BB) in one chromosome (Ultra-bar) and none in the other (round). The round-eyed flies arising from homozygous Bar through crossing-over were entirely normal, both in appearance and in their progeny. The lower frequency with which Ultra-bar arose compared with round was attributed partly to oversight, since Ultra-bar is not very dissimilar from Bar, and partly to a lower viability.

Sturtevant compared the appearance of the eyes in the various Bar genotypes, and made the surprising discovery that the heterozygote of

Ultra-bar and round $\left(\dfrac{BB}{.}\right)$ had narrower eyes (mean number of facets 45*)

than the Bar homozygote $\left(\dfrac{B}{B}\right)$ (mean number of facets 68*), although each fly contained the same two Bar alleles. He concluded that two alleles were more effective in narrowing the eye when they lay in the same chromosome than when there was one in each chromosome. Muller, Prokofyeva and Kossikov (1936) and, independently, Bridges (1936) carried the analysis a

TABLE 9.2   Data of Sturtevant (1925) for the progeny of Bar-eyed (B) *Drosophila melanogaster* with marker genes *forked* bristles (*f*) and *fused* wing-veins (*fu*) on either side of the Bar locus. Plus signs indicate normal alleles.

$$\text{Parents:}\frac{+\,B\,+}{f\,B\,fu}\times f\,B\,fu. \qquad F_1 \text{ Progeny:}\!-$$

Eye-shape	Numbers of Various Genotypes for Outside Markers				
	Parental		Recombinant		Total
	+ +	f fu	+ fu	f +	
Homozygous Bar†	10,631	7,909	187	264	18,991
Heterozygous Bar† (females)	0	0	0	2	2
Normal round (males)	1‡	0	2	1	4
Ultra-bar	0	0	0	2	2

† Homozygous Bar and the heterozygote of Bar and normal can be distinguished by the eye shape, which is more extreme in the homozygote.

‡ Thought to be a contaminant.

stage further when they showed that the Bar phenotype was not due to a simple gene mutation but to a structural change. Study of the salivary gland chromosomes revealed that Bar-eyed flies had a chromosome segment (S) containing 6 transverse bands present in duplicate. The repeated section was adjacent to the original and in the same (not the reversed) sequence, giving the configuration SS. Ultra-bar flies had the same segment in triplicate (SSS), while the normal flies arising from the Bar-eyed ones through crossing-over had normal salivary gland chromosomes with the segment represented only once. Sturtevant and Morgan's discovery of oblique crossing-over was now explained on the supposition that the left-hand S segment in one chromosome of homozygous Bar-eyed flies occasionally paired at meiosis with

the right-hand S segment in the homologous chromosome $\left(\dfrac{SS}{SS}\right)$. A cross-over

* Facet number was found to be smaller the higher the temperature during development over the range 15–30°C. These frequencies refer to flies grown at 25°C.

in these paired segments would then give a gamete with the segment in triplicate (*SSS*) and another in which the segment was represented only once (*S*).
This staggered pairing evidently happened in either direction (the right-hand
segment on one homologue with the left-hand segment of the other, and
vice versa), because the round-eyed flies derived from Bar could have either
of the two complementary crossover genotypes for the marker genes, that
is, either non-*forked fused* or *forked* non-*fused* in Sturtevant's data in Table 9.2.
Sturtevant's earlier deduction that two Bar alleles in one chromosome were
more effective than one in each, had to be replaced by the notion that the
particular segment, *S*, if present in triplicate in one chromosome and represented once in the other $\left(\dfrac{SSS}{S}\right)$ resulted in a narrower eye than the same
segment in duplicate in both chromosomes $\left(\dfrac{SS}{SS}\right)$.

It was evident that the appearance of an organism may be modified
merely by altering the arrangement of the hereditary material in the chromosomes, without mutation and without loss or gain in the quantity of genetic
material. On the bead hypothesis, the only way to accommodate Sturtevant's
discovery of the effect of position on the phenotype was to postulate that the
beads were not the isolated structures that had been supposed, but that
neighbouring beads (genes) could either influence one another, or their
immediate products of activity could interact, thereby modifying the
particular characters of the organism which they controlled. Although
this initial example of an alteration of the phenotype through rearranging
the hereditary material referred to an abnormal situation involving duplicated and triplicated segments, it was later established that the principle
which it illustrates is of wide application and fundamental importance. It
is discussed in § 13.3 and § 16.3.

§ 9.11   Evidence against the bead hypothesis: recombination between alleles

Work on a series of bristle mutants called *scute* of *Drosophila melanogaster*
by a number of authors and extending over many years had suggested that
the units of function, recombination and mutation might not correspond
(cf. Raffel and Muller, 1940). More specific evidence for such lack of
correspondence was obtained when Oliver (1940) discovered recombination
in *D. melanogaster* between two allelic eye-character mutants called *lozenge*.
The mutant alleles were both recessive to normal and sex-linked, and they
gave rise in the homozygote to a reduction in the pigmentation and other
effects on the eye. Oliver found that females heterozygous for the alleles, that
is, with one in one chromosome and the other in the homologue, when
crossed with males carrying either allele, gave small numbers of progeny
with normal eyes, and, furthermore, these reversions were always associated
with crossing-over in the vicinity of the alleles. This remarkable finding
recalled Sturtevant and Morgan's discovery with Bar eye, but differed from
it in an important respect: the normal-eyed progeny from the lozenge-eyed

parents were associated with one particular crossover genotype, whereas with Bar, as indicated above, they were associated with either crossover combination of the marker genes.

Lewis (1941) made a similar discovery with two *star* eye-character alleles in the second chromosome. These alleles, one dominant (S) and the other recessive (s) to normal, caused a reduction in size and an increase in roughness of the eye-surface. Heterozygotes having S in one chromosome and s in the other had *star* eyes as expected with alleles. Females heterozygous for these two alleles and also for the recessive genes *arista-less* (al) and *held-out* wings (ho), which are closely linked on either side of the *star* locus, were crossed with star-eyed males and gave rise to 4 normal-eyed progeny among 31,106 star-eyed. The female parents had the genotype $\dfrac{al\ S\ ho}{+\ s\ +}$ (the $+$ sign indicates the normal alleles), and all 4 normal-eyed progeny had evidently developed from eggs of constitution $+ + ho$, or in other words they were crossovers for the marker genes on either side, having the normal allele of *arista-less* together with the *held-out* mutation. In another experiment using a stock with increased recombination in this region, there were 12 normal-eyed flies from the same cross among 26,370 star-eyed, and again the normals were all non-*aristaless* and *held-out*.

It was evident that the sites of the two star alleles were not quite identical, and it appeared as if crossing-over occasionally took place between them. That the normal-eyed flies carried the mutation *held-out* but not *arista-less* implied that the dominant star allele was slightly nearer to the locus of *arista-less* than the recessive one, such that the genotype of the female parents could be rewritten as $\dfrac{al\ S\ +\ ho}{+\ +\ s\ +}$. In the production of the normal-eyed progeny a crossover was presumed to have occurred at the position of the X: $\dfrac{al\ S}{+\ +} \times \dfrac{+\ ho}{s\ +}$ to give the $+ + + ho$ genotype which was found. The complementary product of such crossing-over would have both alleles in the same chromosome $(al\ S\ s\ +)$. Flies arising from eggs of this genotype were evidently not distinguished from the other star-eyed progeny. Since the normal-eyed recombinants were all of one genotype with respect to the marker genes, there was no reason to suppose that the star alleles were associated with a duplicated segment such as was known to occur with Bar. Lewis confirmed that there was no evidence from the salivary gland chromosomes of any structural changes associated with the star alleles.

The occurrence of recombination between the star alleles could be taken to imply that these were mutations of different genes. Lewis (1945) favoured this explanation and went so far as to re-christen 'star-recessive' as 'asteroid'. For reasons to be discussed in Chapter 13, it now appears that this decision was premature.

A discovery in many ways comparable to those of Oliver and of Lewis with *Drosophila* was made by McClintock (1944) when she discovered an anomaly in a series of alleles at the yellow-green-2 locus $(yg\text{-}2)$ in *Zea mays*. Three mutants which produced yellow-green, pale yellow, and white

seedlings, respectively, were found to be inherited as Mendelian recessives
to the normal green plant-colour, and to behave as alleles, with descending dominance in the order quoted. The anomaly was that the heterozygote
for the two intermediate members of the series, yellow-green and pale
yellow, instead of having yellowish-green leaves as expected, was normal
green.

Two alternative explanations of this observation are possible. If the mutants
are regarded as alleles, then it is necessary to assume that different parts of
the gene are abnormal in the yellow-green and pale yellow mutants,
respectively, such that the normal parts can complement each other.
Alternatively, it could be argued that these two mutants are not allelic,
but are due to mutation of neighbouring genes concerned with a similar
function. On this hypothesis, each would carry the dominant normal allele
of the other's mutation, and hence the heterozygote would be normal.

The gene (or genes) concerned was known to lie close to one end of a
particular chromosome (the short arm of no. 9). From an examination of this
chromosome, McClintock found that whereas the green and the yellow-
green plants had a normal chromosome, the pale yellow plants had a small
terminal segment of the chromosome missing, and the white plants had a
slightly larger terminal deficiency. These observations suggested that part
of the gene (or one of the two on the two-gene interpretation) was missing
in the pale yellow plants, and that the whole gene (or both of them on the
two-gene theory) was missing in the white plants.

On either interpretation the bead hypothesis is undermined. On the
one-gene theory, the alleles for yellow-green and pale yellow plant colour
evidently differ from normal at points which do not correspond, so that in
effect the gene has been split and, contrary to expectation, the parts found to
show autonomy of action in the production of green leaf-colour in the
heterozygote for these alleles. On the two-gene theory, neighbouring genes
are presumed to interact in the production of the green colour in this
heterozygote. A similar argument can be applied to the *Drosophila* data
discussed earlier. There were indications that a comparable situation might
apply with the human rhesus blood-group factors. About 85% of white
people have been found to possess the rhesus antigen, such that their erythrocytes are agglutinated by the antibodies obtained by immunising rabbits
with the blood of the Rhesus monkey *Macacus mulatta*. The remaining 15%
are rhesus negative and lack the antigen. Haemolytic disease of the newborn
(erythroblastosis foetalis) has been shown to be due to rhesus blood group
incompatibility between a rhesus negative mother and a rhesus positive
child. The presence of the rhesus antigen was found by Landsteiner and
Wiener (1941) to be inherited as a Mendelian dominant. A number of
apparently allelic variants within both the rhesus positive (*Rh*) and negative
(*rh*) blood groups have been recognised. R. A. Fisher (in Race, 1944)
suggested that mutant differences at three closely-linked positions (*C/c*,
D/d and *E/e*) were each responsible for the presence or absence of a specific
antigen, of which *D* and *d* corresponded to rhesus positive and negative,
respectively. Further mutant forms at what is possibly a single gene locus
have since been recognised (see Race and Sanger, 1962).

It is evident that both the one-gene and the two-gene explanations of the results obtained by Oliver and by Lewis with *Drosophila* and by McClintock with *Zea* represented a breakdown of the classical theory of the gene, and probably likewise with a one gene (*Rh/rh*) or a three gene (*C/c*, *D/d*, *E/e*) explanation of the rhesus blood-groups. Were these instances to be regarded as exceptional or typical? This question will be discussed in Chapter 13.

10. *The hypothesis of one gene: one enzyme*

§ 10.1 Introduction

The idea of a connection between genes and enzymes is a long-established one. Garrod (1909) showed that the rare human disease called alkaptonuria appeared to be associated with a failure of the breakdown of the benzene ring in the degradation of phenylalanine and tyrosine, with the result that 2,5-dihydroxyphenylacetic acid is excreted in the urine, instead of the normal fumaric and acetoacetic acids. Bateson and Saunders (1902) had shown, on the basis of data collected by Garrod, that alkaptonuria appeared to be inherited as if due to a single Mendelian recessive gene, and Garrod (1909) pointed out that the splitting of the benzene ring in normal metabolism was likely to be the work of a special enzyme which was presumed to be lacking in congenital alkaptonurics. A few years later this specific enzyme was isolated, and its absence from alkaptonurics confirmed. Bateson (1909, p. 266), in discussing the Mendelian unitary factors, came to the conclusion that 'the consequences of their presence is in so many instances comparable with the effects produced by ferments, that with some confidence we suspect that the operations of some units are in an essential way carried out by the formation of definite substances acting as ferments'.

Indications of how different genes may affect related steps in the development of particular characters in an organism were obtained early in the study of Mendelian heredity. Thus, Bateson, Saunders, and Punnett (1905) crossed two pure-breeding white-flowered varieties of *Lathyrus odoratus* and were surprised to find that the progeny had purple flowers. When these F_1 plants were allowed to self-pollinate, and the F_2 generation grown, they found that out of 651 plants which flowered, 382 had coloured petals and 269 were white. These numbers fit a 9:7 ratio (expected numbers 366·2 and 284·8 respectively, $\chi^2 = 1·56$, $n = 1$, $P = 0·3–0·2$). Such a ratio would arise in F_2 if two independent but complementary dominant factors were required for the production of the flower pigment, the 9:7 ratio being a 9:3:3:1 ratio (cf. Chapter 3) in which the last 3 classes were indistinguishable. It was subsequently confirmed by further breeding tests that one parental white-flowered strain had the genotype *CCrr* and the other had the genotype *ccRR*, where *C* and *R* are the complementary dominant genes required for pigment formation.

One possible explanation of these results is that anthocyanin (the pigment in the coloured petals) was formed as the result of two successive biochemical

159

steps, the end-product of the one forming the substrate of the other. If these steps were controlled by the two genes, respectively, and if the end-product of the first step was colourless, it would be necessary for both reactions to occur, that is, for both C and R to be present, for the pigment to be formed.

Bateson, Saunders, and Punnett (1905) crossed a pure-breeding pink-flowered strain of *Salvia horminum* with a pure-breeding white-flowered variety. The F_1 plants had purple flowers. On self-pollination or inter-crossing these F_1 plants, 255 purple, 92 pink, and 114 white-flowered plants were obtained in F_2. These numbers are in agreement with a 9:3:4 ratio (expected numbers 259·3, 86·4, and 115·3 respectively; $\chi^2 = 0·45$, $n = 2$, $P = 0·8$), such as would be expected if the last two classes making up a 9:3:3:1 ratio were indistinguishable. Following confirmation of this explanation from further breeding, it was evident that flower colour in *S. horminum* was determined by two independently-inherited Mendelian factors, such that when both dominant genes were present a purple pigment was produced, while one alone (A) gave a pink pigment, and the other alone (B) the white colour which was also found in the absence of either dominant allele (*aabb*).

A possible explanation in biochemical terms of such a 9:3:4 ratio is that the two genes act sequentially in the synthesis of the purple pigment, gene A leading to the production of a pink anthocyanin and gene B modifying its molecular structure to give a purple anthocyanin. In the absence of A, no anthocyanin is formed and gene B is then ineffective, the flower-colour remaining white. Bateson (1907*b*), using the metaphor 'higher and lower', proposed the term *epistatic* for the factor (A in this instance) which stands above the other or *hypostatic* factor (B in this instance) and determines whether it shall take effect.

Numerous examples of the occurrence in F_2 of modified 9:3:3:1 ratios such as 9:7 and 9:3:4 are known. They point to interaction in development between independently-inherited genes, but the precise nature of such interaction requires identification of the biochemical steps which the genes control. Extensive studies of the nature of such biochemical steps have been made, particularly with the pigments in the fur of mammals, the eyes of insects, and the petals of flowers. Thus, from work on the biochemistry and inheritance of the anthocyanin and anthoxanthin flower pigments, it has been established that individual genes appear to be concerned with specific chemical operations such as methoxylation and glycosidation at particular positions in the molecule (cf. Scott-Moncrieff 1936; Lawrence 1950). This is precisely the kind of result anticipated if there is a relationship between particular genes and specific enzymes.

§ 10.2　Nutritional mutants in fungi and bacteria

A major step forward in the study of biochemical genetics was taken by Beadle and Tatum (1941). They reversed the ordinary procedure, and instead of attempting to work out the chemical basis of known genetic characters, they set out to determine if and how genes control known biochemical reactions.

Conidia of *Neurospora crassa* and *N. sitophila* were X-rayed, and then used to fertilize a strain of the opposite mating-type. About 2000 of the resulting ascospores were germinated and cultured on a 'complete' medium containing agar, inorganic salts, malt extract, yeast extract and glucose. The ability of the cultures to grow on a 'minimal' medium was then tested. This medium comprised agar (optional), inorganic salts, biotin, and a disaccharide, fat or more complex carbon source. Three mutants were found which grew essentially normally on complete medium and scarcely at all on the minimal medium with sucrose as the carbon source. These strains were then tested systematically by adding particular vitamins, amino-acids, etc. in turn to the minimal medium to determine what substance or substances they were unable to synthesise. In this way it was found that the three mutants had lost the ability to synthesise pyridoxin, thiamin, and para-aminobenzoic acid, respectively. Study of the inheritance of these character-differences showed that each differed from normal by a single gene.

Taking advantage of the method which Beadle and Tatum had devised, Srb and Horowitz (1944) obtained by X- or ultraviolet irradiation 15 mutants of *N. crassa* which lacked the ability to synthesise arginine. When these mutants were crossed with wild-type, it was found that each differed from normal by a single gene. When they were crossed with one another it was found that a number of them gave only arginine-requiring progeny, or in other words appeared to be independent mutations of the same genes. On the other hand, others gave many arginine-independent progeny and were evidently not allelic. When allowance was made for the alleles, the 15 mutants were resolved into mutations of 7 different genes.

These authors also used a second method of testing for allelism based on heterokaryosis (see § 5.4). Beadle and Coonradt (1944) had shown that when two recessive mutants of *Neurospora* of the same mating-type but having different nutritional requirements were grown together on minimal medium, a cell fusion (but no nuclear fusion) occurred to form dikaryotic mycelium, and this heterokaryon had a growth rate similar to that of the normal fungus. In other words, each mutant could supply the other's deficiency. Many combinations were tested, for example, a strain requiring *p*-aminobenzoic acid and another requiring nicotinic acid. Confirmation of heterokaryon formation was obtained by isolating hyphal tips and breeding from them: in this instance, from one hyphal tip it was found that some of the progeny required *p*-aminobenzoic acid and others required nicotinic acid for growth. Beadle and Coonradt also demonstrated the value of such heterokaryons in testing for allelism. Two mutants requiring nicotinic acid for growth were shown to complement one another, or in other words, in the heterokaryon each kind of haploid nucleus could supply what the other lacked. It was concluded that they were due to mutations of different genes. (Later work has shown that this inference is not necessarily valid: see Chapter 13.) Using this method, Srb and Horowitz were able to show that certain of their arginine mutants were allelic and others not, and they found that this heterokaryon complementation test gave results in agreement with the progeny-testing method.

By testing the ability of the arginine mutants to respond to the related substances ornithine and citrulline, Srb and Horowitz found that those in 4 of the 7 classes (*A–D* in Fig. 10.1(*a*)) would respond to both these substances,

(a)

$$\xrightarrow{A}\xrightarrow{B}\xrightarrow{C}\xrightarrow{D} \underset{R}{\overset{}{NH_2}} \xrightarrow{E}\xrightarrow{F} \underset{R}{\overset{CO\cdot NH_2}{NH}} \xrightarrow{G} \underset{R}{\overset{NH_2 \atop C\cdot NH}{NH}}$$

Ornithine   Citrulline   Arginine

R stands for —$CH_2\cdot CH_2\cdot CH_2\cdot CH(NH_2)\cdot COOH$

(b)

Anthranilic acid   Indole

Tryptophan

FIGURE 10.1   Steps in the synthesis of (a) arginine and (b) tryptophan in *Neurospora*.

those in a further 2 classes (*E, F* in the figure) would respond to ornithine but not to citrulline, and the 7th class (*G* in the figure) would respond to neither substance. They concluded that ornithine and citrulline were precursors, in the order quoted, in the biosynthesis of arginine, and that there was an ordered series of chemical steps, with each gene controlling a single step in a chain of reactions. The mutations were regarded as the loss of the ability to carry out the appropriate step, so that the sequence was blocked at that point. Since there were 7 different genes involved, it was assumed that there must be at least 7 steps in arginine synthesis. Much more is now known about these steps (cf. Fincham and Day, 1965).

Tatum, Bonner and Beadle (1944) made comparable studies with tryptophan-requiring mutants of *Neurospora*. One (*A* in Fig. 10.1(*b*)) was found able to use either anthranilic acid or indole in place of tryptophan, while another (*B* in the figure), which was non-allelic with the first, grew well on indole but was unable to use anthranilic acid. It thus appeared that anthranilic acid was an intermediary in the synthesis of indole, and thence of tryptophan. Moreover, mutant *B* accumulated anthranilic acid in its tissues, as expected if the succeeding biosynthetic step was blocked. Mitchell and Lein (1948) discovered a third class of tryptophan mutant, *C*, which lacked the ability to couple indole and serine to produce tryptophan, and furthermore, cell-free extracts appeared to lack the appropriate enzyme, tryptophan synthetase, while the *A* and *B* mutants did not. Again, later work along the same lines has provided more information about the steps in tryptophan synthesis (see §13.7).

In view of the remarkable association found in *Neurospora* between mutation of specific genes and blocking of specific biosynthetic steps, it was natural for Beadle (1945) to assume that every biochemical reaction had a specific gene directing its course, and to suppose that the gene's primary and possibly sole function was in directing the configurations of protein molecules.

Critics of the one gene: one enzyme hypothesis pointed out that the method of analysis employed in the *Neurospora* work is a selective one favouring the detection of mutants with single deficiencies, because mutants with multiple defects would probably not survive. This criticism is not easily discounted. Nevertheless, it soon became evident that the apparent one-to-one relation applied very widely, and this tended to weaken though not to invalidate the argument that mutants with multiple effects were being overlooked. The fermentation of a number of sugars by *Saccharomyces cerevisiae* and other yeasts appeared to be controlled by specific genes, and in bacteria mutants were obtained comparable to those found in fungi. Gray and Tatum (1944), by X-ray treatment of cells, obtained a mutant of *Escherichia coli* requiring biotin for growth, and another requiring threonine. This led directly to the discovery by Lederberg and Tatum (1946) of recombination in *E. coli* (see § 15.3), which, in turn, enabled the genetic basis of the biochemical mutants to be established. It soon became evident that, as in fungi, each step in a biosynthetic pathway appeared to be controlled by a specific gene, and in a number of instances it was possible to demonstrate that a specific enzyme was apparently lacking.

Many instances have since been found of mutants associated with the lack of a specific enzyme: Fincham (1959b) listed 54 examples in organisms ranging from bacteria to man. A particularly clear example of a relation between a specific gene and a specific enzyme is due to Horowitz, Fling, Macleod and Sueoka (1961), who found 4 different forms of the enzyme tyrosinase in different wild-type strains of *Neurospora crassa*, and the differences were found to be due to allelic mutations.

§ 10.3   Apparent exceptions to the one gene : one enzyme hypothesis

Several apparent exceptions to the one gene-one enzyme hypothesis have been found, but on detailed study they have proved to be in keeping with the hypothesis.

Following irradiation of conidia of *Neurospora crassa* with ultraviolet light, Teas, Horowitz and Fling (1948) discovered a mutant which had a double

$$
\begin{array}{l}
R\\
|\\
CHOH\\
|\\
CH_3\\
\text{Threonine}
\end{array}
$$

$$
\begin{array}{l}
R\\
|\\
\xrightarrow{A} CH_2\\
|\\
CH_2OH\\
\text{Homoserine}
\end{array}
$$

$$
\begin{array}{l}
SH\\
|\\
\rightarrow CH_2\\
|\\
R\\
\text{Cysteine}
\end{array}
\quad
\begin{array}{l}
R\\
|\\
\xrightarrow{B} CH_2\\
|\\
CH_2\\
|\\
S\\
|\\
CH_2\\
|\\
R\\
\text{Cystathionine}
\end{array}
\xrightarrow{C}
\begin{array}{l}
R\\
|\\
CH_2\\
|\\
CH_2\\
|\\
SH\\
\text{Homocysteine}
\end{array}
\xrightarrow{D}
\begin{array}{l}
R\\
|\\
CH_2\\
|\\
CH_2\\
|\\
S\\
|\\
CH_3\\
\text{Methionine}
\end{array}
$$

$$
R \text{ stands for } \begin{array}{l} -CH\cdot NH_2 \\ | \\ COOH \end{array}
$$

FIGURE 10.2   Steps in the synthesis of threonine and methionine in *Neurospora*.

requirement for growth: it was found to need both methionine and threonine. It was not due to two simultaneous mutations because a cross with wild-type showed that it differed from it by only one gene. Methionine-requiring mutants were already known controlling the steps *B*, *C*, and *D* in Fig. 10.2. Since the methionine requirement of the new mutant was satisfied also by homocysteine or by cystathionine, but not by cysteine, it was inferred that the double requirement was due to the blocking of a biosynthetic step in a common precursor of cystathionine and threonine. This was confirmed when it was discovered that homoserine alone was active in promoting growth. It was concluded that the mutant was blocked in step *A* in Fig. 10.2, and that threonine was derived from homoserine.

Another example of a double requirement was found to have a different explanation. A number of mutants of *N. crassa, Escherichia coli* and other organisms are known which require both isoleucine and valine for growth. It appears that the 4 final steps in the synthesis of these aminoacids are essentially the same (see Fig. 10.3), and that the same enzymes control these steps whether isoleucine or valine is being synthesised (see Wagner, Radhakrishnan and Snell, 1958).

$$
\begin{array}{ccccc}
CH_3 & CH_3 & CH_3 & CH_3 & CH_3 \\
| & | & | & | & | \\
CO & R\!-\!COH & R\!-\!COH & R\!-\!CH & R\!-\!CH \\
| \quad\rightarrow & | \quad\rightarrow & | \quad\rightarrow & | \quad\rightarrow & | \\
R\!-\!COH & CO & CHOH & CO & CH\cdot NH_2 \\
| & | & | & | & | \\
COOH & COOH & COOH & COOH & COOH
\end{array}
$$

R stands for $-CH_3$ in valine pathway

R stands for $-CH_2 \cdot CH_3$ in isoleucine pathway

FIGURE 10.3   The four final steps in the synthesis of valine and isoleucine.

Early in the study of biochemically-deficient mutants in fungi it was discovered that apparent back-mutation to wild-type was sometimes due, not to a reversal of the original mutation, but to mutation of a different gene. The effect of this mutation was to suppress the effect of the original mutation. The suppressor mutation usually showed no linkage to the mutant it suppressed, the two separating from one another in many of the progeny. If the suppressor gene can take over the function of the gene it suppresses, this might imply that two genes can control one enzyme. However, more detailed study, such as has been made of suppressors of tryptophan synthetase deficient mutants (*tryp*-3) in *N. crassa* by Yanofsky and Bonner (1955), has revealed that the suppressor mutants are allele-specific. Thus, one (called su_2) was found to suppress the effect of allele no. 2 at the *tryp*-3 locus, two others (su_3 and su_{24}) suppressed both allele no. 3 and no. 24, while a fourth (su_6) suppressed alleles nos. 2 and 6. The suppressor mutations su_3 and su_{24} appeared to be allelic with one another, but the others were due to mutation at unlinked loci. None was capable of suppressing all the *tryp*-3 alleles: su_2 and su_6 were tested against 25 *tryp*-3 alleles and it was found that only those mentioned above were suppressed.

It was evident that the suppressor genes were not capable of taking over the function of the *tryp*-3 gene. Instead, it seems likely that they act by restoring the functioning of this gene. Such restoration might come about in a number of ways, and there is evidence for diversity of action of different suppressor mutations (see §14.9). Irrespective of the precise mechanism of action, which is not known in most instances, it appears that suppressors are to be regarded as modifiers of the functioning of the mutant gene they suppress. Their existence therefore does not conflict with the idea that enzyme structure is essentially determined by one gene.

12

Another type of complication which has often been encountered in studies of nutritional mutants of fungi is competitive inhibition of growth of, for example, an arginine-requiring mutant by lysine, and *vice versa*. Pontecorvo (1952*a*) found that the growth of heterokaryons of an arginine-requiring and a lysine-requiring mutant of *Aspergillus nidulans* was much affected by the concentrations of these substances in the medium, whereas a diploid strain heterozygous for both mutants was unaffected. It was evident that the site of aminoacid competition was in the cytoplasm, and presumably concerned a carrier molecule or other transport system which provides an essential pathway in the cell.

The examples given of multiple growth-requirements, suppressor mutations, and competitive inhibition, which on first discovery appeared to contradict the one gene:one enzyme hypothesis, have been found on detailed study not to do so. This has given considerable support to the hypothesis, which is based on the many examples now known of the lack of a specific enzyme (or its existence in a modified form) in mutant strains of various organisms. It has now been possible to specify the nature of the relationship between gene and enzyme in much more precise terms, and this is discussed in Chapters 13 and 14.

11. *The DNA theory of the chemical basis of heredity*

§ 11.1 Introduction

It has been known since the work of Miescher (1871, 1897) that the chief constituent of the cell nucleus is nucleoprotein, a combination of nucleic acid and basic proteins. It was later established that the nucleic acid which occurs in combination with protein in the chromosomes is deoxyribonucleic acid (DNA). DNA also occurs in the nuclei of bacteria, where it is associated with little or no protein.

Bacterial geneticists have used the term chromosome for the fine DNA thread found in the nuclei of bacteria and in bacterial viruses. However, these threads differ in a number of respects from the chromosomes of higher organisms. In addition to the chemical difference, the bacterial threads do not show the cycles of behaviour which chromosomes undergo at mitosis and meiosis. Other differences between bacteria and higher organisms in the organisation of their DNA are referred to in later chapters. In order to avoid the confusion caused by this misapplication of the term chromosome to bacteria, the word *chromoneme*, meaning 'coloured thread', has been adopted in the present work for the DNA thread in bacteria and viruses. There is evidence that the primary division of living organisms is not into Plants and Animals, but into the Chromonemal and Chromosomal King-doms, since the differences between chromonemes and chromosomes appear to be associated with a number of other fundamental differences in cell structure and organisation (see Appendix 1, p. 317). In this primary sub-division, the Cyanophyceae (Blue-green Algae) belong with the Bacteria. Recognition of these two Kingdoms is important, because their differences are so great that conclusions about the mechanism of heredity, based on observations in the one, do not necessarily apply to the other.

For nearly 30 years after the acceptance of the chromosome theory of heredity, it was assumed more or less implicitly that the specificity of the gene resided in the protein part of nucleoprotein. The reason for this assumption was that proteins were known to occur in a very large number of highly specific forms, whereas nucleic acids were not thought to have a structure capable of much variety. DNA was found on hydrolysis to yield the purines, adenine and guanine; the pyrimidines, cytosine and thymine; phosphoric acid; and a sugar, deoxyribose. However, in a period of little more than a decade beginning in the year 1944, a complete revolution of

167

thought took place, and it is now generally accepted that it is the DNA which forms the chemical basis of heredity.

§ 11.2   Bacterial transformation

The discovery which initiated this remarkable change in ideas was the finding by Avery, MacLeod, and McCarty (1944) that DNA was the carrier of a specific hereditary character in *Diplococcus pneumoniae* (the pneumococcus). Griffith (1928) had discovered the phenomenon of genetic *transformation*. He had taken a virulent strain of the pneumococcus having a polysaccharide capsule surrounding the cell-wall giving the colonies a smooth (*S*) appearance. He heated this strain until all the cells were killed and then mixed with it a small quantity of living cells of an avirulent non-encapsulated strain giving rough (*R*) colonies, and injected the mixture into mice. He found that the mice frequently succumbed to the infection, that living virulent encapsulated (*S*) pneumococci could be isolated from them, and that this character combination of the bacteria was quite stable and was inherited. Control experiments using the living avirulent (*R*) culture alone, and others using the heated virulent (*S*) cells alone, showed no lethal effect of either on the mice, and no production of encapsulated (*S*) pneumococci.

Later, others demonstrated transformation *in vitro*, by growing the avirulent (*R*) cells in a fluid medium containing heat-killed virulent (*S*) cells. Subsequently, cell-free extracts of the *S* strain were obtained which could cause the specific genetic transformation from *R* to *S*. After many years' work, Avery and associates isolated in a highly purified form the substance responsible for this genetic change and showed that it was DNA.

Subsequently, many other characters were shown to be capable of transfer by DNA, both in this and a number of other species of bacteria. In 1952, the importance of DNA in heredity was also demonstrated with bacteriophage.

§ 11.3   Bacteriophage multiplication

Filter-passing agents pathogenic to specific bacterial strains were called bacteriophages before their viral nature, demonstrated by their infectivity and by their dependence for multiplication on their host, was established. Seven different phages, all active on a strain called *B* of *Escherichia coli*, have been given the type numbers 1 to 7 (*T*1, *T*2, etc.). Nos. 3 to 6 were isolated in America from sewage. The sources of the other three do not appear to have been recorded, but were almost certainly similar. These phages can be distinguished by their serological properties, by the range of strains of the host which they will attack, and by the shape and size of the clear area (plaque) which is produced in a bacterial colony by their destruction of the bacterial cells. The *T*-even phages (*T*2, *T*4, *T*6) are similar in many respects, and might be regarded as belonging to the same 'species', but each of the other four evidently belongs to a different species of virus.

The morphology of the *T*-even phages has been revealed in great detail (see Fig. 11.1) from electron micrographs obtained by Brenner, Streisinger, Horne, Champe, Barnett, Benzer, and Rees (1959) using a new technique involving phosphotungstate for negative staining. These viruses are alike in

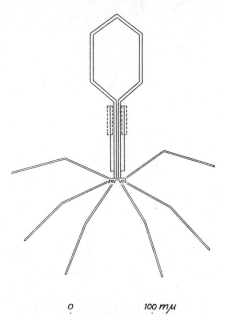

o   *100 mμ*

FIGURE 11.1   Diagrammatic representation of the structure of
the *T*-even phages of *Escherichia coli*, from the electron micrographs obtained
by Brenner *et al.* (1959).

appearance, and are tadpole-shaped with a head and tail. The head is a bipyramidal hexagonal prism measuring about 100 × 65 mμ. The contents are enclosed by a membrane about 3·5 mμ thick. The cylindrical tail, which is about 100 mμ long, consists of a core, surrounded by a contractile sheath. The core, which is attached to the head, is a hollow cylinder of diameter 7 mμ externally and 2·5 mμ internally. The sheath, which is not attached to the head, is about 80 mμ long and 16·5 mμ in diameter when extended. The virus becomes attached to the host cell by the tip of the tail, and the sheath then contracts towards the head to a length of about 35 mμ and diameter 25 mμ externally and 12 mμ internally, exposing the tail end of the core. The sheath appears to be composed of helically arranged sub-units. At the tip of the core, where contact with the bacterium is made, electron micrographs have revealed a hexagonal base plate bearing six short spikes and six long tail fibres measuring about 130 × 2 mμ and with a kink in the middle.

FIGURE 11.2   Appearance of *T*2 phage
of *Escherichia coli* following
osmotic shock and gentle
diffusion of the DNA on a
film of protein on water.
The drawing is based on
an electron micrograph
obtained by Kleinschmidt
et al. (1962).

Physical and chemical studies have established that the *T*-even phages
are composed wholly of DNA and protein, and that the DNA, which accounts
for 40% by weight of the total, occurs within the head. Brenner *et al.* (1959)
have shown that the head membrane, the sheath, and the tail fibres are
composed each of a different protein.

If *T*2 phage is suspended in a concentrated solution of sodium chloride
and then the solution is rapidly diluted with water, the virus particles suffer
an osmotic shock and are inactivated. Under the electron microscope
tadpole-shaped ghosts are then seen—empty shells from which the contents
have been removed. The shells will specifically adsorb to the bacteria
although incapable of producing progeny virus. This adsorption appears to
be determined by the tail fibres since detached fibres become attached to
bacterial cells with the same specificity as the whole virus. The osmotic
shock releases the DNA into the solution. This is shown by the vulnerability
of the DNA to the enzyme deoxyribonuclease to which it was previously
resistant, no doubt through protection by the protein membrane of the head.
This release of DNA has also been beautifully demonstrated by Kleinschmidt *et al.* (1962) who floated the DNA on a film of protein on water and
then examined the preparation under the electron microscope (see Fig. 11.2).

Hershey and Chase (1952*b*) isotopically labelled the protein and, in a separate experiment, the DNA of virus *T*2, using radioactive sulphur (^{35}S) for the protein and radioactive phosphorus (^{32}P) for the DNA. After infection of bacteria, unadsorbed virus was removed by centrifugation, and then the bacteria were agitated in a high-speed mixer in order to detach the virus particles from the bacterial cells-walls. It was found that at least 80% of the sulphur had remained at the cell surface and was removed by the agitation, while most of the phosphorus entered the cells. Despite this violent treatment the bacteria remained capable of yielding phage progeny, and it was found that little or none of the sulphur was incorporated in the progeny virus particles, while the phosphorus was transferred to the progeny to the extent of 30% or more. When labelled *T*2 was inactivated by osmotic shock, nearly all the sulphur was found in the ghosts. From these experiments, Hershey and Chase inferred that the bulk, if not all, of the protein of the virus takes no part in infection after the attachment of the virus to the bacterium. On the other hand, the DNA evidently entered the bacterium and played a part in the virus multiplication, since many of the same atoms appeared in the progeny. The structure of the virus bears out these conclusions. The elaborate tail appears to be a device for attaching the virus to the bacterial cell-wall, and injecting the virus DNA through it.

Hershey and Chase's experiments established that the genetic material of the virus is its DNA. This agrees with Avery, MacLeod and McCarty's discovery with *Diplococcus pneumoniae* in showing that hereditary characters may be carried by DNA alone, since little or no protein appears to be associated with the hereditary transmission. These discoveries gave support to the idea that in higher forms of life (chromosomal as distinct from chromonemal organisms) it might also be the DNA alone which was the chemical basis of heredity, with the protein part of the chromosome having some other function.

§ 11.4   The DNA content of nuclei

Boivin, Vendrely, and Vendrely (1948) made chemical analyses of the DNA content of the nuclei of the thymus, liver, pancreas and kidney of *Bos taurus* (Domestic Cattle). The primary method used was hydrolysis, followed by estimation of the deoxyribose content by a specific colour reaction. The number of nuclei in each preparation was estimated, and the DNA content per nucleus calculated. This led to two remarkable discoveries. First, the nuclei of the various tissues were found all to have essentially the same DNA content of approximately $6 \cdot 5 \times 10^{-12}$ grams. Secondly, the DNA content of the sperm nuclei was found to be approximately half that of the nuclei of the diploid tissues, namely, $3 \cdot 4 \times 10^{-12}$ grams. It appeared that within a species the DNA content of non-dividing nuclei was independent of the tissue or the individual, and dependent solely on the chromosome content (haploid or diploid). Vendrely and Vendrely (1948), in reporting their results in more detail, pointed out that this was a strong argument in favour of the theory that the DNA is the carrier of the hereditary factors.

Mirsky and Ris (1949) obtained similar results for a number of other animal species, and moreover found significant differences in the DNA content of the nuclei of different species: in diploid tissues, the amount of DNA ranged from about 2×10^{-12} grams per nucleus in *Alosa* (Shad) to about 15×10^{-12} grams in *Rana* (Frog). They pointed out that, while supporting the DNA theory of heredity, these results did not necessarily mean that the gene consists of nothing but DNA.

Ris and Mirsky (1949) found that it was possible to obtain reliable information about the relative DNA content of different nuclei by measuring the intensity of pigmentation after staining by the Feulgen reaction. This staining method involves mild hydrolysis in warm dilute hydrochloric acid, followed by staining with decolorised basic fuchsin, and is specific for DNA, since it depends on the Schiff reaction with aldehydes derived from the deoxyribose. These authors showed the existence in the liver of *Rattus* (Rat) of three classes of nuclei with a ratio of intensity of Feulgen staining of $1 : 1\cdot9 : 3\cdot6$. This was in agreement with expectation from the knowledge that diploid, tetraploid and octoploid nuclei occur in this tissue.

§ 11.5   The time of replication of DNA

Swift (1950) studied the DNA content of nuclei in developing tissues of *Mus* and *Amblystoma* using the Feulgen staining method. He found DNA values ranging between that of the normal diploid and twice this amount. He concluded that DNA synthesis occurs in interphase. A similar conclusion was reached for plant material by Howard and Pelc (1951*a*) who demonstrated autoradiographically that radioactive phosphorus (^{32}P) was incorporated into nuclei in the meristematic region of *Vicia faba* root-tips during interphase, but not during mitosis. Walker and Yates (1952) confirmed the interphase synthesis by measuring the absorption of ultraviolet light of wavelength 265 mμ by nuclei in living cells in tissue cultures of particular organs of *Gallus*, *Mus*, *Oryctolagus*, *Rana*, and *Triturus*. There is strong absorption by nucleic acids at this wavelength. The previous history of the individual cells had been recorded by phase-contrast photographs, and so the density of each nucleus on the ultraviolet negatives could be plotted against the time since the previous division of the cell. From this it was established that the doubling of the DNA took place in interphase and extended over a comparatively long period of time.

Swift (1950) showed that at meiosis, like mitosis, the replication of DNA took place in interphase before the nuclear division began. By measurement of the intensity of Feulgen staining, he showed that DNA synthesis was completed before prophase of the first division of meiosis in spermatocytes of *Mus*. This pre-meiotic synthesis was confirmed autoradiographically by Taylor (1953) using plant material. Following incorporation of radiophosphorus (^{32}P) into flower-buds of *Lilium longiflorum* and *Tradescantia paludosa*, he found that the period of DNA synthesis in the pollen-mother-cells of *Lilium* ended before the leptotene stage of meiosis, while in *Tradescantia* it extended to early leptotene, but was completed well before the zygotene stage when homologous chromosomes begin to associate. Confirmation of this time of DNA synthesis in relation to meiosis has been obtained from further autoradiographic studies made by Taylor (1959*b*) with *L. longiflorum*, and by Monesi (1962) with male *Mus musculus* (cf. Pl. 2(*a*)). These observations are important in connection with the mechanism of crossing-over (see Chapter 15).

It appears that the synthesis of the protein of the chromosome also takes place in the interphase before nuclear division. This has been shown by observing autoradiographically the uptake of radioactive sulphur (³⁵S) supplied in sulphate. By this means, Howard and Pelc (1951*b*) demonstrated that protein synthesis at mitosis in *Vicia faba* root-tips occurs at approximately the same time as DNA synthesis, and Taylor and Taylor (1953) showed the same thing for meiosis in flower-buds of *Lilium*. They found there was also some incorporation of ³⁵S into chromosomes whenever the cell was metabolically active as indicated by uptake of ³⁵S into cytoplasmic protein. Taylor (1959*b*) obtained similar results from autoradiographic study of the uptake of glycine labelled with carbon-14 (¹⁴C) in the pollen-mother-cells of *L. longiflorum*.

If both DNA and protein synthesis are completed before nuclear division, whether mitotic or meiotic, Darlington's hypothesis (Darlington 1931*b*) that meiosis is to be regarded as a precocious mitosis appears untenable (see § 8.18).

§ 11.6   The base composition of DNA

Almost simultaneously with the discovery that the quantity of DNA per diploid nucleus was a specific character came the discovery that its composition showed a similar specificity. Chargaff, Vischer, Doniger, Green, and Misani (1949) found that in *Bos taurus* the DNA of calf thymus had the same proportion of the four nitrogenous bases adenine, guanine, cytosine, and thymine, as beef spleen, while Vischer, Zamenhof, and Chargaff (1949) found that the DNA of *Saccharomyces cerevisiae* (Yeast) and *Mycobacterium tuberculosis avium* had quite different base compositions from that of *Bos taurus* and from one another. The technique developed for these analyses involved hydrolysis, followed by chromatographic separation of the bases and their quantitative estimation by ultraviolet spectrophotometry.

Chargaff (1950), in reviewing these findings, drew attention to a remarkable feature, namely, that in every instance the number of molecules of the purine adenine liberated in the hydrolysis of the DNA was approximately equal to the number of molecules of the pyrimidine thymine, and likewise the molar quantities of the other purine, guanine, and the other pyrimidine, cytosine, were equal. On the other hand, the proportions of the two pairs varied widely depending on the species. On a molar basis, the adenine-thymine pair formed 30% of the total in *M. tuberculosis*, 58% in *Bos*, 62% in *Homo*, and 64% in *S. cerevisiae*. These proportions were independent of the tissue or individual from which the DNA was obtained, and were evidently characteristic for each species.

Wyatt (1951) reported that in the DNA of *Bos taurus* about 6% of the cytosine was in fact 5-methylcytosine, and similarly in a number of other animal species the cytosine component included from 1% to 8% of 5-methylcytosine. In *Triticum* sp. (Wheat), he found that no less than 25% of the cytosine component was 5-methylcytosine. In every instance, however, the total molar quantity of cytosine and 5-methylcytosine was equal to the molar quantity of guanine. In the *T*-even viruses of *Escherichia coli*, Wyatt and Cohen (1952) found that the whole of the cytosine of their DNA was replaced by 5-hydroxymethylcytosine, which occurred in approximately equimolar quantities with guanine. On the other hand, the bacterium itself had a normal DNA composition with cytosine and no 5-hydroxymethylcytosine.

§ 11.7   The structure of DNA

The formulae for the chemical groups which make up DNA, that is, the four primary nitrogenous bases (adenine, guanine, thymine, and cytosine), the sugar (2-deoxy-D-ribose), and phosphoric acid, are given in Fig. 11.3. The glycosidic combination of base and sugar which occurs in DNA is called a *nucleoside*, and the phosphate ester of a nucleoside is known as a *nucleotide*. DNA consists of unbranched polymers of nucleotides. The backbone of these nucleotide chains is quite regular and consists of alternate sugar and phosphate groups joined in 3′,5′-phosphate-di-ester linkages. Side groups consisting of one or other of the four bases are attached one to each sugar molecule. The covalent linkages by which the various groups are united to form the polynucleotide are shown in Fig. 11.4.

That DNA was composed of such nucleotide chains had been established and the filamentous shape of the molecule was known from electron microscopy, but no satisfactory detailed structure for the molecule as a whole had been proposed, until Watson and Crick (1953*a*) suggested a structure having several remarkable features. They postulated:

(*a*) that the number of polynucleotide chains in the molecule was two,

(*b*) that the chains followed right-handed helices, with 10 bases in each to one turn of the spiral,

(*c*) that the two chains were coiled plectonemically, that is, in an interlocked way, about the same axis,

(*d*) that the sequences of atoms in the two chains ran in opposite directions, or in other words, that one chain was inverted relative to the other,

(*e*) that the phosphates were on the outside of the double helix and the bases on the inside, with their planes set at right angles to the axis of the helix and spaced at intervals of 0·34 mμ along it,

(*f*) that the two chains were held together by hydrogen bonding between the bases, which were joined together in pairs, a single base from one chain being hydrogen-bonded to a single base from the other chain, and

(*g*) that this bonding was of a highly specific kind, such that the purine adenine in either chain was associated with the pyrimidine thymine in the other, and likewise the purine guanine in either chain with the pyrimidine cytosine in the other.

Details of this proposed structure are shown in Fig. 11.5.

Adenine
(6–aminopurine)

Guanine
(2–amino–6–hydroxypurine)

Thymine
(2,6–dihydroxy–5–methylpyrimidine)

Cytosine
(2–hydroxy–6–aminopyrimidine)

2–deoxy–D–ribose

Phosphoric acid

FIGURE 11.3   The components of DNA.

FIGURE 11.4 The covalent linkages between the components of a polynucleotide chain of DNA.
(a) Part of a polynucleotide chain.
(b) Part of a nucleoside showing the glycosidic linkage between a pyrimidine base and the sugar.
(c) As (b) when the base is a purine.
(d) Part of a 3′-nucleotide showing the linkage between nucleoside and phosphoric acid.
(e) As (d) for a 5′-nucleotide.

FIGURE 11.5   Diagrams to show the structure of DNA as proposed by Watson
and Crick (1953*a*). The diagrams incorporate the inferences from
later X-ray crystallographic work and are based on those of
Wilkins (1957).
  (i) A cross-section of the molecule to show the two phosphate
     sugar chains. N = Nitrogen. O = Oxygen. P = Phosphorus.
     1, 2, 3, 4, 5 = Carbon atoms of deoxyribose. Hydrogen atoms
     are not shown, nor the oxygen atoms attached to the phos-
     phorus atoms, other than the oxygen atoms which form part
     of the backbones of the chains. The Roman numerals indicate
     the positions of successive base pairs numbered from below
     upwards.
 (ii) The adenine-thymine base pair.
(iii) The thymine-adenine base pair.
 (iv) The guanine-cytosine base pair.
  (v) The cytosine-guanine base pair.
 (vi) The molecule seen from the side, lettered and numbered as in
     (i). The phosphate sugar chains in the foreground are
     thickened.

The way in which these postulates for the structure were arrived at have been set out by Crick and Watson (1954). The primary evidence came from the X-ray crystallographic work of Wilkins and associates (Wilkins, Stokes, and Wilson, 1953; Franklin and Gosling, 1953), the general nature of which had been made known to Watson and Crick prior to its publication. The specific base pairing was in agreement with the chemical evidence that certain bases regularly occur in equimolar quantities (see § 11.6), and the occurrence of hydrogen bonding within the molecule was supported by anomalous titration curves which DNA was known to give with acids and bases.

The method which Watson and Crick used, in attempting to find the structure of DNA, was to build models using the known interatomic distances and bond angles for the constituents of DNA, and see if each structure so produced was stereochemically feasible and if it would fit the X-ray data. Wilkins, Stokes, and Wilson (1953) had found that DNA from the animals *Bos* and *Salmo* (Trout), the bacteria *Escherichia coli* and *Diplococcus penumoniae*, and the virus *T*2 of *E. coli*, all gave the same X-ray pattern. This led Watson and Crick to the idea that the sugar and phosphate groups have the same relative positions irrespective of the base attached to the sugar, since it was known that the DNA of different species had a different base composition (see § 11.6). The crystallographic data pointed to a helical structure of pitch 3·4 mμ, and also to the supposition, first suggested by Astbury and Bell (1938), that the bases were set perpendicular to the long axis of the molecule and spaced at 0·34 mμ, which is equal to their thickness. Density measurements from the X-ray patterns indicated that there were two polynucleotide chains.

Watson and Crick first attempted to construct models with the phosphates of the two chains near the helix axis, but they found that, because of the awkward shape of the sugar, there were relatively few configurations which the backbone can assume, and no satisfactory model could be devised along these lines. This led them to the belief that the bases form the central core and the sugar-phosphate chains the circumference of the molecule. The X-ray data suggested a molecular diameter of about 2 mμ measured perpendicular to the length of the filament. This severely limits the types of model that can be constructed, and it appeared probable that each chain was nearly fully extended and made one revolution of the helix every 3·4 mμ. The two chains would have to be intertwined because it is impossible to have paranemic coiling (a pair of helices which can be directly separated laterally) with two regular simple helices going round the same axis.

Watson and Crick considered it likely that the two chains would be held together by hydrogen bonds between the bases. These bonds are strongly directional in character, and can form only in the plane of the bases. However, since within one chain the bases appeared to be set partially on top of each other like a staggered pile of plates, hydrogen bonds can be expected to form only between bases belonging to different chains, thereby uniting the bases in pairs. If each sugar-phosphate chain is in the form of a regular helix, as has been supposed, the link between sugar and base (the glycosidic bond) will always have the same orientation to the axis of the helix. The space available between the two chains will therefore be constant, and pairing between bases in opposite chains can only be done by joining bases of the right size. The space appeared to be such that the purine adenine in one chain could pair with the pyrimidine thymine in the other, and the purine guanine in one chain with the pyrimidine cytosine in the other, in agreement with the chemical evidence of their equality within each pair. For all other combinations there was either too little or too much space between the chains. The base pairing was thought to occur between positions no. 1 on the purine and the pyrimidine, and also between positions no. 6 on each, with the possibility of a third hydrogen bond at positions no. 2 in the guanine-cytosine pair (but not in the adenine-thymine pair). Hydrogen bonding could occur at a number of other places in isolated nucleotides, which can pair in many ways. The specific pairing is imposed by the regularity of the phosphate-sugar chains, and is therefore to be regarded, not as an intrinsic feature of these nucleotides, but as a property which is manifest by them when they occur in a polynucleotide chain.

The occurrence of 5-methylcytosine and 5-hydroxymethylcytosine in some sources of DNA (see § 11.6) is unaccounted for on the Watson and Crick model, but the 5 position is not involved in the hydrogen bonding with guanine, and the occurrence of equimolar quantities of guanine and of total cytosine, whichever derivatives are present, is in agreement with the specific pairing hypothesis.

The proposed structure imposes no restriction on the sequence of bases within a chain, but the specific base-pairing implies that the second chain will have a base sequence complementary to that of the first.

When models were constructed using the specific base pairs, further features of the structure became evident. It was found that the helices must be right-handed. Left-handed helices could be constructed only by violating the permissible separations of atoms. It was also found that the two glycosidic bonds of each base-pair must be symmetrically disposed about a line perpendicular to the axis of the helix. This means that each base-pair, if it could be detached and inverted, would fit between the chains just as well the other way round (see Fig. 11.5(ii)–(v)). It follows that all four bases may occur in both chains. Furthermore, one nucleotide chain must always be inverted relative to the other (but with the complementary base sequence). The sequence of atoms in the backbone of one chain will be

$$\ldots -C_3-C_4-C_5-O-P-O-C_3-C_4-C_5- \ldots$$

and in the same physical direction in the other it will be

$$\ldots -C_5-C_4-C_3-O-P-O-C_5-C_4-C_3- \ldots$$

(see Fig. 11.5(vi)).

The Watson and Crick model obtained immediate support from the work of Wilkins, Stokes, and Wilson (1953) and of Franklin and Gosling (1953), who, independently of Watson and Crick, deduced that the structure was probably helical, that the phosphates were on the outside, and that there were two unequally spaced co-axial components. Nevertheless, some features remained hypothetical until the model had been tested with experimental X-ray evidence. This was obtained by Wilkins and associates, when Feughelman, Langridge, Seeds, Stokes, Wilson, Hooper, Wilkins, Barclay, and Hamilton (1955) showed that the Watson and Crick structure was in all essentials correct, although some modification of details was necessary, notably the placing of the bases closer to the axis of the helix. It is this slightly modified version which is shown in Fig. 11.5.

§ 11.8   The biological implications of the structure of DNA

Watson and Crick (1953*b*, 1954) had drawn attention to the genetical implications of their proposed structure for DNA. That this structure was established as substantially correct did not necessarily imply that the biological hypotheses were also true. These hypotheses were:

1. that replication occurs by breakage of the hydrogen bonds, unwinding and separation of the two chains, and the formation of a new complementary chain alongside each, and
2. that the precise sequence of the bases in the nucleotide chain is the code which carries the genetical information.

The first of these hypotheses is discussed in Chapter 12, and the second in Chapters 13 and 14. As a corollary to the sequence hypothesis, Watson and Crick suggested that mutation may be due to a base occasionally occurring in one of its less likely tautomeric forms, so that at replication the wrong base is inserted at this position in the complementary chain. The molecular basis of mutation is discussed in § 14.2. Watson and Crick also suggested that pairing between homologous chromosomes at meiosis may depend on pairing between specific bases.

The brilliant idea underlying the Watson and Crick model of DNA was that there were two complementary nucleotide chains, and that replication of the gene involved each chain acting as a template or mould for the formation of its complement. Such a mechanism for copying the gene would not require gene specificity to be transferred to protein and then back to DNA again, such as previous hypotheses of self-duplication had assumed to be necessary. Watson and Crick's idea thus gave support to the theory that the chemical basis of heredity might be DNA alone. This theory was based on Avery, MacLeod, and McCarty's discovery that DNA alone, without protein, appeared to be the carrier of hereditary factors in *Diplococcus pneumoniae* (see § 11.2), and Hershey and Chase's comparable discovery for virus *T*2 of *Escherichia coli* (see § 11.3). Applied to higher forms of life, this would mean that the protein part of the nucleoprotein of the chromosome played no direct part in heredity. This idea was diametrically opposed to that which had been generally held prior to 1944.

12. The theory of semi-conservative replication of DNA

§ 12.1 Introduction

Delbrück and Stent (1957) gave the name semi-conservative to the mechanism of replication of DNA postulated by Watson and Crick (1953*b*), since each new DNA molecule would consist of one old nucleotide chain and one new one, complementary to the old. Watson and Crick (1953*b*, 1954) had visualised the replication process as involving breakage of the hydrogen bonds between the two chains, followed by uncoiling, and synthesis of a new complementary chain alongside each old one. They assumed that the uncoiling and separation of the two chains would occur progressively from one end of the molecule like the opening of a zip-fastener, and that the new synthesis would follow at once, and hence also occur progressively along the molecule. This mechanism would imply that the synthesis would extend from the same physical end in both chains. Owing to the inverted polarity of the two chains, this would mean that in a chemical sense the synthesis was occurring in opposite directions in the two chains. Fig. 12.1 is a diagrammatic representation of this replication process.

§ 12.2 Evidence for semi-conservative replication of chromosomes

One of the first indications that the replication of DNA might be occurring in the way that Watson and Crick had suggested was obtained by Taylor, Woods and Hughes (1957) with root-tips of *Vicia faba* (Broad Bean) labelled with tritiated thymidine. Thymidine is the nucleoside of thymine and deoxyribose and is incorporated exclusively into DNA. Tritium (^{3}H) has the great advantage over other radioactive isotopes that the β-particles which it emits are of such low energy that they will penetrate only for a distance of about 1 μ in photographic emulsion. This means that the position of the labelled atoms can be determined with corresponding precision.

Vicia faba was chosen because it has large chromosomes and because Howard and Pelc (1951*a*) had established the time of replication of the DNA in the meristematic cells of the root-tip in relation to mitosis. At room temperature mitoses succeed one another at about 24-hour intervals, but the divisions are not synchronised so that at any given time there are nuclei at all stages of the mitotic cycle. The DNA replication extends over an 8-hour period ending about 8 hours before metaphase. Accordingly, if *Vicia faba*

181

FIGURE 12.1   Diagrammatic representation of the method of replication
of DNA proposed by Watson and Crick.

(*a*) Part of a DNA molecule. The arrows indicate the
polarity of the two nucleotide-chains. Their spiral
coiling is not shown. *A* = adenine, *C* = cytosine,
G = guanine, *T* = thymine.

(*b*) The molecule in process of replication. The arrow
shows the direction in which chain separation and
synthesis occur.

seedlings are grown in tritiated thymidine solution for 8 hours, then thoroughly washed with water, and some 8 hours later the root-tips are removed, fixed, stained by the Feulgen method, and squashed on microscope slides, then any cells at metaphase should have incorporated tritiated thymidine at the preceding DNA replication. Photographic film is then placed in contact with the squashed cells, and the preparation is kept in the dark for about two weeks before developing the film to find the position of the tritium.

The technique which Taylor, Woods and Hughes adopted differed slightly from this. During the interval between washing to remove the tritiated thymidine and fixing, the roots were placed in a non-radioactive mineral solution containing colchicine. There were two reasons for introducing colchicine. In the first place, colchicine causes the two chromatids of each chromosome to diverge, being held together only at the centromere. This facilitates observation of the presence or absence of the isotope in the individual chromatids. Secondly, colchicine inhibits the formation of the mitotic spindle, with the result that the chromosome number is doubled at each mitosis. Hence, the number of mitoses which have occurred since the roots entered the colchicine can be determined from the chromosome number. Taylor *et al.* kept some of the roots in the colchicine solution for 10 hours before fixing, and others for 34 hours.

Cells at metaphase after 10 hours in colchicine had the normal diploid chromosome number of 12, and the two chromatids of each chromosome were found to contain tritium, indicated by dark grains of silver above each chromatid where the photographic emulsion had been exposed. Each chromatid was uniformly labelled, and the two chromatids of a pair equally. Many of the cells at metaphase after 34 hours in colchicine contained 24 chromosomes, as was to be expected if a second mitotic cycle had intervened before the fixation. These 24-chromosome cells showed a remarkable feature: of the two chromatids making up each chromosome, one contained tritium and the other did not. A few of the metaphases after 34 hours in colchicine showed 48 chromosomes, indicating that two successive mitoses had occurred in the colchicine and implying that the 24-hour division cycle was by no means constant. In the 48-chromosome cells, half the chromosomes in each cell showed one labelled and one unlabelled chromatid, while the other half showed no label in either chromatid. The washing prior to placing the roots in the colchicine solution was evidently sufficient to remove the isotope solution, so that subsequent replications of the DNA took place in the absence of labelled thymidine.

These remarkable observations are shown diagrammatically in Fig. 12.2(*a*). It is evident that as far as its DNA is concerned, the chromosome is composed of two sub-units, one old and one new, which extend the whole length of the chromosome, and are such that the DNA of each sub-unit is conserved. This inference is shown in Fig. 12.2(*b*). The chromosome evidently replicates semi-conservatively, but it does not follow from this that the DNA molecule or molecules that form part of it necessarily also show this method of replication. The results are compatible with each of the following structures:

(*a*) The chromosome contains a single giant DNA molecule which replicates semi-conservatively in the way Watson and Crick proposed.

(*b*) The chromosome contains a number of DNA molecules each replicating semi-conservatively and held together in such a way that the new nucleotide chains form a unit which at the next replication separates from the unit formed by the old chains.

(*c*) The chromosome sub-units contain one or a number of DNA molecules replicating conservatively, that is, maintaining the whole molecular structure through the replication process, and the new molecule or

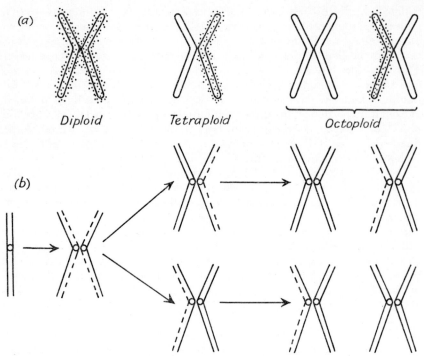

FIGURE 12.2   Diagram to show the observations and inferences made by Taylor
et al. (1957) from autoradiographs of the chromosomes of *Vicia
faba* in root-tips grown in tritiated thymidine for 8 hours.

  (*a*) Observations. The drawings represent chromosomes at meta-
       phase of mitosis. Following colchicine treatment, the two
       chromatids of each chromosome are held together only at the
       centromere. The dots represent silver grains in the photo-
       graphic emulsion and indicate the position of the tritium
       incorporated into DNA.

  (*b*) Inferences. The lines represent the two longitudinally-arranged
       sub-units inferred to exist within each chromatid. Broken lines
       indicate sub-units containing tritium, and unbroken lines sub-
       units without tritium. Circles represent centromeres. Of each
       group of 4 lines representing a colchicine-metaphase chromosome,
       the two outer lines represent old and the two inner new sub-units.

molecules form a unit which at the next replication separates from the
unit formed by the old molecule or molecules.

Although their results are thus open to a variety of interpretations, a further
observation led to more information about the nature of the chromosomal
sub-units, and made it appear highly probable that the DNA molecules were
replicating semi-conservatively. Taylor *et al.* noticed that in some of the
24-chromosome cells the tritium was in one chromatid for part of the
length of the chromosome, and in the other chromatid for the remainder
of the length. It appeared that an exchange of segments had occurred
between the two chromatids.

Taylor (1958) investigated these exchanges in more detail, using *Bellevalia romana* as his experimental material, since it has only 8 chromosomes in the diploid cells, and two of the 4 pairs of chromosomes are individually recognisable. Using essentially the same procedure as before but rather different timing (6–8 hours in the isotope, then 10 hours in a mineral solution free of isotope, and then 12–14 hours in colchicine solution before fixation), Taylor found that exchanges between chromatids were quite frequent, and moreover within one cell two homologous chromosomes often showed exchanges between their chromatids at corresponding positions. These twin exchanges, as he called them, evidently reflected a single exchange before the chromosomes had separated. Observation of the 4 individuals of chromosome no. 1 (the largest chromosome) in each of 18 tetraploid cells showed 15 single exchanges and 36 twin exchanges (72 apparent exchanges). For the other chromosomes the frequencies were comparable but lower, as expected if the exchange frequency were proportional to chromosome length. All the exchanges observed appeared to involve both sub-units of each chromatid.

Let the frequency of exchange for a particular chromosome be denoted by p for the replication in the presence of tritiated thymidine and by q for the subsequent replication in the absence of the label. Exchanges could presumably occur at any time during the interval between replication and the prophase of the mitosis which follows it. If the two sub-units composing each chromatid are alike, such that rejoining is at random, the expected frequency of single exchanges observed at the tetraploid stage is $\frac{1}{2}p + 2q$ and of twin exchanges is $\frac{1}{4}p$ (see Fig. 12.3). The observed frequencies conflict with this hypothesis, since with $\frac{1}{2}p + 2q = \frac{15}{36} = 0.42$ and $\frac{1}{4}p = \frac{36}{36} = 1$, q must be negative. On the other hand, if the two sub-units of each chromatid have a structural difference and reunion is restricted to within like sub-units, the expected frequencies of single and twin exchanges are $2q$ and p, respectively (see Fig. 12.4). The observed data give

$$p = \frac{36}{36} = 1 \qquad \text{and} \qquad q = \frac{7.5}{36} = 0.21.$$

The lower frequency (q) of exchanges at the mitosis in the absence of tritiated thymidine might be due to the lower tritium concentration or to the presence of colchicine, which is known to inhibit X-ray-induced chromosomal aberrations.

Taylor (1959a) found that $p = q$ if colchicine is present throughout the experiment, the roots being placed in colchicine from two hours before the beginning of the tritiated thymidine treatment. In 24 tetraploid cells following such treatment, chromosome 1 showed 26 single exchanges and 14 twins, giving

$$p = \frac{14}{48} = 0.29 \qquad \text{and} \qquad q = \frac{13}{48} = 0.27.$$

The conclusion reached from the relative frequency of single and twin exchanges was that the sub-units of the chromosome are structurally different, such that reunion can occur only between similar ones. This inference,

FIGURE 12.3 Diagrammatic representation of the origin of single and twin exchanges between sister-chromatids, as revealed by tritium labelling, if rejoining can occur freely between the broken ends of sub-units. The lines and circles have the same meaning as in Fig. 12.2(*b*). The numbers 1 and 2 show the fate of the segments of the two original sub-units.

FIGURE 12.4   Diagrammatic representation of the origin of single and twin exchanges between sister-chromatids, as revealed by tritium
labelling, if the two sub-units of each chromatid are structurally
different, and if rejoining between the broken ends of sub-units
can occur only between similar sub-units. The lines, circles and
numbers have the same meaning as in Fig. 12.3. The structural
difference between the sub-units is indicated by arrows.

taken in conjunction with the semi-conservative replication which the
chromosomes showed, was in such remarkable agreement with Watson and
Crick's proposals for the structure and mode of replication of the DNA
molecule, that it appeared highly probable that the DNA of the chromosome
was replicating in the way they suggested. The two nucleotide chains of the
DNA molecule (or molecules) in the chromosome would then correspond to
the two chromosomal sub-units. The inverted polarity of these chains
would preclude rejoining after an exchange except between chains of the
same polarity (see Fig. 12.4). It thus appears that the chromosome contains
one or a number of DNA molecules which replicate semi-conservatively
such that all the old nucleotide chains form one sub-unit and all the new

chains another. This conclusion needs to be accepted with reserve until a satisfactory explanation has been found for some contradictory evidence (cf. La Cour and Pelc, 1959; Peacock, 1963; Marimuthu and Threlkeld, 1964). Peacock's results disagree with those of La Cour and Pelc, but nevertheless are not in entire agreement with those of Taylor. On the other hand, Prescott and Bender (1963), using mammalian cells in tissue culture, have confirmed Taylor's discovery that mitotic chromosomes replicate semi-conservatively, and Taylor (1965) has shown that the replication prior to meiosis is also semi-conservative.

§ 12.3   Evidence for semi-conservative replication of DNA

More decisive evidence about the mechanism of replication of DNA molecules was obtained by Meselson and Stahl (1958) using DNA from *Escherichia coli*. Their technique was to cultivate the bacteria for 14 successive cell generations in a medium where the nitrogen was all the heavy isotope ^{15}N, and then abruptly to change to a normal ^{14}N medium. The growth of the bacterial population was exponential and was recorded by cell counts. Samples of about 4×10^9 bacteria were withdrawn from the culture just before the transfer to ^{14}N and at intervals for several cell generations afterwards. The generation time at the temperature of the culture, 36°C, was approximately 50 minutes. The cell contents of each sample were suspended in a concentrated solution of caesium chloride and centrifuged at 44,770 revolutions per minute for 20 hours. After this time the opposing processes of sedimentation and diffusion had set up a continuous increase of density in the caesium chloride away from the axis of rotation, and the DNA became concentrated at a point in this gradient which is dependent on its own density. The position of the DNA was recorded by ultraviolet absorption photographs. It had previously been established by centrifuging a mixture of DNA from ^{14}N and ^{15}N bacteria that two separate bands then appeared on the ultraviolet photographs due to the difference in molecular weight.

After one generation in the ^{14}N medium, all the DNA showed a band at a position halfway between the ^{14}N and ^{15}N positions, while after 2 generations, bands were present at this position, and at the ^{14}N position, and they were of equal intensity (see Fig. 12.5). The interpretation of these results is shown in the diagram. It is concluded that the DNA molecules consist of two sub-units containing equal amounts of nitrogen and which survive intact for many generations, and that each daughter molecule receives only one parental sub-unit. This is in precise agreement with the expectations from the Watson and Crick model for DNA replication, although the experiment does not establish that the sub-units are single nucleotide chains. However, Meselson and Stahl took the DNA of intermediate density obtained after one generation in ^{14}N medium, and heated it to 100°C for 30 minutes in the caesium chloride solution. Such heat treatment was thought to separate the nucleotide chains of DNA molecules. When the heated DNA was centrifuged, two bands were obtained instead of the previous one, and moreover they corresponded in position with the bands obtained when pure ^{14}N and pure

FIGURE 12.5   Meselson and Stahl's observations of the position of the
DNA of *Escherichia coli* in a caesium chloride density
gradient, after successive cell generations following
transfer from a ^{15}N to a ^{14}N culture medium. The
deductions concerning the mode of replication of DNA
are shown on the right. The rectangles represent the two
sub-units inferred to exist within each molecule, open
rectangles containing ^{14}N and shaded rectangles ^{15}N.

^{15}N DNA from *E. coli* were heated and then centrifuged. It was concluded that
the DNA of intermediate density consisted of molecules with one heavy
and one light polynucleotide chain, and that these were separated by the
heat treatment.

Sueoka (1960) applied the density gradient centrifugation technique to a
chromosomal organism: *Chlamydomonas reinhardi*. The generation time for
mitotically dividing cells at 25°C was about 3 hours. Samples of the culture
were removed immediately before transfer from ^{15}N to ^{14}N culture solution,
and at 2-hourly intervals for the next 10 hours, and the DNA from each
sample was centrifuged in concentrated caesium chloride solution. DNA
from *Bos* was used as a density reference. It did not interfere with the
observation of the *Chlamydomonas* DNA because of a difference in their
densities. The results obtained by Sueoka with *Chlamydomonas* were the same
as Meselson and Stahl had obtained with *Escherichia*, namely a single band
midway between the ^{14}N and ^{15}N positions after one generation, and two
bands of equal intensity, one at this position and one at the ^{14}N position,
after two generations. It was concluded that the DNA of *Chlamydomonas*
replicates semi-conservatively as in *Escherichia*.

Djordjevic and Szybalski (1960) obtained similar results using a culture
of human cells. Instead of cultivating them in a heavy nitrogen medium,

190 Mechanism of Heredity § 12.4

they transferred the cells to a medium containing the nucleoside of 5-bromouracil and deoxyribose (5-bromodeoxyuridine). This base analogue is incorporated into DNA in place of thymidine (see § 12.4), and has a higher molecular weight, thereby allowing separation by density gradient centrifugation of normal DNA from DNA containing 5-bromouracil. The first generation cells after transfer to the base analogue gave an intermediate band in the centrifuge tube, and the second generation gave intermediate and heavy bands of equal intensity. Clearly the DNA molecules in the human cells were replicating semi-conservatively as in *Chlamydomonas* and *Escherichia*.

The conclusion seems clear from these experiments that the DNA replicates in the way Watson and Crick proposed, although doubts are still expressed by some authors (cf. Cavalieri and Rosenberg, 1963).

§ 12.4   The *in vitro* synthesis of DNA in one chemical direction

Lehman, Bessman, Simms and Kornberg (1958) purified an enzyme obtained from *Escherichia coli* which would bring about the synthesis of DNA *in vitro*. The enzyme catalysed the incorporation of deoxyribonucleotides into DNA, using as substrate the four deoxynucleoside 5'-triphosphates, that is, of adenine, guanine, cytosine and thymine. Highly polymerised DNA was necessary as a primer and the presence of magnesium ions was also required. The triphosphates needed as substrate had been synthesised by enzymic phosphorylation by adenosine triphosphate (ATP) of the 5'-monophosphates. The existence in *E. coli* of a specific kinase for the phosphorylation of each of the four nucleotides had already been established.

Bessman, Lehman, Simms and Kornberg (1958) showed that in the polymerisation process the omission of any one of the four nucleoside triphosphates reduced the reaction rate to about $\frac{1}{200}$, and omission of the DNA primer abolished it entirely (although it was later shown that some synthesis could occur after a lag period of 3 to 6 hours). They achieved a synthesis *in vitro* of up to 20 times the initial quantity of DNA, and they showed that an amount of inorganic pyrophosphate ions was released equal to the amount of nucleotide incorporated. The synthetic reaction is shown diagrammatically in Fig. 12.6. The necessity for all four nucleoside triphosphates was remarkable and, with the need for DNA as a primer, suggested that synthesis was by a template mechanism such as Watson and Crick had proposed.

Confirmation of the template action of the primer was obtained by Lehman, Zimmerman, Adler, Bessman, Simms and Kornberg (1958) who showed that the base composition of the synthesised DNA was the same as that of the primer. They experimented with DNA from *Aerobacter aerogenes*, *Bos taurus*, *Escherichia coli* and its *T*2 virus, and *Mycobacterium phlei*. The adenine plus thymine contents of the DNA of these organisms, expressed as molar percentages of the total bases, cover a wide range, from 33% for *M. phlei* to 66% for *T*2, and in every instance the product of the polymerase reaction did not differ significantly in base composition from the primer.

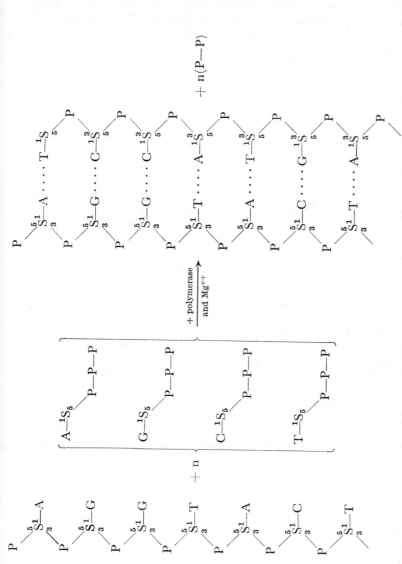

FIGURE 12.6   The synthesis of DNA from the four deoxynucleoside 5′-triphosphates, in the presence of the specific polymerase, magnesium ions, and DNA of high molecular weight as a primer. Inorganic pyrophosphate ions are released in proportion to the number of nucleotides incorporated.
A = adenine, C = cytosine, G = guanine, P = phosphate, S = sugar (deoxyribose), T = thymine.

Moreover the components of each complementary pair of bases on the Watson and Crick model occurred with equal frequency, as in the primer. Variation in the proportions of the four nucleoside triphosphates in the reaction mixture did not affect their proportions in the product, which appeared to be determined solely by their proportions in the primer.

Dunn and Smith (1954) and Zamenhof and Griboff (1954) had discovered that 5-bromouracil and 5-iodouracil, although not occurring naturally, were incorporated into the DNA of *E. coli* and of its *T*2 virus in place of thymine (5-methyluracil) such that the total molar quantity of the uracil derivatives (including thymine) was equal to the molar quantity of adenine. This was in keeping with the base-pairing predictions of the Watson and Crick model, since these uracil compounds differ from thymine only in the substituents at position 5 of the pyrimidine ring, which is a part of the molecule not involved in hydrogen bonding with adenine. In view of the incorporation of these compounds into the DNA of living cells, Bessman, Lehman, Adler, Zimmerman, Simms, and Kornberg (1958) tested the ability of the polymerase obtained from *E. coli* to accept these unnatural bases (in the form of the deoxynucleoside triphosphates) as substrates for DNA synthesis. They found that uracil and 5-bromouracil were incorporated specifically in place of thymine; 5-methyl- and 5-bromo-cytosine in place of cytosine; and hypoxanthine (6-hydroxypurine) but not xanthine (2,6-dihydroxypurine) in place of guanine (2-amino-6-hydroxypurine). These results were in agreement with the specific base pairing in the Watson and Crick model, since the replacements are all by analogues with similar hydrogen-bonding capacities, although the failure of xanthine to be incorporated is unexplained. The specific replacement by nucleotides with similar base-pairing properties, revealed in this experiment, demonstrated that specific hydrogen bonding must be involved in DNA synthesis.

The *in vitro* incorporation into DNA of a pyrimidine as abundant in living organisms as uracil raised the question of why it is absent from natural DNA. Bessman *et al.* suggested that this might be due to the lack of an enzyme for phosphorylating the uracil nucleotide, for there is no evidence for the existence of such an enzyme. The deoxynucleoside triphosphate of uracil used in the experiment was obtained by deamination of that of cytosine by means of nitrous acid.

There are indications that the priming function of the high molecular weight DNA depends on separation of the two nucleotide chains. Bollum (1959) found that a DNA polymerase obtained from *Bos* (calf thymus) would not function unless the DNA used as primer had first been heated in order to separate the chains. The DNA polymerase obtained from *E. coli* differs, however, from that derived from *Bos*, since Richardson, Schildkraut and Kornberg (1964) have shown that it can use the double-chain molecule as effectively as the single chains.

In order to study the very slight incorporation of nucleotides into DNA which was found to occur by the action of the *E. coli* polymerase when only one deoxynucleoside triphosphate was present instead of all 4, Adler, Lehman, Bessman, Simms and Kornberg (1958) devised an ingenious

FIGURE 12.7   Diagram to show the action of various enzymes in DNA synthesis
               and breakdown. The *Escherichia* polymerase adds 5′-nucleotides
               progressively to the 3′ end of the chain, and the *Crotalus* venom
               phosphodiesterase reverses this, detaching 5′-nucleotides pro-
               gressively from the 3′ end. The *Micrococcus* deoxyribonuclease and
               Bos spleen phosphodiesterase cause breakdown into 3′- nucleotides.

technique. The 5′-nucleotide of cytosine, labelled with ^{32}P, was phosphoryl-
ated to obtain the nucleoside triphosphate, and then this was incorporated
into DNA through the action of the polymerase. Sedimentation coefficients
in the ultracentrifuge showed that the incorporated radioactive nucleotides
had formed covalent linkages to molecules of the same average size as those
of the *Bos* DNA primer. The DNA molecules containing the ^{32}P were hydrolysed, first with deoxyribonuclease from *Micrococcus pyogenes*, and then with a
phosphodiesterase from *Bos* spleen. These enzymes break down the molecule
into 3′-nucleotides. It was found that all 4 of these 3′-nucleotides (that is, of
adenine, guanine, cytosine, and thymine) showed radioactivity, indicating
that the phosphate which had entered the DNA molecule attached by a 5′
linkage to the nucleoside of cytosine emerged attached by a 3′ linkage to
any of the 4 nucleosides. This showed that the action of the polymerase was
to attach 5′ nucleotides to the 3′ position at the nucleoside end (as distinct
from the phosphate end) of a nucleotide chain, and to do this irrespective
of the base in this terminal nucleotide (see Fig. 12.7). Similar results were
obtained when the experiment was repeated using adenine or thymine in
place of cytosine as the ^{32}P-labelled 5′-nucleotide.

     Confirmation that the polymerase adds nucleotides at the nucleoside end
of the chain was obtained by hydrolysis of the product with phosphodiesterase
from the venom of the snake *Crotalus adamanteus*. This enzyme hydrolyses
DNA nucleotide chains to 5′-nucleotides, and does so stepwise from the
nucleoside end of the chain. It was found that nearly all the radioactivity was
liberated when less than 3% of the nucleotides had been released, indicating
that the venom phosphodiesterase reversed the action of the polymerase
(see Fig. 12.7).

Richardson, Schildkraut and Kornberg (1964) have shown that under the action of the *E. coli* DNA polymerase the two chains of DNA act one as template and one as primer, nucleotides being added at the 3′-hydroxyl terminus of the primer chain complementary to those in the other or template chain. It was found that DNA synthesis is inhibited by a 3′-phosphate terminus.

§ 12.5 Demonstration of the inverse polarity of the two nucleotide chains

By an ingenious experiment using essentially the same techniques as were used to establish the mechanism of the *in vitro* synthesis of DNA by the *E. coli* polymerase (see § 12.4), Josse, Kaiser and Kornberg (1961) demonstrated that the two nucleotide chains of the DNA molecule are relatively inverted in just the way Watson and Crick (1953a) had supposed. The principle underlying the experiment was to assemble the molecule using 5′-nucleotides and then dismantle it again, but into 3′-nucleotides. Radioactive phosphorus (^{32}P) introduced as part of, say, adenine 5′-nucleotides, would be recovered distributed among all four 3′-nucleotides with frequencies that could be determined and would depend on the source of the primer. The experiments differed from those used to establish the mechanism of synthesis (§ 12.4) in that all four nucleoside triphosphates were provided, with the result that extensive DNA synthesis could occur. In any particular experiment only one of the four bases was associated with the label in the phosphorus of the nucleotide, but each, in turn, was so labelled.

It is conventional to indicate 3′-phosphates with the phosphate symbol (p) to the right of the nucleoside symbol and 5′-phosphates with the phosphate symbol to the left. Thus GpA stands for $G3p5A$, where G and A are the deoxynucleosides of guanine and adenine, respectively. One can imagine the experiment as the passing of the radio-phosphorus from the left hand of one nucleoside to the right hand of the adjacent nucleoside to the left. If the two chains of the molecule 'face the same way', passage of the radio-phosphorus will occur to the neighbour to the left in each chain. In other words, transfer from, for example, adenine to guanine will be expected to occur with the same frequency as transfer from thymine to cytosine ($GpA = CpT$). On the other hand, if the chains 'face opposite ways', passage to the left in each will mean passage in opposite directions physically. Hence, transfer from adenine to guanine would be expected to occur with the same frequency as transfer from cytosine to thymine ($GpA = TpC$). Thus, by determining the relative frequencies with which each base has each of the others to its left as its nearest neighbour, it should be possible to determine whether or not the two chains are relatively inverted. This is on the assumption that the nucleotide sequence is non-random.

Josse, Kaiser and Kornberg obtained such data using, in turn, as primer, DNA from 6 species of bacteria, 5 strains of bacterial viruses and *Bos* (calf thymus). Without exception, the results agreed with the hypothesis that the two chains were relatively inverted, and they contradicted any suggestion that the chains were of similar polarity. A selection of their data is given in Table 12.1, together with some of the data of the same kind obtained by

TABLE 12.1   Some of the data of Josse, Kaiser and Kornberg (1961) and Swartz, Trautner and Kornberg (1962) for the frequencies of different base sequences in the DNA of various organisms. For explanation, see text.

Base Sequence	Myco-bacterium phlei	Aerobacter aerogenes	Chlamydo-monas reinhardi	Homo sapiens	Haemo-philus influenzae	Para-centrotus lividus
A + T	32·6	44.3	46.2	59.5	61·8	64·2
G + C	67·4	55·7	53·8	40·5	38·2	35·8
⌐A3p5A	2·4 (2·7)	5·9 (4·9)	6·0 (5·3)	9·7 (8·9)	11·6 (9·5)	11·0 (10·3)
⌊T5p3T	2·6 (2·7)	6·1 (4·9)	5·9 (5·3)	9·7 (8·9)	11·6 (9·5)	10·2 (10·3)
⌐A3p5T / T5p3A	3·1 (2·7)	5·3 (4·9)	5·4 (5·3)	8·1 (8·9)	9·5 (9·5)	10·4 (10·3)
⌊T3p5A / A5p3T	1·2 (2·7)	3·6 (4·9)	5·3 (5·3)	6·7 (8·9)	7·3 (9·5)	9·0 (10·3)
⌐A3p5G	4·5 (5·5)	5·6 (6·2)	6·0 (6·2)	7·0 (6·0)	5·0 (5·9)	5·3 (5·7)
⌊T5p3C	4·5 (5·5)	5·7 (6·2)	5·7 (6·2)	7·1 (6·0)	4·9 (5·9)	5·9 (5·7)
⌐T3p5C	6·1 (5·5)	5·7 (6·2)	4·6 (6·2)	5·7 (6·0)	5·2 (5·9)	5·9 (5·7)
⌊A5p3G	6·5 (5·5)	5·8 (6·2)	4·4 (6·2)	6·1 (6·0)	5·4 (5·9)	5·7 (5·7)
⌐A3p5C	6·4 (5·5)	5·2 (6·2)	6·0 (6·2)	5·4 (6·0)	4·9 (5·9)	5·8 (5·7)
⌊T5p3G	6·0 (5·5)	5·2 (6·2)	5·5 (6·2)	4·9 (6·0)	4·8 (5·9)	5·3 (5·7)
⌐T3p5G	6·3 (5·5)	6·9 (6·2)	7·3 (6·2)	7·4 (6·0)	6·7 (5·9)	6·7 (5·7)
⌊A5p3C	6·3 (5·5)	6·7 (6·2)	7·7 (6·2)	7·4 (6·0)	6·7 (5·9)	6·7 (5·7)
⌐G3p5G / C5p3C	9·0 (11·4)	6·7 (7·8)	7·1 (7·2)	5·0 (4·1)	3·6 (3·7)	3·3 (3·2)
⌊C5p3C	9·0 (11·4)	6·5 (7·8)	7·4 (7·2)	4·7 (4·1)	3·7 (3·7)	3·8 (3·2)
⌐G3p5C / C5p3G	12·2 (11·4)	10·3 (7·8)	9·2 (7·2)	4·3 (4·1)	5·3 (3·7)	3·1 (3·2)
⌊C3p5G / G5p3C	13·9 (11·4)	8·8 (7·8)	6·3 (7·2)	1·0 (4·1)	3·8 (3·7)	2·0 (3·2)

Swartz, Trautner and Kornberg (1962) for a further range of organisms (2 species of plants, 10 species of animals and several more bacterial viruses). The 16 possible combinations of the 4 nucleosides are shown in the first column, and those expected to occur with equal frequency if the two chains are of opposite polarity are paired, and separated by horizontal lines. Those expected to occur with equal frequency if the chains were of the same polarity are joined by arrows. From the data the percentage frequencies of the two base-pairs have been obtained and are given at the top of the table for each species. From these values the expected frequencies of each of the 16 combinations have been calculated on the assumption that the nucleotide sequence is a random one. These frequencies, as percentages, are given in brackets after each observed percentage frequency.

In addition to the clear indication that the chains are of opposite polarity (equality within the pairs associated in the table, and frequent inequality between the pairs joined by arrows), the data show that each species has a unique pattern of base neighbours. Swartz, Trautner and Kornberg found evidence of fairly consistent differences between bacteria and chromosomal organisms in some of the sequence patterns, notably the low frequency of cytosine to the left of guanine (*CpG*) in chromosomal organisms (illustrated by *Chlamydomonas*, *Homo*, and *Paracentrotus* in the table) and the high frequency of guanine to the left of cytosine (*GpC*) in bacteria (illustrated by *Mycobacterium*, *Aerobacter*, and *Haemophilus* in the table). These peculiarities appear to be independent of the guanine-cytosine frequency, which varies widely in different species of both bacteria and chromosomal organisms.

Josse, Kaiser and Kornberg found that, for any particular species, the same sequence patterns were obtained when DNA obtained directly from the organism was used as primer and when the DNA prepared enzymatically was itself used as primer. This indicated that the base sequence was preserved in the replication process. Swartz, Trautner and Kornberg found that a number of different tissues of *Bos* gave the same sequence pattern, and similar results were obtained with *Mus*. It was evident that, like DNA content (§ 11.4), and overall base composition (§ 11.6), the base sequence was species-specific and tissue-independent.

Confirmation that the two nucleotide chains of DNA are of relatively inverted polarity (antiparallel) has been obtained by Chargaff *et al.* (1965) by hydrolysis of the DNA of *Bos taurus*, and isolation of purine dinucleotides and pyrimidine dinucleotides by chromatography. It was found that the sequence *A3p5G* was 1·3 times as frequent as the sequence *G3p5A*, and the inverted complements of these sequences had corresponding frequencies, *T5p3C* being 1·3 times as frequent as *C5p3T*.

§ 12.6   The *in vivo* synthesis of DNA in both chemical directions

The mechanism of DNA synthesis shown by the polymerase extracted from *Escherichia coli* by Kornberg and associates, and discussed in § 12.4 and § 12.5, involves the addition of 5′-nucleotides to the nucleoside end of a nucleotide chain. This mechanism alone would not explain how both chains of a DNA molecule could replicate from the same physical end, as Watson and Crick had postulated, since this would require the attachment of nucleotides at the phosphate end of one of the chains. However, several authors have found evidence that replication can occur in the same physical direction (and therefore in opposite chemical directions) alongside both nucleotide chains.

Cairns (1963) demonstrated this with *E. coli*. His technique was to grow the bacteria in the presence of tritiated thymidine for a known length of time and then find the position of the tritium by gentle extraction of the DNA followed by autoradiography. The film was exposed to the emissions from the tritium for about 2 months before being developed. It was already known that each bacterium in an exponentially growing culture synthesises DNA almost continuously. When bacteria were grown in the presence of tritiated thymidine for 3 minutes, it was found that two pieces of DNA each 60 to 80 μ long were labelled, and about twice this length was labelled with 6 minutes of treatment. At this rate of synthesis, up to about 800 μ of DNA could be covered in the cell generation time, which at 37° was about 30 minutes. If the DNA was extracted immediately after the labelling the two labelled pieces of DNA were close-together, but if the bacteria were allowed to continue to grow for 15 minutes in unlabelled thymidine, the two labelled pieces of DNA were found to be further apart. It was inferred that two labelled molecules were being formed simultaneously in the region of replication as would be expected on the Watson and Crick zipper model.

In a second series of experiments, Cairns grew the bacteria in the presence of the tritiated thymidine for a period of 1 hour. This would allow the occurrence of up to two complete replications of the DNA in the presence of the label. The autoradiographs so obtained revealed up to 900 μ of DNA labelled in an unbroken piece. This indicated that the whole of the bacterial DNA occurs in one piece, since assuming it contains two nucleotide chains and has the Watson and Crick structure, this length is in reasonable agreement with previous estimates of the DNA content of *E. coli* nuclei.

Furthermore, whenever a fork was visible, indicating that the DNA had been caught in the act of replicating, one limb of the fork always showed twice the density of grains in the emulsion compared with the other limb and with the remainder of the molecule (see Fig. 12. 8). This is what would be expected if the molecule replicates semi-conservatively, because the first replication in the presence of the tritium would label one nucleotide chain, and at the second replication in the presence of the tritium these labelled and unlabelled chains would separate and a new labelled chain would be laid down alongside each. Hence, at the end of the second replication one daughter molecule would be labelled in one of its chains and the other in both. Different molecules showed the second duplication at various stages of completion and it was evident that the replication was proceeding progressively from one end of the molecule to the other. Moreover, replication was evidently occurring simultaneously in the same physical direction in both nucleotide chains, or otherwise the double labelling of one limb would not always have extended right to the fork. Some further discoveries made by Cairns by autoradiography of the DNA of *E. coli* are discussed in the next section.

Evidence that replication of DNA *in vivo* can occur in the same physical direction alongside both nucleotide chains has also been obtained by Yoshikawa and Sueoka (1963) with *Bacillus subtilis*. The frequency of genetic transformation of 10 different characters was studied, using the DNA from an exponentially growing population, and also of a culture in the stationary phase. On the assumption that the cells from the stationary phase have a complete chromoneme*, and not one that has partially replicated, comparison of the relative transforming activity of the DNA from the exponential and stationary growth phases should provide information about the mechanism

---

* Chromoneme = bacterial chromosome—see § 11.1.

14

FIGURE 12.8   Appearance of an autoradiograph of the chromoneme of
Escherichia coli labelled with tritium for one hour (from
Cairns, 1963). It is inferred that *A* is the point of initiation
of replication, *B* the point to which replication had
reached at the time of fixation, and *CD* a gap due to
breakage during extraction.

of replication of the DNA. It was found that a genetic map could be constructed such that the relative transforming activity of a gene near one end was approximately double that of a gene near the other end, with a progressive decline in between. This is what would be expected in an unsynchronized cell population if there was oriented replication from one end of the chromoneme to the other, with both chains undergoing replication and with little interval between the end of one replication and the beginning of the next. Genes near the replication origin would then be represented almost twice as often in the DNA of the exponentially growing population as genes near the replication terminus.

Bonhoeffer and Gierer (1963) incorporated 5-bromouracil labelled with radioactive carbon (^{14}C) into the DNA of *Escherichia coli* for varying periods of time, and then studied the distribution of radioactivity in a caesium chloride density gradient. They found that as the average size of the labelled section of the molecule was increased, the radioactivity shifted towards a density of pure hybrid thymine-bromouracil molecules. From quantitative studies, it could be inferred that the chromoneme grew at only one point.

All these results, obtained by various methods, are in agreement with the hypothesis that the DNA in these bacteria is in one piece, and that it replicates progressively from one end to the other in the way Watson and Crick proposed. It is evident that although the *E. coli* polymerase isolated by Kornberg and associates will bring about synthesis *in vitro* in one chemical direction only, synthesis *in vivo* can occur in both, that is, by addition of 5′-nucleotides at the free 3′-hydroxyl end and at the free phosphate end of a polynucleotide chain. Presumably there are either two enzymes, or, alternatively, the same enzyme under conditions not achieved *in vitro* can also function in the inverse way.

§ 12.7   The mechanism of separation of the two nucleotide chains

From the evidence given in this chapter, there is reason to believe that DNA replicates semi-conservatively in the way Watson and Crick proposed. As pointed out in § 12.1, in order to allow the parental nucleotide chains to separate prior to such replication, it would be necessary to break the hydrogen bonds between the complementary bases and to uncoil the chains. The breaking of the comparatively weak bonds would be a simple matter compared with the formidable problem posed by the uncoiling.

Levinthal and Crane (1956) suggested a possible solution. If the molecule rotated about the helix axis the chains could readily separate progressively from one end of the molecule, provided the direction of rotation was anti-clockwise as seen looking down on the end where separation was occurring, and provided the chains as they separated continued to rotate each about its own helix axis. As suggested by Watson and Crick, the molecule was visualized as shaped like a letter Y during the separation process with the crotch of the Y moving progressively downwards. Levinthal and Crane, using data for virus *T*2 of *Escherichia coli* multiplying at 37°C, made estimates of the viscous drag and of the time taken for separation to occur (100 seconds), and came to the conclusion that the energy required for the rotation of the molecule in order to separate the chains was only about one thousandth of that required for the formation of the new phosphate-sugar bonds in the polymerisation of nucleotides to form the two new chains produced in the replication process. They assumed that the DNA of $T2$ consisted of molecules about 20 μ long (6,000 turns of the helix).

It is now known that the whole of the DNA of virus $T2$ occurs in a single molecule, which measures about 50 μ in length and contains about 150,000 nucleotide pairs, implying 15,000 turns of the double helix. This has been shown by measurement of the length of the thread when gently released from the head of the virus by extraction with phenol or after rupture by osmotic shock. Such measurement can be made either from autoradiographs (Cairns 1961) or from electron micrographs (Kleinschmidt *et al.* 1962; cf. Fig. 11.2). Since the molecule is known to replicate many times in the interval of about 30 minutes between infection of the host and release of the progeny virus, it is evident that an exceedingly efficient uncoiling mechanism must exist. Similar arguments apply to DNA replication in other organisms. Indeed, it now appears highly probable, from the evidence given in § 12.6, that the whole of the DNA of an *E. coli* nucleus is contained in a single molecule. With a length of approximately 1 mm, this molecule would contain 3×10^6 nucleotide pairs, implying 300,000 turns of the spiral. Replication in 30 minutes would require the molecule to spin at 10,000 revolutions per minute.

Kuhn (1957) considered that rotatory Brownian motion of the molecular axis was capable of achieving an essential uncoiling of a DNA molecule 3 μ long (900 turns of the helix) within one second and a complete separation of the chains of such a molecule within 50 to 80 seconds. Longuet-Higgins and Zimm (1960) have suggested that in addition there may be a decrease of free energy which would produce a small torque near the axis of the coil at the point of separation in the partly untwisted coil, and so drive the uncoiling.

Cairns (1963) from tritium autoradiographs of intact chromonemes of *Escherichia coli* (see § 12.6) made a quite unexpected discovery: each replicating molecule had the ends of the fork joined (see Fig. 12.8). Furthermore, from the autoradiographs the chromoneme appeared to be circular. No intact circles were seen, but no other configuration could generate all the structures observed merely by breakage during the process of extraction. Cairns (1964), using a slightly modified technique involving extraction of the tritium-labelled DNA with lysozyme, obtained autoradiographs showing the *E. coli* DNA as an intact circle of circumference approximately 1.1 mm. Usually the DNA was in process of duplication, having the form of two contiguous loops, as in Fig. 12.8. Similarly, the extraction and purification of the DNA of the *E. coli* viruses phi-ex(ϕX)174 (Hayashi, Hayashi and Spiegelman, 1964) and $T2$ (Thomas and MacHattie, 1964), followed by examination under the electron microscope, has revealed intact circles. These had a mean circumference of 1.86 μ for the replicating form of ϕX (cf. § 14.6 and § 14.7) and of 55 μ for $T2$.

FIGURE 12.9   (*a*) Chromoneme of *Escherichia coli* with its single replicon.
              (*b*) Part of a chromosome showing four replicons at various stages
                     of replication.
                     Dots indicate replicon junctions, where chains can rotate inde-
                     pendently of one another. Curved arrows show the direction of
                     rotation and straight arrows the direction in which chain separation
                     and synthesis are occurring.

A circular chromoneme, both for *E. coli* and for a number of bacterial
viruses, is supported by genetic data which indicate circular linkage maps
(see Chapters 15 and 16). On the assumption that rotation occurs in
separation of the chains, a circular thread with the fork ends joined implies a
device at the junction to allow independent rotation of the chains (see
Fig. 12.9(*a*)). However, there is as yet no direct evidence from any organism
that the chains of the DNA molecule do in fact separate by rotation in the
way Levinthal and Crane have postulated.

As already indicated, the 55 μ long chromoneme of virus *T*2 and the
1100 μ long chromoneme of its host, *E. coli*, each constitute one replicating unit. Jacob and Brenner (1963) proposed the term *replicon* for
such a unit of replication. It is established on good evidence that a fragment
of a chromoneme transferred to another cell (see § 15.3), is unable to replicate
but may recombine with the intact chromoneme of the acceptor cell.
Jacob and Brenner suggested that the capacity of chromonemes to replicate
only as a whole and not when fragmented implies the presence and activity
of specific determinants controlling replication (see § 16.1).

Chromosomes contain so much more DNA than the chromonemes of
bacteria and viruses that it is not surprising that the replication mechanism
appears to be differently organised. If the whole of the DNA in a chromosome
consisted of one molecule it would have a length of many centimeters. It
appears that a chromosome does not replicate progressively from one end
to the other. This has been particularly clearly shown by Schmid (1963)
with human cells in tissue culture. Each of the chromosomes has its own
specific pattern of early and late replicating regions, as revealed by tritium
labelling. This suggests that a chromosome may be made up of a series of
replicons. Since inversions of chromosome segments occur regularly in
evolution (cf. § 8.15), it appears likely that the replicating units will
not all be oriented the same way. A hypothetical linear sequence of replicons

is shown in Fig. 12.9(*b*) to illustrate the kind of organization which would fit the data. As with the bacterial chromoneme, if rotation of DNA about the helix axis occurs in replication, the replicon junctions will have to allow free rotation of chains. In order to reconcile the existence of a number of replicons in a chromosome with the observations of Taylor and associates that old and new sub-units separate from one another throughout the length of the chromosome (see § 12.2), it is necessary to assume that, when replication has been completed in two adjacent replicons, old chain is linked to old chain and new to new across the replicon junction. The simplest way in which this linking could be maintained would be if the old chains were of one polarity and the new of the other.

These speculations about the organization of chromosomes illustrate how much has still to be discovered about chromosome structure from the point of view of replication. In later chapters, chromosome organization from other points of view will be discussed.

13. The theory of the genetic code

§ 13.1 Introduction

Zamenhof, Brawerman, and Chargaff (1952) had found large differences in the base composition of the DNA of different species of bacteria, and this led them to suggest that there were specific differences in the sequences of nucleotides along the polynucleotide chains of DNA molecules. This idea received strong support from Watson and Crick (1953b), who regarded the precise sequence of the bases as the code which carried the genetical information. Their proposed replication mechanism for DNA was admirably adapted to maintain the same order of the bases in the daughter-molecules.

Dounce (1952) and, apparently independently, Gamow (1954) had the brilliant idea that the linear sequence of nucleotides in nucleic acids was responsible for determining the linear sequence of aminoacids in the polypeptide chains of protein molecules. That the linear construction of the genetic material might reflect the linear structure of specific polypeptides was a highly original idea of attractive simplicity. Moreover, it accommodated so well the one gene:one enzyme hypothesis, since all known enzymes are proteins. Gamow drew an analogy between polynucleotides as a long number written in a four-digital system (the four bases) and polypeptides as long words based on a 20-letter alphabet (the 20 different kinds of aminoacids), and he raised the question of how the four-digital numbers could be translated into such words.

Dounce and Gamow's idea has been variously called the sequence hypothesis, the co-linearity hypothesis, and the theory of the genetic code.

§ 13.2 The linear construction of the gene

One of the first questions raised by the co-linearity hypothesis is how the gene is constructed. It had been known ever since Sturtevant (1913) discovered that crossover frequencies fitted a linear map, that the genes appeared to be arranged in a line along the chromosome (§ 7.3). Did this linear construction extend to the intragenic organization?

Several instances of recombination between alleles had been discovered in *Drosophila melanogaster* (see § 9.11). These suggested that the classical bead hypothesis of the gene might not be valid. However, little significant information about the detailed structure of the gene was obtained until the advent of selective techniques for the recovery of recombinants. Such techniques were made possible by Beadle and Tatum's discovery of fungal mutants with specific nutritional requirements (§ 10.2). If two mutants are very closely linked and have the same biochemical requirement for growth, recombinants could be detected even if of very low frequency by crossing the mutants and germinating the progeny spores on minimal medium, since neither parental type of spore would be able to grow.

Roper (1950) applied this technique to 3 biotin-requiring mutants (bi_1, bi_2, bi_3) of *Aspergillus nidulans* which had been independently obtained by X-ray treatment, and found that crosses of one with another gave recombinants not requiring biotin (prototrophs) with frequencies of about 1 per 2,000 (bi_1 and bi_2) and 1 per 5,000 progeny (bi_1 and bi_3). It was deduced that the biotin-independent progeny were arising by recombination and not by back-mutation because of their genotype for linked character-differences. Furthermore, no prototrophs were obtained from crosses between strains with the same biotin alleles. The three mutants all appeared to be concerned with the same biochemical step, since they each required biotin or desthiobiotin for growth and did not respond to pimelic acid. Moreover, Roper (1953) found that heterokaryons obtained from pairs of them were still biotin-requiring. In other words, each mutant was unable to supply the other's deficiency. Similarly, rare diploid strains of *Aspergillus* which Roper obtained by a selective technique from the heterokaryons, were also biotin-requiring. These had one biotin mutation in one chromosome and the other in the homologous chromosome. By the definition of multiple alleles given in § 9.1, these mutants would qualify as allelic, since they are functionally similar, do not complement one another, and are due to mutations in essentially the same region of the linkage map. However, as with the *Drosophila* examples discussed in § 9.11, the discovery of recombination between such mutants raises the question of what is meant by the terms gene and allele. Pontecorvo (1952*b*) tentatively concluded that the biotin-requiring strains were due to mutations at different sites distinguishable by recombination but within a single gene. On this supposition the gene as a unit in physiological action is a larger chromosome segment than either the unit of mutation or of recombination.

Pritchard (1955) investigated 7 closely-linked and apparently allelic adenine-requiring mutants of *Aspergillus nidulans* which had been obtained independently of one another. Twelve of the 21 possible combinations of the 7 alleles in pairs were tested for recombination by crossing the mutants and plating the progeny ascospores on medium free of adenine. In every instance adenine-independent progeny were obtained. Their frequencies depended on the alleles crossed and ranged from 1 in 1250 to 1 in over 150,000 progeny. Marker genes (*y*, yellow conidia, and *bi*, biotin-requiring), linked to the adenine locus on either side, enabled the behaviour of the neighbouring parts of the chromosome to be followed and confirmed that the prototrophs were arising by recombination and not mutation. Moreover, tests established that the mutants were stable and showed mutation back to adenine independence only with very low frequency. A majority of the adenine prototrophs had a particular crossover genotype for the marker genes, such as would be expected if crossing over had occurred between the alleles. For example, by crossing a strain having adenine-8 and yellow conidia with a strain having adenine-11 and biotin requirement, heterozygous asci of constitution $\dfrac{y \; 8 \; +}{+ \; 11 \; bi}$ were obtained, where 8 and 11 represent the adenine alleles and plus (+) stands for the appropriate normal allele (green conidia, biotin independence) of the marker genes. A majority of the adenine-independent ascospores from this cross had the genotype *y bi* for the markers. It was deduced that the *ad* 8 and *ad* 11 sites of mutation were placed such that the genotype of the diploid nuclei in the young asci could be rewritten $\dfrac{y \; + \; 8 \; +}{+ \; 11 \; + \; bi}$. Conversely, the most frequent class of adenine independent strains derived from asci of genotype $\dfrac{y \; 8 \; +}{+ \; 10 \; bi}$ had the + + genotype for the markers (green conidia, biotin independent), from which it was inferred that the formula for the diploid ascus nuclei was $\dfrac{y \; 8 \; + \; +}{+ \; + \; 10 \; bi}$, with allele no. 10 to the right of allele no. 8. In this way a map giving the sequence of the 7 alleles was constructed. A map was also prepared from the recombination frequencies, both between the alleles and with the markers. The various mapping data were reasonably consistent with one another, and pointed to a linear construction for the adenine gene. Moreover, it was evident that the allele map was collinear with the gene map; for instance, the analysis above indicates a single linear structure with the sequence *y* 11 8 10 *bi*.

§ 13.3   The cis-trans position effect

Roper and Pritchard (1955) had obtained a diploid strain of *Aspergillus nidulans* heterozygous for two adenine alleles (nos. 8 and 16). It had been obtained from a heterokaryon of the two mutants and hence had one allele in one chromosome and the other in the homologous chromosome. Its genotype was $\dfrac{y \; + \; 8 \; +}{+ \; 16 \; + \; bi}$, using the same notation as previously. This diploid, as expected with allelic mutants, was adenine-requiring. However, by attempting to grow conidia from it on a medium lacking adenine it was possible to select for adenine-independence among them. About 1 conidium in 10^7 was found to show such independence, and from the behaviour of the linked character-differences (*y*, *bi*) it was evident that a process of mitotic crossing-over had taken place. Somatic crossing-over had been discovered by Stern (1936) as a rare occurrence in *Drosophila melanogaster*, and was found not to be associated with any reduction in chromosome number. From crosses involving the adenine-independent diploids, Roper and Prichard found that some of them had the genotype $\dfrac{y \; + \; + \; bi}{+ \; 16 \; 8 \; +}$, such as would be expected if reciprocal recombination had occurred between the alleles. This genotype was identified by the recovery of both *ad* 8 and *ad* 16 from the progeny. These alleles could be distinguished because *ad* 16 allowed slow growth on minimal medium while *ad* 8 failed to grow.

From this experiment it was evident that the $\dfrac{+\ +}{16\ \ 8}$ genotype (with the two normal alleles in one chromosome and the two mutations in the homologous chromosome) does not require adenine for growth, while the $\dfrac{+\ \ 8}{16\ +}$ genotype (with one mutation in each chromosome) does. This was an example of position effect, but it differed from Sturtevant's classical example of Bar eye in *Drosophila melanogaster* in that it did not involve a duplication of a segment of the chromosome (see § 9.10).

Haldane (1941), using a chemical analogy, introduced the terms *cis* and *trans* for the two geometrically isomeric types of double heterozygote previously described by Bateson's terms coupling and repulsion, respectively. Pontecorvo (1950) applied these terms to closely-linked mutations, where differences in the appearance of individuals with the cis and the trans configurations might be expected. Such differences had been discovered by Lewis (1945) with the *star* eye characters in *Drosophila melanogaster* described in § 9.11. He had found that flies with the double mutant in one chromosome and the normal alleles in the other $\left(\dfrac{S\ \ s}{+\ +}\right)$ had eyes similar to dominant Star $\left(\dfrac{S}{+}\right)$ and appreciably larger than those of the repulsion heterozygote $\left(\dfrac{S\ +}{+\ \ s}\right)$ with its very small and rough eyes. A classic example of the same phenomenon was due to the work of Green and Green (1949) with 3 recessive *lozenge* alleles of *D. melanogaster*. They had followed up Oliver's discovery of recombination between alleles at this locus (see § 9.11). Denoting the 3 alleles by 1, 2, and 3, Green and Green showed that flies of genotype $\dfrac{+\ +}{1\ \ 2}$, $\dfrac{+\ +}{1\ \ 3}$, or $\dfrac{+\ +}{2\ \ 3}$ had normal eyes whereas flies of genotype $\dfrac{+\ \ 2}{1\ +}$, $\dfrac{+\ \ 3}{1\ +}$, or $\dfrac{+\ \ 3}{2\ +}$ had the lozenge characters of glossy eyes with less pigmentation than normal. Several other examples of this cis-trans position effect were discovered in *Drosophila* shortly afterwards, and they included the classic example of multiple alleles, namely, the white eye locus (w). MacKendrick and Pontecorvo (1952) and Lewis (1952) found small numbers of recombinants with wild-type (red) eyes from crosses between certain pairs of alleles at this locus. All the red-eyed flies showed recombination for marker genes on either side of w. It thus began to appear as if recombination between alleles, together with the cis-trans position effect, might be normal features of the gene.

§ 13.4   The cistron

Genetic recombination in viruses was discovered by Delbrück and Bailey (1947) and by Hershey (1947) with the *T*-even phages of *Escherichia coli*. Hershey and Rotman (1948) studied recombination with a particular class of mutants which had arisen spontaneously in virus *T*2. In these mutants the clear areas (plaques) produced by the destruction of the bacteria were larger and with a sharper margin than those caused by normal (wild-type) virus. They were called *r* mutants because breakdown (lysis) of the host cells was more *rapid* than normal. Hershey and Rotman found that when a mixture of two *r* mutants of independent origin was added to a liquid culture of the bacterial host (strain *B*), such that there were about 5 times as many virus particles of each kind as there were bacterial cells, many of the bacteria were simultaneously infected with both strains of virus. When fresh bacteria were infected with the progeny virus particles released by the breakdown of the cell-walls of the doubly-infected bacteria, besides many mutant plaques, a certain number of small rough-edged (wild-type) plaques were produced. These had evidently arisen by re-combination, because each *r* mutant alone gave none. Moreover, their frequency of occurrence was characteristic for each pair of mutants. From the recombination frequencies, the mutants could be grouped into two classes, which were subsequently called I and II. There was much closer linkage within each class than between them. It was remarkable that every mutant tested by 'crossing' (mixed infection) with another gave rise to recombinants. Eleven *r* mutants were studied in this way, and 47 out of the 55 possible crosses were made. Moreover, there was some indication that the recombination frequencies might fit a linear map.

It was subsequently found that the *r*I and *r*II classes of mutants (and also a third group) could be distinguished by their behaviour on other strains of *E. coli*. In particular, the *r*II mutants, unlike *r*I and *r*III, were found not to grow on a strain called *K* of *E. coli*. This inability was taken advantage of by Benzer (1955), since it allowed selection for wild-type recombinants between any two of the mutants, in much the same way as Roper (1950) had selected for recombinants between biotin-requiring mutants of *Aspergillus nidulans*. Benzer used virus *T*4 and crossed 8 *r*II mutants of independent origin in 23 of the 28 possible pairs. Crossing was done by infecting strain *B* of *E. coli* with an equal mixture of the two virus mutants, such that in total there were 6 times as many virus particles as bacterial cells. The progeny virus particles were tested for their ability to multiply on strain *K* of the host. Although neither parent can propagate on *K*, a small proportion of the progeny from every cross produced plaques. The frequency of these was, nevertheless, much higher than could be attributed to back-mutation, and it was concluded that the plaques on *K* were arising through recombination. This was confirmed by the finding that the recombination frequencies from the various crosses gave a reasonable fit with a linear map. The sites of the 8 mutations were found to be in the sequence

47   104   101   103   105   106   51   102

where the figures are the identification numbers of the mutants. These results are what might have been expected from Hershey and Rotman's earlier findings with *T*2 virus using the original non-selective technique.

Benzer tested whether the *T*4 mutants which he had mapped were allelic, by making mixed infections of them in pairs on strain K of the host. Although none of the mutants alone would propagate on K, he found that certain combinations of them could supply each other's deficiency and so multiply and produce plaques. When strain K is infected with an rII mutant, the virus is adsorbed to the host and the bacterial cells are killed, but no progeny virus is produced. With a mixed infection by two rII mutants, a situation comparable to the *Aspergillus* heterokaryons studied by Pontecorvo and associates evidently prevails, with two dissimilar hereditary contributions within one cell. When Benzer classified the behaviour of the rII mutants by this test for allelism, he made a remarkable discovery. All combinations in pairs of the 6 mutants to the left on the map, that is, nos. 47, 104, 101, 103, 105, and 106 failed to produce plaques, and were evidently alleles (see Fig. 13.1(f)). He called this part of the map segment A. Similarly, the other two mutants, nos. 51 and 102, also failed to complement one another (Fig. 13.1(g)): they formed segment B. But any mutant in segment A when paired with either of the B mutants produced plaques on strain K of the host (Fig. 13.1(h)). There thus appeared to be two segments within the rII region corresponding to independent functional units.

If K bacteria were infected with a mixture of wild-type virus and an rII mutant (Fig. 13.1(a) and (b)), the virus was found to multiply and both types appeared in the progeny. It was evident that the rII mutants were recessive to the normal condition, and that the wild-type virus could supply whatever was needed to allow the rII mutants to multiply. It was presumed that the *cis* configuration of a double mutant and wild type (Fig. 13.1(c)–(e)) would similarly allow multiplication to occur, irrespective of the position on the map of the mutant.

The situation which Benzer had found in virus $T4$ was evidently similar to that known for several genes in *Drosophila* and *Aspergillus*, with recombination between alleles and a cis-trans position effect. The rII mutants were particularly interesting, firstly, because of the proximity of two functional units, mutation of either giving the same phenotype, and secondly, because of the neat way in which the recombination and complementation data established this. Benzer suggested that the A and B segments might affect sequential steps in a chain of synthesis. Alternatively, the two segments might each control the production of a specific polypeptide chain, the two chains later being combined to form an enzyme. With either of these explanations, the end-product of the action of the two segments would be a single substance, the lack of which was presumed to cause the rII phenotype.

Benzer (1955, 1957) found that certain rII mutants gave no detectable wild-type recombinants with any of several other mutants, which nevertheless gave wild-type recombinants with each other. Such mutants can be represented as occupying a segment of the linkage map rather than a point. It was significant that back-mutation of such a mutant had never been observed, whereas some of the point mutations showed reversion to wild-type not infrequently. The most likely explanation for both the recombination behaviour and the stability of these mutants appeared to be that they had originated through the loss of a segment of the hereditary material covering

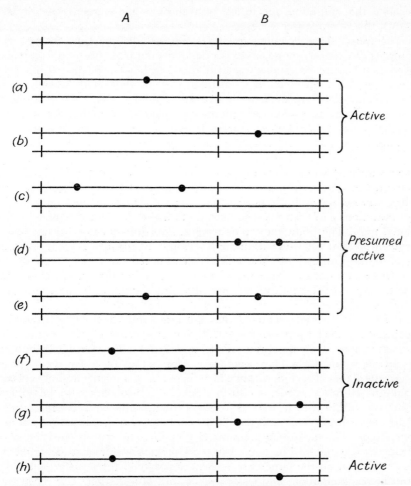

FIGURE 13.1   Diagram to show Benzer's results from mixed infection of
Escherichia coli strain *K* by two strains of virus *T*4. The
dots show the position of the *r*II mutations on the linkage
map. 'Active' means that extensive virus multiplication
took place.

(*a*), (*b*) Single virus mutants mixed with wild-type virus.

(*c*)–(*e*) Double mutants mixed with wild-type (that is,
cis configuration).

(*f*)–(*h*) Mixed infection by two single mutants (that is,
trans configuration).

A and *B* are the two cistrons inferred to be present.

the length which they appeared to occupy on the linkage map. It will be recalled that mutation due to loss of a chromosome segment was already known in *Drosophila* (see § 9.7).

The use of these deletions greatly facilitated the mapping of new *r*II mutants. Moreover, by means of a series of overlapping deletions, a method of mapping point mutations was available independent of the mapping by recombination frequencies. Both methods were in agreement. Mapping was also facilitated by study of the behaviour of mixed infections on strain *K* of the host, because even if two mutants belonged to the same segment, a few plaques were in fact often produced. It appeared that a limited amount of multiplication in *K* bacteria was possible even with some *trans* configurations of alleles, and this allowed wild-type recombinants to form. In consequence, the number of plaques obtained was a measure of the distance apart of the mutant sites. A very rapid technique for mapping sites was therefore available, and Benzer (1961) reported that over 2400 spontaneous and induced *r*II mutations had been mapped, and that all the data fitted a one-dimensional map. The point mutations were at 200 different sites within the *A* segment, and at 108 sites within the *B* segment. By fitting a Poisson distribution to the numbers of sites which had mutated once and the numbers which had mutated twice, he estimated that, taking the whole *r*II region, there were at least another 120 sites at which mutation had not yet been observed.

Benzer (1957) had suggested that the functional unit of the hereditary material, defined by a comparison of the phenotype of the *cis* and *trans* configurations of a pair of mutations, be called a *cistron*. On his definition, a cistron would be a map segment corresponding to either the *A* or *B* segments of the *r*II region, within which there is no complementation between mutants. In other words, a cistron would be a segment of the hereditary material within which the cis configuration produced a normal (non-defective) phenotype, and the trans configuration produced a mutant phenotype. This definition amounts to equating the cistron with the gene defined as a unit of function. Alleles as previously understood would be mutations within the same cistron. Benzer proposed the terms *recon* for the unit of recombination, and *muton* for the unit of mutation. The recon was defined as the smallest element in the one-dimensional array that is interchangeable (but not divisible) by genetic recombination, and the muton as the smallest element that, when altered, can give rise to a mutant form of the organism. The introduction of these terms was a recognition that the bead hypothesis was inadequate, and that the term gene, hitherto used more or less indiscriminately for the unit of function, of recombination, and of mutation, was insufficiently precise.

Benzer drew attention the the remarkable parallelism between genetic maps, which appear to be one-dimensional at all levels of analysis, and the one-dimensional character of DNA. On the basis of (*a*) the total length of the linkage map for all the mutant characters in virus *T*4 that had been recognised and mapped, and (*b*) the total content of DNA, which was assumed to have the Watson and Crick structure, Benzer estimated that the *r*II cistrons probably contained several hundred or perhaps a few thousand nucleotide pairs, whereas the recon and the muton comprised a very small number of nucleotide pairs, and possibly only one.

Benzer's results with virus *T*4 implied that the functional units (cistrons) in the hereditary material could be defined unambiguously by the normal test for the allelism of closely-linked recessive mutants such as had been in use for many years. This test was to observe whether the trans (repulsion) heterozygote or heterokaryon had the mutant phenotype indicating alleles, or the wild-type phenotype indicating that the mutations were in different functional units (see § 9.1). However, experimental results with fungi suggested that the functional units of the hereditary material could not always be defined so easily.

Fincham and Pateman (1957) found that two apparently allelic mutants of *Neurospora crassa* of independent origin, both of which formed no detectable quantity of the enzyme glutamate dehydrogenase, would nevertheless produce the enzyme, although with lower than normal specific activity, when they were grown together as a heterokaryon. This remarkable discovery concerned amination-deficient (*am*) mutants which were unable to synthesize from ammonia the alpha(α)-amino groups (see § 13.5) of a wide range of aminoacids, this being the reaction which is catalysed by glutamate dehydrogenase. The mutants were regarded as allelic because of the extremely low frequency (about 1 per 10^5) with which wild-type progeny were obtained when they were crossed.

Similarly, Giles, Partridge, and Nelson (1957) found that certain pairs out of 21 apparently allelic adenine-requiring mutants (*ad*-4 locus) of *N. crassa*, of independent origin, formed heterokaryons which were able to grow in the absence of adenine and which synthesized adenylosuccinase. This enzyme was not formed in detectable quantities by the individual mutants.

The outcome of these unexpected discoveries of complementation between mutants affecting the same enzyme, and the modifications to Benzer's concept of the cistron which they necessitated, are discussed in § 13.6.

§ 13.5   The effect of mutation on protein structure

From the evidence in the preceding sections of this chapter, and from similar results obtained subsequently for other genes, it appears that the first question raised by the genetic code idea, namely, how the gene is constructed, has been answered. As a unit of function it appears to be a linear structure, and to contain numerous smaller units capable of mutation and of recombination with one another. This is the construction that might be expected if the genetic material is DNA, with nucleotide sequence of paramount importance, and such that alteration of one or more nucleotides at any point incapacitates the whole gene. A second question raised by the Dounce-Gamow hypothesis of aminoacid sequence in polypeptides determined by nucleotide sequence is whether gene mutation can be shown to alter aminoacid sequence.

Neel (1949) established that the human disease called sickle cell anaemia is inherited as a Mendelian recessive. This disease is widespread in West Africa and in American negroes (see § 2.6), and is characterized by a severe anaemia which is usually fatal in childhood. In individuals with the disease, the erythrocytes change their form when the oxygen concentration is low, taking on the shape of a sickle instead of the normal biconcave disc. Neel found that the parents of such individuals were quite healthy, but always had a rather similar condition of the blood called sicklaemia or sickle cell trait. In sicklaemia the crescentic shape of the erythrocytes occurs only at lower oxygen concentrations such as are not encountered in the circulating blood, and there are no anaemic symptoms. From the regular occurrence of sicklaemia in the parents of individuals with sickle cell anaemia, it was inferred that sicklaemia was the heterozygous and sickle cell anaemia the homozygous condition for the sickling gene (cf. Fig. 13.4(*a*)).

Pauling, Itano, Singer, and Wells (1949) found that the difference between sickling and normal erythrocytes was in their haemoglobins, which showed different electrophoretic mobilities. Moreover, sicklaemia haemoglobin was found to consist of about equal proportions of normal haemoglobin and sickle cell anaemia haemoglobin, as expected of the heterozygote. Ingram (1956) showed that there was a specific chemical difference between the two globins (the protein part of haemoglobin). He had devised a rapid technique for characterising the chemical properties of a protein in considerable detail. Trypsin was used to split the peptide chains of haemoglobin and then the small peptides formed, which numbered about 30, were separated by a two-dimensional combination of paper electrophoresis and paper chromatography. Most of the peptides differ in net charge, and hence migrate at different speeds in an electric field on wet filter paper. The paper is then turned through 90° and a further separation brought about by their differing rates of migration in particular solvents. Finally, the position of the spots corresponding to the different peptides is revealed by staining with ninhydrin. Ingram called the resulting chromatogram the fingerprint of the protein.

Proteins are made up of one or more polypeptide chains. In haemoglobin there are 4, comprising 2 of one kind (alpha (α)-chains) and 2 of another (beta (β)-chains). Polypeptide chains consist of aminoacids linked together in a linear sequence by peptide bonds. In each of the 4 chains of the haemoglobin molecule there are about 150 aminoacids. All aminoacids have a carboxyl group (—COOH), an amino group (—NH$_2$), a hydrogen atom (—H), and a particular radical (—R), attached to one carbon atom called the alpha (α)-carbon (Fig. 13.2(i)). With 4 different groupings joined to the α-carbon, there are 2 stereo-isomers of each acid (except glycine, where R = —H). Only the L-isomers (Fig. 13.2(i)) ordinarily occur in proteins. The radicals (R) are very diverse in structure and are listed in Fig. 13.2(iii) for the 20 aminoacids normally found in proteins. One of them, proline, is strictly-speaking an iminoacid: the R group is joined at its far end to the α-carbon amino group. In the formation of the peptide bond, aminoacids link together by the attachment of the α-carbon carboxyl group of one to the α-carbon amino group of the next, with the elimination of a water molecule (see Fig. 13.2(ii)). A polypeptide chain will, therefore, have a free amino group at one end and a free carboxyl group at the other.

FIGURE 13.2 Structure of aminoacids and polypeptide chains.
     (i) An aminoacid.
    (ii) Part of a polypeptide chain. The peptide linkages are numbered from the amino group end of the chain.
   (iii) The formulae of the 20 aminoacids normally found in proteins. In (i) and (ii), bold type and italics indicate projection in front of and behind the plane of the page, respectively.

The primary structure of a protein is determined by the sequence of aminoacids in its polypeptide chain or chains. X-ray crystallography has shown that in proteins the polypeptide chain (or chains) is coiled in such a way that hydrogen bonding can occur between each peptide linkage (—CO·NH—) and the next-but-two in the chain. More specifically, there is hydrogen bonding between the oxygen atom of peptide linkage no. 1 and the hydrogen atom of peptide linkage no. 4, and similarly between O of 2 and H of 5, O of 3 and H of 6, and so on. The numbering of the bonds is from the free amino group end of the chain. This alpha (α)-helix, as the coiled polypeptide is called, forms the secondary structure of a protein. Many proteins, including all those that are active in promoting chemical reactions, have the α-helix folded in an irregular way to give a characteristic shape to the molecule, which is called its tertiary structure. The association of a number of polypeptide chains in one protein molecule, as in haemoglobin, gives rise to a quaternary structure.

Ingram (1956) found that the fingerprint of haemoglobin *A* (the normal molecule) differed from that of haemoglobin *S* (from patients with sickle-cell anaemia) in respect of just one of the 30 or so peptides obtained by trypsin digestion. Trypsin breaks peptide links derived from the carboxyl groups of the aminoacids lysine and arginine. It was evident that the difference between the two haemoglobin molecules was confined to one small part of one of the polypeptide chains. Ingram (1957) analysed this peptide and showed that the aminoacid sequences were as follows (the abbreviations refer to the italicized letters in Fig. 13.2(iii)):

A   His–Val–Leu–Leu–Thr–Pro–Glu–Glu–Lys

S   His–Val–Leu–Leu–Thr–Pro–Val–Glu–Lys

The histidine is at the amino end and the lysine at the carboxyl end of the peptide. (All peptides formed by trypsin digestion will have either lysine or arginine at their carboxyl end.) It is evident that the two peptides differ by only one aminoacid, the glutamic acid residue at a specific point in *A* being replaced in *S* by valine. In each half-molecule of haemoglobin, comprising nearly 300 aminoacids, this single substitution constituted the only difference between haemoglobins *A* and *S* as regards their primary structure. Previous investigations had failed to establish whether the difference was in the primary or the tertiary structure. Ingram's work did not eliminate the possibility that there might be differences in the tertiary structure as well. However, for the first time, the effect of a single gene mutation was shown to be a change in one aminoacid in a polypeptide chain.

It is tentatively assumed that the tertiary structure of a polypeptide chain is determined exclusively by its primary structure. The tertiary structure is maintained by disulphide (—S—S—) links between cysteine residues, and by chemical or physical bonds between other aminoacid residues. It thus seems possible that the folding to give the tertiary structure could occur largely spontaneously during the synthesis of the polypeptide chain, which is known to occur progressively from the free amino end (see § 14.8). Although the change in the primary structure of haemoglobin due to the sickling mutation is confined to $\frac{1}{300}$th part of the molecule, its effects are profound. It seems likely that the replacement of 2 charged glutamic acid residues in normal haemoglobin (one in each half-molecule) by 2 uncharged valines alters the charge distribution on the surface of the molecule sufficiently to cause the abnormally low solubility of reduced haemoglobin S, which causes the sickling of the erythrocytes in the anaemia. This seemingly trivial change of one aminoacid in each half-molecule would then be wholly responsible for this lethal disease.

§ 13.6   The hybrid-protein hypothesis of allelic complementation

In attempting to explain the complementation between mutants of *Neurospora crassa* affecting the same enzyme, which had been discovered by Fincham and Pateman (1957) and Giles, Partridge and Nelson (1957) (see § 13.4), four observations were of importance. Firstly, and most remarkably, it was discovered that the patterns of complementation between alleles could be represented by a linear map. This was shown by Pateman and Fincham (1958) for *am* mutants, Catcheside and Overton (1959) for *arg*-1 mutants, and Woodward, Partridge, and Giles (1958) for *ad*-4 mutants of *N. crassa* (see Fig. 13.3). The sequence of the mutants on the complementation map is based on the supposition that the mutants have overlapping non-functional regions. These non-functional regions are indicated by the horizontal lines to the right of the tables of complementation data in Fig. 13.3. If two mutants are shown on the map by lines which overlap, this means their non-functional regions overlap and they fail to complement one another in a heterokaryon. The ability to represent allelic complementation by a linear map suggests that there is interaction between linear structures with defects in different regions. These linear structures need not be the genes themselves, but could be products of gene action.

Secondly, complementation between alleles seemed on the whole to be the exception rather than the rule. A majority of allelic mutants, including many which behaved genetically as if they were point mutations rather than deficiencies (cf. § 13.4), were found to be non-complementary. This suggested that the gene could not be subdivided into regions of distinct and non-overlapping function. Instead, it appeared that the linear complementation maps reflected the behaviour of gene products rather than the gene itself.

Thirdly, Fincham and Pateman (1957), found that the level of glutamate dehydrogenase activity through interallele complementation was comparatively low compared with that of wild-type fungus. Woodward, Partridge, and Giles (1958) made a similar discovery with adenylosuccinase-deficient mutants. The enzyme activity rarely exceeded 25% of that of the wild-type.

Fourthly, Fincham (1959a) discovered that the enzyme resulting from interallele complementation was qualitatively abnormal. He found that a heterokaryon of alleles nos. 1 and 2 at the amination (*am*) locus produced a peculiar kind of glutamate dehydrogenase. It differed from wild-type enzyme in its low thermostability. Similar results were obtained with

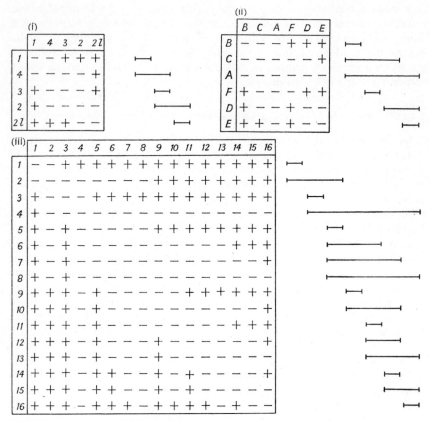

FIGURE 13.3   Results obtained from tests for complementation between allelic
mutants of *Neurospora crassa*.
    (i) Data of Pateman and Fincham (1958) for 5 alleles at the
amination (*am*) locus.
    (ii) Data of Catcheside and Overton (1959) for 6 alleles at the
arginine-1 (*arg*-1) locus.
    (iii) Data of Woodward, Partridge and Giles (1958) for 16 alleles
at the adenine-4 (*ad*-4) locus.
The letters or numbers specify the mutants, a plus sign (+)
indicates complementation, and a minus sign (−) indicates no
complementation. The set of horizontal lines to the right of each
table shows the one-dimensional complementation map derived
from the data. Non-overlapping lines indicate complementation,
and overlapping lines no complementation. In (ii), the sequence
of *B* and *F* on the complementation map is arbitrary.

the enzyme produced by the heterokaryon of alleles nos. 1 and 3, and this enzyme had in addition a lower than normal affinity for glutamate.

Fincham and Pateman (1957) suggested that allelic complementation might be due to the partial reconstitution of a component of the enzyme-forming system. It was assumed that two different defective nuclear products interacted in the cytoplasm of the heterokaryon. Giles, Partridge and Nelson (1957) also favoured nuclear product interaction as an explanation. Catcheside and Overton (1959) suggested that the complementation might be due to the enzyme consisting of an aggregate of two or more normally identical polypeptide chains. This would give an opportunity in a hetero-karyon for the chains produced by each mutant to become associated, and through interaction of some kind, to restore the enzyme activity which the individual mutants lacked. They suggested that genes in which all the alleles failed to complement one another might control proteins consisting of only a single polypeptide chain. This possibility is exemplified by the histidine-6 (*his*-6) locus in *N. crassa*, where Catcheside (1960) found no complementation among 95 mutants tested in all pairwise combinations.

Strong support for this hybrid-protein hypothesis of allelic complementa-tion was obtained when Fincham (1959*a*) found that the heterokaryon enzyme was qualitatively abnormal, and the hypothesis was confirmed by the demonstration of complementation *in vitro* between proteins isolated from mutants. Woodward (1959) obtained complementation by mixing extracts from pairs of mutants individually deficient for adenylosuccinase. Fincham and Coddington (1963) found that purified proteins from mutants nos. 1 and 3 at the *am* locus could interact to form a mixture of enzyme types very similar to that found in the heterokaryon of these mutants.

Clear evidence for the hybrid-protein model of complementation was also obtained by Schlesinger and Levinthal (1963) with mutants of *Escherichia coli* deficient for the enzyme alkaline phosphatase. This enzyme has been shown to consist of two normally identical sub-units, and so can be described as a dimer. Proteins serologically related to alkaline phosphatase were extracted from several mutants and purified. The sub-units of the protein were separated by reduction with thioglycollate in urea. The monomers derived in this way from different mutants known to complement one another *in vivo* were then mixed pairwise, after acidification, and it was found that partially active enzyme was obtained. It was shown by starch electrophoresis, by sedimentation in a sucrose gradient, and from the quantity of enzyme formed with different proportions of the parental monomers, that this enzyme was a hybrid dimer consisting of a monomer from each of the mutant proteins used in the reaction.

It thus appears that allelic complementation results from association between polypeptide chains derived from the two parent strains to produce active enzyme molecules. As Fincham (1959*a*) pointed out, this explanation of complementation means that Benzer's term cistron can be retained as the functional unit of the hereditary material, provided the definition of a cistron is modified such that the trans phenotype has to be non-defective at the enzyme level before two mutants are recognised as belonging to different cistrons. In other words, two mutants in the trans configuration in a heterokaryon or diploid will give normal enzymes if they are in different cistrons, and abnormal enzyme (or none) if in the same cistron.

§ 13.7 The one cistron:one polypeptide hypothesis

It is known that some protein molecules, such as insulin and the protein part of haemoglobin, contain dissimilar polypeptide chains. Are the amino-

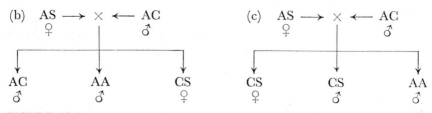

FIGURE 13.4

(a) The expectations on Neel's hypothesis of the inheritance of sickle cell anaemia.

(b) and (c). The two families in which Itano and Neel (1950) discovered haemoglobin C.

A, C, S. Three kinds of haemoglobin. *A*—Normal adult haemoglobin. *S*—Sickle cell haemoglobin. *C*—Another abnormal haemoglobin. The phenotypes of individuals with various haemoglobin combinations are as follows:

AA—Normal.

AC—Normal, but erythrocytes contain haemoglobin *C* as well as *A*.

AS—Normal, but erythrocytes sickle at low oxygen concentrations (sickle cell trait).

CS—Mild form of sickle cell anaemia.

SS—Sickle cell anaemia.

acid sequences in these chains determined by the same cistron or by different cistrons?

Itano and Neel (1950), in studying the inheritance of sickle cell anaemia in man, encountered two families in which there were children with a mild form of the disease. It was found that in each instance only one of the parents had sicklaemia (sickle cell trait), whereas with the normal severe anaemia both parents show sicklaemia (see § 13.5 and Fig. 13.4(*a*)). Further investigation showed later that the anaemic children had sickle cell haemoglobin (*S*) and also a new kind of haemoglobin (*C*) which differed electrophoretically from normal haemoglobin (*A*) and from haemoglobin *S*.

Moreover, the non-sickling parent in both families was found to have haemoglobin C as well as A. The families and their haemoglobins are shown in Fig. 13.4(b) and (c). It seemed likely that the C and S haemoglobins were inherited as a pair of alleles since each is recessive to normal and yet the individuals with both abnormalities (CS) are anaemic. Hunt and Ingram (1958) found that haemoglobin C, like haemoglobin S, had an aminoacid substitution in the β-chains of the molecule. Indeed, rather surprisingly, the substitutions were at identical positions, with the glutamic acid at this position in normal adult haemoglobin (A) replaced by valine in S and by lysine in C.

Itano and Robinson (1960) found that an abnormality in the α-chains appeared to be determined by a different genetic locus, which was probably not closely linked to the β-chain gene. The evidence for this came from study of the haemoglobin of relatives of an individual who was heterozygous for the α-chain defect and for haemoglobin S. Itano and Robinson (1959) had found that when another kind of haemoglobin called I, which is abnormal in the α-chain of the molecule, is mixed with either haemoglobin S or haemoglobin C (both abnormal in the β-chain), two new kinds of haemoglobin could be produced as well as the original forms. At low pH the α sub-unit of the molecule separates from the β sub-unit, and complete molecules are regenerated when the solution is neutralized. The new kinds of haemoglobin formed in this way consisted of normal haemoglobin A and a doubly abnormal molecule combining the defects of both the original types. Baglioni and Ingram (1961) described a comparable situation *in vivo*—a person with four kinds of adult haemoglobin in her blood. These were the normal haemoglobin A; haemoglobin G, with a lysine residue in place of asparagine at a particular point in each α-chain; haemoglobin C, with lysine in place of glutamic acid at a particular point in each β-chain; and haemoglobin X, which was found to have both the G and C substitutions. These four kinds of haemoglobin occurred with approximately equal frequency, suggesting that the mechanism for association of α- and β-chains to form complete molecules did not discriminate between the two kinds of α- or the two kinds of β-chain.

It is evident from these observations that the α- and β-chains are determined by different genes, are synthesized separately, and are then assembled to give haemoglobin by the random association of α- and β-sub-units. In individuals heterozygous for a defect in the α-chain, the two α-chains of each molecule always appear to be alike, and similarly with the β-chain. This is in contrast to the situation described in § 13.6, where association of mutant forms of normally identical sub-units appears to be responsible for the phenomenon of allelic complementation.

Gross (1962) has suggested that two genes in *Neurospora crassa* concerned with the synthesis of leucine, namely *leu*-2 in linkage group IV and *leu*-3 in linkage group I, may be responsible for specifying the aminoacid sequence in two different polypeptide chains which form part of a single enzyme molecule. If the one cistron-one polypeptide chain hypothesis is found to apply generally, this will mean that the earlier idea of one gene specifying each enzyme will be true only for enzymes containing one kind of polypeptide chain.

It appears that the number of cistrons determining a particular enzyme may differ in different organisms. Tryptophan synthetase, the enzyme which catalyses the condensation of indole and serine to give tryptophan (see Fig. 10.1(b)), appears to be a double structure, one part (A) of the protein molecule having a site which combines with an indole compound (indoleglycerol phosphate), and the other part (B) a site which combines with a serine compound (serine + pyridoxal phosphate). In *Escherichia coli*, the A and B components are specified by different cistrons (Crawford and Yanofsky, 1958), but in *Neurospora crassa* one cistron (*tryp*-3) determines both activities, which appear to be contained in different parts of a single polypeptide chain (Bonner, Suyama and De Moss, 1960).

Another example of a bifunctional protein is provided by the enzymes responsible for steps 7 and 9 in the synthesis of histidine in *Salmonella typhimurium* (see Fig. 16.1(b)). Both of these steps appear to be catalysed by the same protein, and four cistrons appear to be concerned in specifying it. Loper (1961) found that mutants lacking the specific dehydrase catalysing step no. 7 were due to mutation in any of the four cistrons, but only those mutants due to mutation in one particular cistron also lacked the phosphatase activity of step no. 9. Loper suggested that this protein might be active as the phosphatase under certain conditions, and in a different state of polymerisation would be capable of the dehydrase activity.

§ 13.8   Evidence for co-linearity of gene and polypeptide

Case and Giles (1960) studied the complementation in all pairwise combinations of 75 mutants of *Neurospora crassa* at the *pan*-2 locus. These mutants required pantothenic acid for growth. Of the 75 mutants, 23 showed ability to complement in one or more combinations, while the remaining 52 failed to complement in any combination. The complementation map of the mutants (which are numbered) is shown in Fig. 13.5(a). All the complementing mutants and 13 of the 52 non-complementing mutants were mapped genetically. This was done by crossing one with another, selecting for recombinants, and observing the frequency of recombination and the behaviour of outside marker genes. The sequence of the mutant sites on the linkage map so obtained is shown in Fig. 13.5(b). No attempt has been made to indicate the recombination frequencies, and the sites are shown uniformly spaced. On this genetic map, the complementing mutants are shown above the line, and the sample of non-complementing mutants below the line.

Comparison of the complementation and genetic maps shows a distinct tendency for the sequence of sites on the two maps to correspond. There are some exceptions to this correspondence, but on the whole the relationship is clear. This is what would be expected if complementation is due to non-overlapping defects in otherwise identical polypeptide chains, and if the site of modification of the polypeptide chain corresponds to the site of mutation in the gene. Such a relationship between sites in DNA and in the corresponding

FIGURE 13.5   Data of Case and Giles (1960) for mutants at the pantothenic
acid 2 (*pan-2*) locus in *Neurospora crassa*. The numbers specify the
mutants.

(*a*) Complementation map.

(*b*) Recombination map. No attempt has been made to indicate
recombination frequencies and the mutants are shown uniformly spaced. Complementing mutants are numbered above
the line and non-complementing below. A further 39 non-
complementing mutants (comparable to the 13 on the bottom
line of (*i*)) were not mapped genetically.

protein is what would be expected on the Dounce-Gamow hypothesis
that nucleotide sequence determines aminoacid sequence. The exceptions to
correspondence between genetic map and complementation map would be
accounted for if the gene determines the primary structure and the complementation reflects the tertiary structure of the protein, since the pattern of
folding to give the tertiary structure is likely to depend on interactions between
aminoacid residues in different parts of the polypeptide chain.

Carlson (1961) obtained a circular complementation map for allelic
mutants at a locus called *dumpy* in *Drosophila melanogaster* (see Fig. 13.6). In
Neurospora crassa, circular complementation maps were obtained by Gross
(1962) with leucine-requiring mutants (*leu-2*) and by Kapuler and Bernstein (1963) with adenine-requiring mutants (*ad-8* locus). With *ad-8*, if
the genetic map was drawn as a spiral it was found largely to correspond to
the complementation map. The significance of these circular complementation maps is uncertain. Kapuler and Bernstein suggested that the

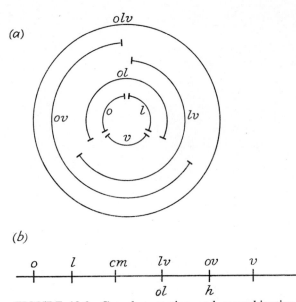

FIGURE 13.6 Complementation and recombination maps for allelic mutants at the locus called *dumpy* in *Drosophila melanogaster* (from Carlson, 1961).
(*a*) Complementation map.
(*b*) Recombination map.
Mutations at this locus show one or more of three recessive effects: an obliquity (*o*) or truncation of the wings; distrubed thoracic bristle patterns known as vortices (*v*); and a lethal effect (*l*). *Comma* (*cm*) is a mutant with weak *o* and *v* effects, and *humpy* (*h*) is a mutant with exaggerated *o* and *v* effects.

tertiary configuration of the enzyme may be in the form of a spiral. Crick and Orgel (1964) have concluded that the folding of the polypeptide chain is the key to the relationship between the complementation and genetic maps, but that there is no simple general way of deducing this tertiary structure from them. In a hybrid dimer they believe that the potentially misfolded region of one chain is corrected by the homologous region of the other.

Study of the changes in the primary rather than in the tertiary structure of a polypeptide resulting from allelic mutations, in conjunction with genetic mapping of the mutants has provided conclusive evidence that gene and polypeptide are co-linear, or in other words, that the positions of the alterations in gene and polypeptide correspond. Sarabhai, Stretton, Brenner and Bolle (1964) studied a series of mutants of virus *T*4 of *Escherichia coli* affecting the protein coat of the head of the virus. These mutants were

(a) H11   C140   B17   B272   H32   B278   C137   H36   A489   C208

(b)

H11

C140

B17

B272   Cys

H32   Cys His T7c

B278   Cys His T7c Tyr C12b

C137   Cys His T7c Tyr C12b Try T6

H36   Cys His T7c Tyr C12b Try T6 Pro T2a

A489   Cys His T7c Tyr C12b Try T6 Pro T2a Try T2

C208   Cys His T7c Tyr C12b Try T6 Pro T2a Try T2 Tyr C2

Normal   Cys His T7c Tyr C12b Try T6 Pro T2a Try T2 Tyr C2 His C6

FIGURE 13.7   Data of Sarabhai *et al.* (1964) for 10 mutants
affecting the protein coat of the head of virus *T*4 of
Escherichia coli.
(*a*) Genetic map showing the sequence of the
mutant sites. No attempt has been made to
indicate recombination frequencies, and the
mutants are shown uniformly spaced.
(*b*) The structure of the protein of the coat produced by each mutant, and by the normal virus.
The abbreviations refer to the peptides obtained by digestion with trypsin.

described as ambivalent ('amber') because they would grow on one strain
of the host (strain *CR*63) but not on another (strain *B*) (see § 14.10 and § 16.1
In other words, host strain *CR*63 appeared to suppress the mutant character
of the virus. Ten mutants induced by base analogues, and due to mutation
at different sites in the cistron concerned with this protein, were mapped by
means of their recombination frequencies with one another. Their sequence
on the map is shown in Fig. 13.7(*a*). The defective protein produced by these

mutants when they infect strain B of the host was purified and then digested with trypsin to give a series of peptides. Compared with normal virus, specific peptides were found to be missing in the mutants. When the mutants were placed in order according to the number of peptides present, it was found that the sequence was the same as that of the mutant sites on the genetic map. This establishes the truth of the co-linearity hypothesis, because the sequence in which the peptides occur in the polypeptide chain can be inferred from the progressive deficiencies of the mutants (see Fig. 13.7(b)). Evidence was obtained that the free amino end of the chain is to the left in the diagram. Since it is known that synthesis of polypeptides begins at the amino end (see §14.8), the inference is that in the mutants, polypeptide synthesis is arrested before completion. Thus, the positions of the mutant sites on the genetic map appear to correspond with the positions where chain synthesis stops in the polypeptide, which is evidently co-linear with the gene. How it comes about that protein synthesis is allowed to go to completion when the virus mutants are grown on host strain $CR63$ instead of strain B, is discussed in § 14.10.

Yanofsky, Carlton, Guest, Helinski, and Henning (1964) have also obtained evidence of the truth of the co-linearity hypothesis. A number of tryptophan-requiring mutants of *Escherichia coli* were obtained by irradiation with ultraviolet light. Those which were unable to convert indoleglycerol phosphate to tryptophan in the presence of serine were selected for study. They were found to be defective in the A protein of the enzyme tryptophan synthetase (see § 13.7). This protein appears to be a single polypeptide chain containing approximately 280 aminoacids. From analysis of the A protein produced by the mutants, it was found that each mutant differed from wild-type by a single aminoacid substitution. Details of these substitutions are shown in Fig. 13.8(i), where the letters refer to Fig. 13.2(iii) and identify the aminoacids. The reference numbers of the mutants are given at the top of the diagram. Nearly all the aminoacid substitutions found were within one quarter of the polypeptide, which is represented by the sequence of 70 letters in the diagram.

In Fig. 13.8(ii) is shown the genetic map of the mutants, which is based primarily on recombination frequencies, but supported by study of crosses with mutants having a segment of the gene deleted. The results show four features of particular significance. First, the genetic map of the mutant sites has the same sequence as the alterations to the polypeptide, thereby demonstrating

---

FIGURE 13.8   Data of Yanofsky *et al.* (1964) for tryptophan-requiring mutants of *Escherichia coli* defective in the A protein of the enzyme tryptophan synthetase.

(i) The diagram shows the sequence of aminoacids in about one quarter of the polypeptide chain of the protein, and the substitutions caused by the numbered mutants. The letters refer to Fig. 13.2 (iii). Where the sequence of aminoacids is uncertain, the letters are in italics. * = Uncertain if l or m. † = Uncertain if j or k.

(ii) Genetic map of the mutants. The recombination frequencies are in arbitrary units.

(i)

(ii)

the truth of the co-linearity hypothesis. It is evident that the position of a mutation in the gene determines the position of the corresponding aminoacid change. Secondly, certain of the mutants, for example, nos. 23 and 46, show recombination with one another and yet have an aminoacid substitution at the same position in the polypeptide. The significance of this discovery is discussed in § 14.10. Thirdly, the recombination frequencies (which are expressed in arbitrary units in the diagram), are roughly proportional to the number of aminoacids between the points of substitution in the polypeptide. This implies that the recombination frequency is related to the distance between the nucleotide substitutions in the DNA, and that this in turn is related to the distance between the aminoacid substitutions. Fourthly, certain mutants give consistently higher recombination frequencies than others, for example, nos. 23 and 187 compared with 46, and nos. 487 and 223 compared with 446. It is evident that recombination frequency is partly dependent on the nature of the mutations which are recombining. This remarkable conclusion is discussed further in Chapter 15.

All the essential pieces of evidence required to establish the Dounce-Gamow theory that nucleotide sequence specifies aminoacid sequence have now been obtained. When this idea was put forward there were no data available with which to test it, but it now appears that the gene is a linear structure with numerous sites of mutation within the functional unit; that mutations cause changes in aminoacid sequence in specific polypeptides; and moreover, that there is an exact point-by-point relationship between the position of the mutation in the gene and the position of the aminoacid substitution in the polypeptide. How nucleotide sequence in DNA is translated into aminoacid sequence in polypeptides is discussed in the next chapter.

14. *The theory of consecutive non-overlapping triplets of nucleotides as the aminoacid code*

§ 14.1   Introduction

When Dounce (1952) and Gamow (1954) independently put forward the basic idea that nucleotide sequence in nucleic acids might determine aminoacid sequence in polypeptides, they also suggested means by which this translation might be brought about. With four different nucleotides in DNA (having adenine, thymine, guanine, and cytosine respectively as bases), there are 16 possibilities for a sequence of 2 bases, 64 possibilities for a sequence of 3, 256 for a sequence of 4, and so on. Since there are 20 different aminoacids in proteins, it is evident that a minimum of 3 nucleotides is required to specify each. Both Dounce and Gamow therefore suggested that a sequence of 3 consecutive nucleotides was responsible for each aminoacid. Astbury and Bell (1938) had found from X-ray crystallography that the spacing between nucleotides in DNA was approximately the same as the spacing between aminoacid residues in a fully extended polypeptide chain. They considered that this correspondence was likely to be of biological significance, and this led both Dounce and Gamow to suggest that the nucleotide sequence was read at single nucleotide intervals. In other words, if a segment of the nucleic acid is represented by the letters $A\ B\ C\ A\ C\ D$, where A–D specify the 4 individual nucleotides, the triplet $A\ B\ C$ would represent one aminoacid, $B\ C\ A$ the next, $C\ A\ C$ the third, and so on.

Gamow and Ycas (1955) pointed out that overlapping triplets such as these impose restrictions on the aminoacid sequences that are possible in polypeptides, and yet from an analysis of known sequences which they had made it appeared likely that all possibilities were permitted. They therefore rejected overlapping codes in favour of one in which the number of determining nucleotides exceeded by a factor of 3 the number of aminoacid residues in the synthesized protein, so that neighbouring residues did not share nucleotides. In other words, they favoured a non-overlapping triplet code.

From the range of dipeptides known to occur naturally, Brenner (1957) confirmed that a fully overlapping triplet code was unlikely to be correct. He analysed the published data on aminoacid sequences in polypeptides and found that of the 400 possible sequences in a dipeptide, 239 were already

227

known. The data referred predominantly to various mammals (*Oryctolagus cuniculus, Balaenoptera borealis, Equus caballus, Bos taurus, Ovis aries, Sus domesticus, Homo sapiens*), but also included one bird (*Gallus domesticus*), one fish (*Salmo* sp.), one flowering plant (*Carica papaya*) and tobacco mosaic virus. If the code was the same in all these organisms, and was fully overlapping and based on trinucleotides, then there could not be more than 256 different dipeptides, since this is the number of ways of arranging a sequence of 4 nucleotides (4^4). Although near this limit, the known number did not exceed it. However, with full overlapping, only 4 different triplets can follow any given one. Thus, after a nucleotide trio represented as *A B C*, the possibilities are *B C A, B C B, B C C*, and *B C D*. In terms of aminoacid sequence, this would mean that the aminoacid represented by *A B C* could be followed only by four others. In order to allow for the possibility of more than 4 different aminoacids succeeding a particular one in the sequence, it would be necessary to postulate that a second triplet, for example *A B A*, represented the same aminoacid as *A B C*. If all the 20 possible dipeptides which begin with a particular aminoacid are found to occur naturally, a minimum of 5 different triplets would be required to code for this one aminoacid.

Brenner found that there was such diversity in the aminoacids which followed or preceded each particular one, that in total 70 different triplets would be required to code for all 20 aminoacids. This is more than the number possible with a triplet code ($4^3 = 64$). Hence, on the assumption that the organisms from which the aminoacid sequences were obtained had the same code, it was apparent that all fully overlapping codes based on trinucleotides could be ruled out. It could be inferred that if Astbury and Bell's discovery of a similar periodicity in DNA and protein was biologically important, its significance was unlikely to relate to the genetic code.

§ 14.2   The molecular basis of mutation

In order to understand the aminoacid code, it is essential to know in chemical terms the nature of the changes in DNA caused by mutation. Watson and Crick (1953b) had suggested that mutation might be due to a base in DNA occasionally occurring in one of its less likely tautomeric forms*, so that at replication the wrong base is inserted at this position in the complementary nucleotide chain. Following the discovery by Dunn and Smith (1954) and Zamenhof and Griboff (1954) that certain base analogues such as 5-bromouracil were incorporated into DNA in place of the specific bases which they resembled chemically (see § 12.4), Litman and Pardee (1956) discovered that 5-bromouracil had a powerful mutagenic effect on virus *T*2 of *Escherichia coli*. This led to a study by Benzer and Freese (1958) of the mutagenic effect of 5-bromouracil on the *r*II cistrons of the *T*4 virus. They made the outstanding discovery that 5-bromouracil did not enhance the spontaneously occurring mutations in a general way, but instead

* Tautomerism is the wandering of a mobile hydrogen atom from one multivalent atom to a neighbouring one within a molecule. Tautomeric forms of a molecule are usually in dynamic equilibrium with one another.

caused mutation at certain sites with characteristic frequencies. Their data relating to the end of the *B* cistron which adjoins the *A* cistron are given in Table 14.1. The pattern of mutations in the *A* cistron and the remainder of the *B* cistron was similar to that shown in the table.

Brenner, Benzer, and Barnett (1958) made similar studies using proflavin as mutagen. Proflavin is known to interact with DNA, but unlike 5-bromo-uracil does not appear to become incorporated. A finding of very great inter-est was that proflavin causes mutation at a completely different series of sites from 5-bromouracil (see Table 14.1). The proflavin sites also differed largely from the spontaneously mutating ones. Furthermore, with proflavin there were single occurrences of mutation at many different sites, whereas with 5-bromouracil and also with spontaneous mutation there was more repetition of mutation at certain sites.

Freese and associates studied the *r*II mutations caused by other mutagens such as 2-aminopurine, nitrous acid, and hydroxylamine. The patterns of mutations caused by some of these mutagens on part of the *B* cistron are shown in Table 14.1, which is based on the collected data given by Benzer (1961). Many features of these patterns remain unexplained. Thus, it is not known why certain sites ('hot spots') show extremely high spontaneous mutation frequencies: a possible explanation is discussed in § 15.6. The mechanisms of action of the various mutagens are not understood in chemical terms with certainty. It is clear, however, that their actions are specific for certain sites. This is in direct contrast to the earlier studies on mutation, such as those described in Chapter 9, where the range of kinds of mutations found was independent of the mutagen used. It is evident from the results with *r*II mutants of virus *T*4 that the specificity of mutagen action is at the level of mutant sites within the gene. The early studies on mutation were concerned with the gene as a whole, and at this level of organization the specific effects are lost, just as the totals of the various columns in Table 14.1 would give no indication of the specificity of action of the different mutagens.

Freese (1959) showed that the *r*II mutants produced by the base analogues 2-aminopurine and 5-bromodeoxyuridine (the deoxynucleoside of 5-bromouracil) could be induced to revert to wild-type by the action of these same substances, whereas proflavin-induced mutants and most spontaneous mutants could not. This confirmed the evidence from the differing site patterns that the base analogues on the one hand and proflavin on the other caused mutation in different ways.

Freese suggested that the base analogues caused mutation through mistakes in base pairing, either at the time of incorporation into DNA, or at a subsequent replication. The mechanism was thought to be similar to Watson and Crick's original suggestion, one base temporarily existing in a tautomeric form so that at replication the wrong purine or the wrong pyri-midine would be inserted (see Fig. 14.1(*b*) and (*c*)). Whatever the exact mechanism, the end-result would be that a purine would always be replaced by the other purine, and the corresponding pyrimidine by the other pyri-midine. Freese found that 5-bromouracil-induced mutations were reverted most readily by 2-aminopurine, and *vice versa*, suggesting that these base

TABLE 14.1 The table shows the numbers of mutations that have occurred spontaneously and with various mutagens at 50 different sites within part of the rII B cistron of T4 virus of Escherichia coli. (From Benzer, 1961.)

Site	Spontaneous	Nitrous Acid	Ethyl Methane Sulphonate	2-amino-purine	2,6-diamino-purine	5-bromo-uracil	5-bromo-deoxy-cytidine	Pro-flavin
B1/1	1							
2	8							
3	3	1	2	1	1			
4	3							
5	4							
6	1		2		1			
7	2							
8	2							2
9	1							
10	32	14	7	9	1	28	13	
11	2							
12	1							1
13	1							
14		1						
15	1							
16	1							
B2/1	1							
2	2							
3	6							
4	2							
B3/1	5							
2	3							
B4/1	1							
2	5	1						
3								1
4	1							
5	1							
6	1		1					
7	1							
8								2
9	1	8	5	1		3	2	
10	51	4						
11								1
12								1
13				1				
14	2							
15	1		1	1				
16		1						
17	17							1
18	3			4	1			
19	1					2		
20	517	23	7		3	5	5	1
B5/1	1							
B6/1		1						
2	1	3	4			3		
3	1							1
B7/1	1							
2	3		1					
3	2	1						
4	9							

FIGURE 14.1   The hypothetical steps in the production of mutations in *T*4 virus of
Escherichia coli by (*a*) hydroxylamine, (*b*) 5-bromouracil and (*c*)
2-aminopurine. The steps outlined in (*b*) and (*c*) could also occur
in the reverse direction, though this appears to happen less often.
Arrows show the insertion of a base complementary to that in the
other chain, and the displacement of the latter at the next replication. *X* indicates where the mutagen has acted.

analogues acted predominantly in opposite directions. Later work (Freese
et al., 1961) showed that mutants induced by hydroxylamine were similar
in properties to those induced by 5-bromouracil. Hydroxylamine is thought
to act by altering 5-hydroxymethylcytosine (which replaces cytosine in the
DNA of the *T*-even viruses—see § 11.6) so that it pairs with adenine instead
of guanine (Fig. 14.1(*a*)). At the next replication, thymine would be inserted
opposite the adenine, and the end-result would be that a guanine cytosine-
analogue base-pair was replaced by an adenine thymine base-pair. From its
behaviour in causing reverse mutation, it was concluded that 5-bromouracil
acts predominantly to give the same overall effect as hydroxylamine (Fig.
14.1(*b*)), while 2-aminopurine acts predominantly in the reverse direction,
causing the transition from an adenine thymine pair to a guanine cytosine-
analogue pair (Fig. 14.1(*c*)). On the other hand, nitrous acid was thought to
cause mutation through the oxidative deamination of either adenine or
cytosine (and its analogues) (see Fig. 14.2), with the result that transitions
from one base-pair to the other could occur more or less equally in both
directions. This hypothesis fitted the findings from the induction of mutations

FIGURE 14.2   The hypothetical steps in the production of mutations in *T*4 virus of *Escherichia coli* by nitrous acid, through the oxidative deamination of (*a*) adenine to hypoxanthine, and (*b*) cytosine analogue to uracil analogue. Arrows show the insertion of a base complementary to that in the other chain, and the displacement of the latter at the next replication. *X* indicates where the mutagen has acted.

by nitrous acid and of their reversion by other mutagens, and *vice versa*. In contrast to these mutagens (nitrous acid, hydroxylamine, and the base analogues), which were thought to act by causing various patterns of *transition* (purine–purine and pyrimidine–pyrimidine substitution), Freese (1959) suggested that the second category of mutations, exemplified by proflavin-induced mutations, were due to the replacement of a purine by a pyrimidine, and *vice versa*. He called this hypothetical process *transversion*. However, Brenner, Barnett, Crick, and Orgel (1961) postulated that proflavin causes mutation by the insertion or deletion of one or more base-pairs in the DNA, and not by transversion as Freese had suggested. Part of their evidence for this was that proflavin-induced mutants appeared completely to lack the normal activity of the gene, whereas mutants produced by other mutagens were often 'leaky', that is, showed some growth on strain *K* of the host (see § 13.4). With many virus characters, proflavin-induced mutants were not found, presumably because loss of the function of the gene controlling them was lethal. This difference in character of proflavin mutants, together with their unique site pattern and the inability of base analogues to cause reversion, suggested that proflavin modified the gene in a fundamentally different way from the other mutagens. That this alteration to the gene was the addition or subtraction of base-pairs was confirmed by the experiments described in the next section.

§ 14.3   Evidence that the code is read in triplets from a fixed origin

Crick, Barnett, Brenner, and Watts-Tobin (1961) performed some ingenious experiments which appear not only to establish the nature of proflavin mutants, but also provide fundamental information about the genetic code. A single *r*II mutant of virus *T*4 of *Escherichia coli* induced by proflavin and situated at a site in segment *B*1 (cf. Table 14.1) formed the starting-point. As indicated in § 13.4, *r*II mutants are unable to grow on strain *K* of the host, thus allowing selection for strains which have reverted to wild-type. A small number of revertants were found. When these were grown on strain B of the host, nearly all were found to differ slightly in plaque morphology from wild-type, which suggested that the revertants did not arise by a precise reversal of the original proflavin-induced mutation, but by some other change which largely compensated for the original alteration to the gene. This was confirmed from the progeny of the revertants. It appeared that in nearly every instance the reversion was due to a second mutation at a different site from the original one. The suppressor mutations were in the same region of the gene, being restricted to segments $B1$ and $B2$ (cf. Table 14.1). This represents about $\frac{1}{10}$ of the whole B cistron, only part of which is shown in the table. Each suppressor mutation, when separated through recombination from the proflavin mutant which it suppressed, was found to be an rII mutant itself.

To account for these observations, Crick *et al.* postulated that the initial proflavin-induced mutation was due to the addition of one nucleotide-pair at the mutant site, and that the suppressor mutations were due to the deletion of one nucleotide-pair. If the nucleotide sequence forming the gene was read from a fixed starting-point, such addition and subtraction of nucleotides would lead to misreading over the interval between the two sites but nowhere else. In consequence, abnormal aminoacids would be inserted in the segment of the polypeptide chain which corresponded with this part of the gene. This would explain why the suppressed mutant was not quite identical with the wild-type, and also why the site of each suppressor was near that of the original mutant. If the two sites were far apart, the polypeptide chain would be expected to be so abnormal that the phenotype would be mutant, and hence not found when selecting for mutants which would grow on strain K.

According to this hypothesis, the original proflavin mutation may be called a plus mutant (Fig. 14.3(c)), and the suppressors of it may be called minus mutants (Fig. 14.3(b)–(d)). By repeating the original procedure, suppressors of the minus mutants were obtained (Fig. 14.3(h) and (i)). They were found to be due to mutation at different sites near the site of the mutant they suppressed, just like the first group of suppressors. According to the hypothesis, this second family of suppressors should be plus mutants, and this was confirmed experimentally, because two plus mutants brought into the same piece of DNA through recombination had the mutant phenotype like each alone (Fig. 14.3(j)), and similarly with two minus mutants (Fig. 14.3(k)), but one plus and one minus mutant suppressed one another and gave the wild-type or nearly wild-type phenotype, provided they were not too far apart. By selecting for revertants of these plus mutants, a third family of suppressors was obtained and found to be minus mutants, as expected. Altogether about 80 rII mutants were obtained by this successive selection of suppressors, and their sites extended over about $\frac{1}{4}$ of the B cistron.

An outstanding discovery was the finding that 3 plus mutants in the same piece of DNA gave a near wild-type phenotype, and similarly with 3 minus mutants (Fig. 14.3(l) and (m)). On their hypothesis, this implied that the *coding ratio*, that is, the ratio of bases to aminoacids, was 3. The addition or deletion of 3 nucleotides within a short segment of the DNA had restored

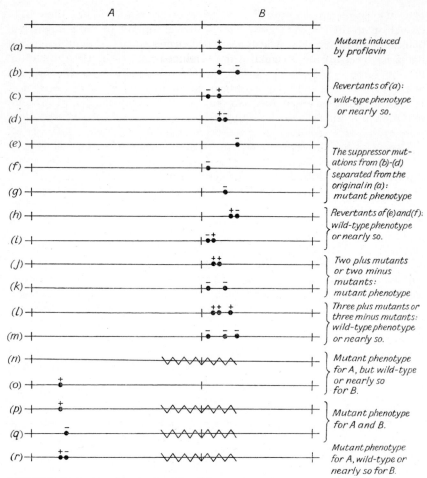

FIGURE 14.3   Results obtained by Crick *et al.* (1961) from study of suppressors of
a proflavin-induced *r*II mutant of virus *T*4 of *Escherichia coli*.

the function of the gene, indicating that the nucleotides were read in threes
from one end. With the addition or subtraction of 1 or 2 nucleotides the gene
is evidently misread to the end, resulting in the mutant phenotype, but with
3 added or removed it is misread only over the interval between the sites.
Thus, their results suggested that a triplet of nucleotides was the coding
unit or *codon* for an aminoacid.

Further evidence that the gene is read from a fixed starting-point was
obtained from the use of a deletion known to cover parts of both *A* and *B*
cistrons in the region where they join. The loss of this segment destroys the
function of the *A* cistron, but not that of the *B*: it covers the part of the *B*
cistron where the mutants used in the present study are situated. This is
presumed to be a non-essential part of the *B* gene (Fig. 14.3(*n*)). A mutant

in the A cistron which reverts freely with proflavin and is therefore presumed to be an addition (or deletion) of a nucleotide pair, destroys the function of the A gene without affecting the B, as might be expected (Fig. 14.3(o)). However, when this mutant and the deletion are combined in the same piece of DNA, it was found that the function of the B cistron was also destroyed (Fig. 14.3(p)). It was presumed that with the loss of the junction between A and B cistrons, both were being read as one, with the result that putting the reading out-of-phase in the A cistron affected the B as well. This was confirmed by the finding that a suppressor of the A cistron mutant restored the B cistron function (Fig. 14.3(r)). It thus appears that the gene (or nucleotide sequence derived from it) is read in trios of nucleotides starting from a fixed origin at one end.

It was assumed that the initial proflavin-induced mutant in this series of experiments had an addition of one nucleotide-pair at the mutant site in the B cistron. However, this mutant might equally well have been a deletion of one nucleotide-pair. This would not affect the argument except to inter-change plus and minus throughout. The initial mutant, and the series of suppressors obtained from it, might represent additions or deletions of 2 or more nucleotide-pairs instead of only 1. Although improbable, this remains a possibility, with its corollary that the coding ratio may be a multiple of 3. However, independent evidence that the coding ratio is 3 has since been obtained (see § 14.9).

§ 14.4   RNA

In attempting to discover how the nucleotide sequence in DNA is trans-lated into aminoacid sequence in protein, it is essential to know whether the translation is direct, or whether other substances intervene in the process. The work of Brachet, Caspersson and many others (see Brachet, 1957) established that ribonucleic acid (RNA) participates in protein synthesis. One of the clearest demonstrations of this was when Brachet showed that treatment of cells with ribonuclease, which catalyses the breakdown of RNA, stops protein synthesis. Whereas DNA is almost confined to the nucleus, RNA occurs predominantly in the cytoplasm, although it is found in the nucleolus as well as in variable quantity in association with the chromosomes. Brachet demonstrated with the green alga *Acetabularia* (cf. § 5.3) that protein synthesis could continue in the cytoplasm in the absence of the nucleus. In many tissues a correlation has been shown between the amount of RNA present and the rate of protein synthesis. From observations such as these the idea developed that RNA provides a link between gene and protein. More specifically, it was suggested that information in the form of base sequence in DNA was transferred to RNA and thence to aminoacid sequence in proteins. The size of the RNA molecule (see below) is such that it could readily pass through the 40 mμ wide pores in the nuclear membrane.

The first clear evidence that RNA has the capacity to carry information about protein structure came from work on tobacco mosaic virus. This virus contains no DNA. It is composed of RNA surrounded by a hollow cylinder of protein measuring 300 mμ in length and 15 mμ in external diameter. Gierer and Schramm (1956) separated the RNA and the protein and showed that the RNA by itself is infective, although to a much lesser degree (0·1%) compared with the intact virus. Fraenkel-Conrat (1956) mixed the RNA of one strain and the protein of another, and produced several very active chimaeras. The serological characters of these mixed

TABLE 14.2   The table shows the results obtained by Fraenkel-Conrat and Singer (1957) from study of two strains of tobacco mosaic virus, and of reciprocal chimaeras of their RNA and protein.

N = Normal *Nicotiana* strain of virus
P = *Plantago* strain of virus, sometimes called ribgrass virus.

The first and last columns of figures give the numbers of the various aminoacid residues in the N and P proteins, according to the data of Tsugita (1962). Both contain a total of 158 aminoacids. The other figures are Fraenkel-Conrat and Singer's values for the percentage weight of each aminoacid in the virus strains. The analyses were not corrected for destruction of acid-sensitive aminoacids during hydrolysis.

Strain of Virus			N	N	P	P	
	RNA		N	N	P	P	
	Protein		N	P	N	P	
Serological character			N	P	N	P	
Nature of disease produced by progeny			N	N	P	P	
Serological character of progeny			N	N	P	P	
	a	Glycine	6	2·3	2·3	1·8	1·6	4
	b	Alanine	14	6·5	6·9	8·5	8·5	18
	c	Serine	16	9·0	8·8	8·1	8·1	13
	d	Threonine	16	8·9	8·9	7·5	7·2	14
	e	Cysteine	1	Not determined (about 0·6%)				1
	f	Methionine	0	0·0	0·0	2·2	2·0	3
Amino -acid compo- sition of protein of progeny	g	Valine	14	9·6	9·0	6·3	5·9	10
	h	Leucine	12	14·2	14·3	12·2	12·2	11
	i	Isoleucine	9					8
	j	Aspartic acid	18	13·8	14·2	14·8	15·0	17
	k	Asparagine						
	l	Glutamic acid	16	12·4	12·1	17·3	16·4	22
	m	Glutamine						
	n	Arginine	11	9·5	9·7	8·5	8·9	11
	o	Lysine	2	1·9	1·8	2·3	2·4	2
	p	Phenylalanine	8	7·2	7·1	5·4	5·3	6
	q	Tyrosine	4	4·1	4·3	6·2	6·3	7
	r	Histidine	0	0·0	0·0	0·7	0·7	1
	s	Tryptophan	3	2·8	2·6	2·2	2·2	2
	t	Proline	8	5·0	5·1	5·1	5·0	8

virus preparations were those of the virus supplying the protein, but all the characters of the progeny were those of the virus supplying the RNA.

Fraenkel-Conrat and Singer (1957) investigated this remarkable discovery in more detail. One of the best examples concerned chimaeras derived from the normal virus and a strain originally isolated from *Plantago lanceolata*. On a Turkish variety of *Nicotiana tabacum*, the normal virus produces mottling of the leaves while the *Plantago* strain produces a distinctive ring pattern of diseased cells. Furthermore, the two strains differ appreciably in the composition of their protein, and in antigenic specificity. The protein of the

D-ribose   Uracil
                                 (2,6–dihydroxypyrimidine)

FIGURE 14.4   The components of RNA which differ from those of DNA (D-ribose in place of 2-deoxy-D-ribose, and uracil in place of thymine; cf. Fig. 11.3).

Plantago strain (P) contains methionine and histidine which are absent from the normal *Nicotiana* strain (N), and there are differences in frequency of nearly all the aminoacids (see Table 14.2). Indeed, the *Plantago* strain differs so much that it is regarded by some authors as a distinct species and is called ribgrass virus. Fraenkel-Conrat and Singer prepared reciprocal chimaeras, that is, RNA of the N strain with protein of the P strain, and *vice versa*. They found that the progeny of each had protein closely corresponding in aminoacid composition to that of the parent from which the RNA was derived (see Table 14.2). It appeared that the protein part of the virus made no contribution to the progeny, and that the specificity of the virus protein was determined solely by the RNA.

In view of this clear evidence that RNA can carry genetic information about protein structure, it is not surprising that the structure of RNA appears to be quite similar to that of DNA. The essential differences are that the sugar is D-ribose (Fig. 14.4(a)) instead of 2-deoxy-D-ribose, and one of the pyrimidines is uracil (Fig. 14.4(b)) in place of the thymine (5-methyluracil) of DNA. The other three bases (adenine, guanine and cytosine) are the same.

The nucleotides are polymerized by 3′,5′-phosphodiester linkages as in DNA to form polynucleotide chains. These nucleotide chains are thought normally to occur singly, unlike DNA. However, there may be pairing of complementary bases between different parts of the same chain to give double-helical regions.

Grunberg-Manago and Ochoa (1955) isolated from *Azotobacter vinelandii* and enzyme, polynucleotide phosphorylase, which would bring about RNA synthesis *in vitro* from ribonucleoside 5′-diphosphates with release of orthophosphate. The reaction requires magnesium ions, but no primer is needed, and it is not necessary to have all 4 ribonucleoside 5′-diphosphates present. In view of the lack of requirement for primer, it is evident that this enzyme does not provide a mechanism for the maintenance of specific nucleotide sequences. An enzyme is also known which will break the 3′-linkages of RNA chains, and another which will break 5′-linkages, both comparable to the DNA enzymes (see § 12.4, p. 193). Unlike DNA, RNA can also be broken down by hydrolysis with alkali, when it gives the nucleoside 3′-phosphates and also some 2′-phosphates.

§ 14.5   Ribosomes

Tracer experiments with radioactive aminoacids have established that protein synthesis takes place in association with minute particles composed of about 60% RNA and 40% protein. Roberts (1958) proposed the name *ribosome* for these ribonucleoprotein particles. They are found in the microsomal fraction when the components of cells are separated by differential centrifugation. Palade (1955) had shown from electron micrographs of thin sections of about 40 different mammalian tissues that these particles occur in large numbers in all the cells. Many were associated with the membrane system of the endoplasmic reticulum. In bacteria, however, where there may be several thousand ribosomes per cell, they are apparently not associated with membranes.

Ribosomes appear to be a fundamental constituent of all cells, and to be very similar in all organisms. They are more or less spherical in shape, measure approximately 20 mμ across, and have a sedimentation rate of about 73 Svedberg units. At low concentrations of magnesium ions, they dissociate into two unequal components with sedimentation rates of 50 S and 30 S. There is evidence that the ribosomes usually occur in aggregates during protein synthesis (see § 14.9). The size and base composition of the RNA of ribosomes also appears to be remarkably uniform. Thus in bacteria its base composition is about 26% adenine, 20% uracil, 32% guanine, and 22% cytosine (molar proportions), irrespective of the DNA composition of the species from which it is obtained. It is evident from these figures that the complementary pairs (adenine-uracil and guanine-cytosine) are unequal, indicating that at least some of the nucleotides are unpaired. That the RNA composition of the ribosomes should be uniform, and independent of the DNA, suggests that this RNA is not directly involved in the transfer of information from DNA to protein.

§ 14.6   The messenger RNA hypothesis

An exceptionally favourable situation for the study of the part played by RNA in protein synthesis is provided by the infection of *Escherichia coli* with the *T*-even viruses. Upon infection the synthesis of bacterial DNA stops abruptly, and the bacterial nucleus is rapidly destroyed, but synthesis of RNA and protein continue and are followed about 7 minutes after infection at 37°C by the production of virus DNA. Volkin and Astrachan

TABLE 14.3   Base composition of the DNA and RNA of *Escherichia coli* and its *T*-even viruses expressed in molar percentages.

Base	*Escherichia coli*		*T*-even Viruses		
				RNA specific to Virus	
	DNA	Total RNA	DNA	Volkin & Astrachan 1957	Bautz & Hall 1962
Adenine	25	23	32	31	30
Thymine (DNA) or Uracil (RNA)	25	23	32	29	33
Guanine	25	31	18	22	21
5-Hydroxymethylcytosine (virus DNA) or Cytosine (RNA and bacterial DNA)	25	23	18	18	16

(1957) determined the base composition of the newly-synthesized RNA by transferring infected bacteria to a medium containing labelled phosphorus (^{32}P), hydrolysing the RNA shortly afterwards, separating the 4 classes of nucleotides, and measuring their radioactivity. They found that the newly synthesized RNA was similar in base composition to the virus DNA (apart from having uracil in place of thymine, and cytosine in place of 5-hydroxymethylcytosine). This composition was different from that of the bacterial DNA, and from the overall composition of the RNA, 80% of which is in the ribosomes (see Table 14.3). These observations point to the newly synthesized RNA as a carrier of information from DNA to protein. It was notable also that this RNA showed a high turnover rate, with no net synthesis.

Hall and Spiegelman (1961) showed that the RNA synthesized after infection of *E. coli* by *T*2 virus could form hybrid molecules with the DNA of the virus. Owing to its difference in base composition, the newly-synthesized virus-specific RNA can be separated from the bacterial RNA by density-gradient centrifuging in sucrose solution. Hall and Spiegelman then mixed the virus-specific RNA with the virus DNA. The DNA had previously been heated to 95°C for 15 minutes, and then quickly placed in an ice-bath. Marmur and Lane (1960) had shown that such heating of DNA causes the complementary nucleotide chains to separate and that slow cooling allows them to re-associate again in complementary pairs, but quick cooling does not. The mixture of RNA and single-chain DNA was placed in a water-bath at 65°C and allowed to cool very slowly, taking 30 hours to reach 26°C. Hall and Spiegelman found that hybrid DNA-RNA molecules were thereby formed. Their evidence for this was based on radioactive isotope labelling using ^{32}P in phosphate for the culture which provided the RNA, and ^{3}H in thymidine for that which provided the DNA. In a control experiment, the labelled RNA and DNA were mixed, but not heated, and then centrifuged in caesium chloride solution for 5 days to give a density gradient. The contents of the centrifuge tube were then removed drop by drop in sequence and assayed for ^{32}P and ^{3}H. The β-particles emitted by these isotopes have different energies and so can be distinguished. It was found that the ^{32}P and ^{3}H were concentrated at different positions in the tube, as expected since RNA is denser than DNA. By contrast, after heating and slow-cooling the DNA-RNA mixture, the ^{32}P showed a bimodal distribution, the new peak partly overlapping the ^{3}H peak. It was inferred that the heating and slow cooling had allowed hybrid DNA-RNA molecules to form, and that these had a density close to that of DNA. The hybrid complex evidently contained considerably more DNA than RNA, presumably because the RNA was only a short segment.

Confirmation that hybrid molecule formation depends on complementary nucleotide sequences in the DNA and RNA was obtained by slow-cooling mixtures of the $T2$-specific RNA and previously-heated DNA of the host bacterium, *Escherichia coli*. No hybrid molecules were formed. Likewise there was no hybrid formation with the heated DNA of *Pseudomonas aeruginosa* nor with that of virus $T5$ of *E. coli*, which happens to have the same overall base composition as $T2$. Hall and Spiegelman's results thus provide a clear indication that the RNA formed after $T2$ infection is likely to have been synthesized in association with the virus DNA, since the RNA appears able to form double helices with single chains of $T2$ DNA, but not with other sources of DNA.

Weiss and Nakamoto (1961) and Hurwitz, Furth, Anders, Oritz, and August (1962) have described an RNA polymerase, both from bacteria and mammals, which has many features in common with the DNA polymerase described by Kornberg and associates (see Chapter 12). The RNA polymerase requires all 4 ribonucleoside 5′-triphosphates as substrate, and DNA as primer. Divalent metal ions are also needed, and pyrophosphate ions are liberated. This enzyme, first detected in the nuclei of the liver of *Rattus norvegicus*, has since been found in extracts of several bacteria and *Pisum sativum*. The reaction catalysed would appear to provide a means by which base sequence in DNA is transferred to RNA. Following RNA synthesis *in vitro* with this enzyme using 5′-triphosphates one of which was labelled with ^{32}P, the RNA was broken down again by alkaline hydrolysis into 3'-phosphates (some 2'-phosphates were also formed), and the proportion of radioactive phosphorus associated with the 4 different nucleotides was determined. By labelling each nucleoside 5'-triphosphate in turn with ^{32}P, the relative frequencies of the 16 possible sequences of a pair of nucleotides were estimated (cf. § 12.5). Using the DNA from various organisms in turn as primer, it was found that the base sequence in the synthesized RNA always resembled that of the DNA primer.

Chamberlin and Berg (1962) obtained similar results. That the DNA and RNA should have the same proportions of the 4 bases suggests that each of the complementary nucleotide-chains in the primer DNA was used for the synthesis of RNA chains. This was confirmed by Chamberlin and Berg by using as primer the DNA of virus phi-ex(ϕX)174 of *E. coli*. This virus normally contains only one particular nucleotide chain of DNA (Sinsheimer 1959) with a molar base composition of 25% adenine, 33% thymine, 24% guanine, and 18% cytosine. The RNA synthesized when the ϕX single-chain DNA was used as primer had the complementary composition (34% adenine, 24% uracil, 19% guanine, and 23% cytosine). When DNA of this virus with normal complementary pairs of chains, obtained *in vitro* with the DNA polymerase, was used as primer for the RNA polymerase reaction, the resulting RNA had a base composition of 29% adenine, 29% uracil, 21% guanine, and 21% cytosine, which is identical with the DNA composition (except for uracil in place of thymine). This indicates that both DNA nucleotide chains were used for RNA synthesis. However, it cannot be inferred from this that RNA synthesis *in vivo* will necessarily occur in relation to both DNA chains. Indeed, evidence is given in § 14.7 which shows that RNA synthesis *in vivo* occurs in relation to one particular DNA chain only.

The idea that the short-lived RNA formed after virus infection constitutes a messenger between DNA and protein obtained strong support from some ingenious experiments by Brenner, Jacob, and Meselson (1961). *Escherichia coli* was grown for several generations in a culture medium containing the heavy isotopes ^{15}N and ^{13}C, so that all the nitrogen and carbon in the ribosomes would be of these heavy atoms. The bacteria were then infected with virus T4, and transferred immediately to a medium containing normal nitrogen (^{14}N) and carbon (^{12}C). In one experiment the bacteria were fed with phosphate containing radioactive phosphorus (^{32}P) from the second to the seventh minute after transfer, and in another experiment they were given sulphate containing radioactive sulphur (^{35}S) for the first 2 minutes of virus multiplication. The cells were subsequently disrupted and the ribosomes purified and centrifuged in caesium chloride solution to give a density gradient (cf. § 12.3). Control experiments showed that this treatment would separate any newly-synthesized ribosomes containing ^{14}N and ^{12}C from the old heavy ribosomes containing ^{15}N and [13]C. It was found that no wholly new ribosomes were synthesized after the virus infection, and moreover, the newly-synthesized RNA indicated by ^{32}P, and the newly-synthesized protein indicated by ^{35}S, were found to be associated with the heavy band of ribosomes in the caesium chloride gradient. It was evident that at the time of cell disruption virus protein was being synthesized in old bacterial ribosomes under the influence of an unstable RNA fraction which was presumed to act as a messenger from the virus DNA. It appeared that the ribosomes were non-specialized structures which synthesize at a given time the protein dictated by the messenger they happen to contain. The function of the ribosomal RNA was not revealed by these experiments and remains unknown.

Nirenberg and Matthaei (1961) obtained evidence that the messenger RNA must be in the form of a single chain in order to function. In a cell-free system derived from *Escherichia coli*, a synthetic polyribonucleotide containing uracil but no other bases, and hence necessarily in the form of single chains, was found to lead to a specific type of protein synthesis (see § 14.10) whereas when the uracil chains were paired with adenine chains, no such synthesis occurred.

Evidence pointing to the existence of messenger RNA in chromosomal organisms was obtained by Ycas and Vincent (1960). They allowed *Saccharomyces cerevisiae* to grow in the presence of orthophosphate containing radioactive phosphorus (^{32}P), and found that the newly-synthesized RNA into which it was incorporated had a molar base composition of 32% adenine, 29% uracil, 19% guanine, and 20% cytosine. This is similar to the DNA composition: 31·5% adenine, 33% thymine, 18·5% guanine, and 17% cytosine, and quite different from the overall RNA composition (chiefly ribosomes) of 25% adenine, 28% uracil, 23% guanine, and 24% cytosine. A number of authors have since obtained similar evidence from mammalian tissues. Although not conclusive, these observations suggest that messenger RNA may be of general occurrence.

§ 14.7   Evidence that one particular nucleotide chain of DNA is transcribed

Bautz and Hall (1962) isolated virus *T*4 messenger RNA from recently infected cells of *Escherichia coli* by absorbing the RNA at 55°C in a cellulose column containing virus *T*4 DNA in the single-chain condition following heating. The RNA was subsequently separated from the DNA by heating to 65°C, and then purified, and hydrolysed to find its base composition. The results obtained are shown in Table 14.3 and are in reasonable agreement with those of Volkin and Astrachan discussed in § 14.6 and obtained by a different method. In view of this agreement, Bautz and Hall attached real significance to a feature of their data of great interest, namely, that the total content of guanine and cytosine in the messenger RNA (37%) is approximately equal to the corresponding total for the virus DNA (36%), but the individual bases occur unequally in the RNA (21% guanine, 16% cytosine). These observations would be accounted for if the messenger RNA is always synthesized as the complement of one particular nucleotide-chain of the DNA, and if this chain contains 21% cytosine-analogue and 16% guanine. A similar argument can be applied to the data for the other pair of bases.

Evidence that only one specific DNA chain appears to be made use of when the gene functions was also obtained by Champe and Benzer (1962) from study of the effect of 5-fluorouracil on the expression of certain *r*II mutants of *T*4 virus. This base analogue is thought to be incorporated into RNA in place of uracil, but then to show hydrogen bonding similar to cytosine. In consequence, an *r*II mutant which has uracil in place of cytosine at one point in its messenger RNA will lose its mutant character and show the normal phenotype if 5-fluorouracil has taken the place of the uracil. The adenine in the DNA chain complementary to the uracil will be unaffected, so the mutant character will reappear in the progeny. Of 46 *r*II mutants thought from their reversion behaviour with mutagens (see § 14.2) to be due to a transition from a guanine cytosine-analogue base-pair to an adenine thymine pair, 29 were found to give the wild-type phenotype with 5-fluorouracil, while the remaining 17 did not respond. This result would be accounted for if the group of 29 mutants had one orientation of adenine and thymine with respect to the two DNA chains and the group of 17 mutants had the other orientation, and if the messenger RNA was synthesized as the complement of only one specific nucleotide chain of the DNA. The 29 mutants which responded to the uracil analogue were assumed to have adenine in this DNA chain at the mutant site, and hence normally would have uracil in the messenger RNA, while the other 17 were presumed to have thymine in the DNA chain and hence adenine in the messenger RNA.

Further evidence that only one of the two chains of the DNA is transcribed into messenger RNA has been obtained from several sources. In *Diplococcus pneumoniae* the two nucleotide chains of the DNA differ sufficiently in base composition to form separate bands when centrifuged in caesium chloride solution. Guild and Robison (1963) obtained preparations of the two fractions by this means. Using DNA from a novobiocin-resistant strain of the bacterium, they found that the heavy fraction (richer in the heavier purine, guanine, and the heavier pyrimidine, thymine) required about 45 minutes at 37°C to transform novobiocin-sensitive cells to resistance, whereas the lighter fraction modified the phenotype almost immediately. Since the cell generation time is about 40 minutes at 37°, it was inferred that the heavier chain needs to replicate before effective messenger RNA can be synthesized, whereas the lighter chain does not. It appeared likely that the messenger RNA from the gene for novobiocin-resistance was always complementary to the lighter of the two DNA chains.

Fox and Meselson (1963) obtained virus lambda (λ) of *Escherichia coli* in which the thymine of the DNA was replaced by 5-bromouracil. Following mixed infection of the host with this and with normal λ, those progeny virus which had one chain of the DNA normal and the other containing 5-bromouracil were isolated by density-gradient centrifugation. Virus particles in which both chains of the DNA contain 5-bromouracil are rapidly inactivated by exposure to light. It was found that when the virus particles in which one chain contained 5-bromouracil and the other did not were exposed to light, half the population survived. This would be accounted for if one specific chain of the DNA was essential for the synthesis of messenger RNA which was needed for a function upon which the replication of the DNA was dependent. If this DNA chain happened to be the one containing

5-bromouracil, no messenger would be formed and the virus DNA would be unable to replicate. In the other half of the population of virus particles, the 5-bromouracil would be in the complementary DNA chain, damage to which would not prevent the formation of messenger RNA.

Studies by a number of authors using bacterial viruses in which the two chains of the DNA can be separated, either because of a difference in molecular weight or because all the mature virus contains only one specific chain, have shown that the messenger RNA formed after infection has a base composition similar to one chain of the virus DNA and hence complementary to the other. With virus $\phi X174$, progress has been made in understanding why the formation of messenger RNA *in vivo* appears to be complementary to one DNA chain, while *in vitro* it may be formed complementary to both (see § 14.6). This virus has its DNA in the form of a single molecule with the ends joined to form a closed circle (see § 12.7). Hayashi, Hayashi, and Spiegelman (1964) purified chromatographically the DNA of $\phi X174$ obtained during its replication in the host, *E. coli*. Although the mature virus contains only one specific nucleotide chain (see § 14.6), complementary chains are present during replication. It was confirmed both from electron micrographs and from sedimentation patterns that at least 90% of the virus DNA molecules retained their circular form. The RNA synthesized *in vitro* with the RNA polymerase using the circular double-chain $\phi X174$ DNA as primer was found to resemble one of the DNA chains in composition, whereas when the DNA was fragmented by means of a sonic oscillator, the RNA resembled both chains. This was established from the relative frequencies with which ^{32}P, incorporated into the RNA in guanosine 5'-phosphate, was recovered in the 3'- (and 2'-) phosphates of each of the 4 nucleosides after alkaline hydrolysis, because the relative frequency of the 4 bases on the 3' side of guanine in one DNA chain happens to be quite different from that in the other chain. Confirmation of the results was obtained by heating and slow cooling the RNA and the single-chain DNA of the mature virus. The RNA synthesized with disrupted double-chain DNA as primer gave rise to hybrid molecules with the single-chain DNA, whereas the RNA formed with the unbroken double-chain DNA did not. The inference from these experiments is that messenger RNA produced from the unbroken two-chain DNA resembles the single DNA chain of the mature virus in composition. It is evident that fragmentation of the DNA causes breakdown of the mechanism which determines that the messenger RNA shall be formed as the complement of one specific DNA chain.

§ 14.8   The adaptor hypothesis

In considering how base sequence in DNA or RNA could be translated into aminoacid sequence in a polypeptide chain, Crick (1957) pointed out that it was difficult to see how this was possible by direct contact between the coding nucleotides and the specific aminoacid. He predicted that each aminoacid was likely first to be combined with its own specific *adaptor*, and that each of these adaptors would have a highly specific spatial pattern of hydrogen bonds capable of associating it with a particular sequence of bases in DNA or RNA. He further suggested that molecules based on sequences of nucleotides were likely candidates for the adaptors, and that the combination between each aminoacid and its own specific adaptor could be made by a special enzyme. Within a year, Hoagland, Zamecnik, and Stephenson (1957) had discovered the existence of molecules of precisely the kind Crick had anticipated. They had found a low molecular weight RNA in the non-particulate fraction of an extract of the cytoplasm of liver cells of *Rattus norvegicus*. These RNA molecules, at first called soluble RNA to distinguish them from the RNA of the ribosomes, appeared to have the ability

$$\text{(i)} \quad E_1 + aa_1 + Appp \longrightarrow E_1(aa_1 \cdot pA) + pp$$

$$\text{(ii)} \quad E_1(aa_1 \cdot pA) + RNA_1 \longrightarrow aa_1 \cdot RNA_1 + E_1 + Ap$$

$$\text{(iii)} \quad aa_1 \cdot RNA_1 + aa_2 \cdot RNA_2 \xrightarrow[\text{Gppp}]{\text{Tr}} aa_1 \cdot aa_2 \cdot RNA_2 + RNA_1$$

FIGURE 14.5   The three primary steps by which aminoacids are incorporated into proteins.   A = Adenosine (adenine ribonucleoside)
aa_1, aa_2 = Aminoacids nos. 1, 2
E_1 = Activating enzyme no. 1
G = Guanosine (guanine ribonucleoside)
p = Phosphate
RNA_1, RNA_2 = Transfer RNA nos. 1, 2
Tr = Transfer enzyme

to bind aminoacids to themselves and to transfer them to peptide linkages. The names acceptor RNA and *transfer RNA* were subsequently proposed, because of this ability to accept aminoacids and transfer them to protein.

The primary steps in the process of protein synthesis, which were quickly established following the discovery of transfer RNA, appear to be as follows. Each aminoacid is first combined with adenosine triphosphate (ATP) and a specific enzyme to form a single complex consisting of the aminoacid, adenosine monophosphate (AMP) and the enzyme, with the elimination of pyrophosphate (Fig. 14.5(i)). Each of the 20 aminoacids has its own specific activating enzyme. The second step is the interaction of the whole aminoacid-AMP-enzyme complex with a specific transfer RNA to form an aminoacid-RNA-compound. AMP and the enzyme are released in the process (Fig. 14.5(ii)). There is a unique transfer RNA molecule for each aminoacid. The third and final step in protein synthesis takes place in the ribosomes. Each transfer RNA aminoacid complex evidently becomes associated through specific hydrogen bonding of its coding nucleotides with the appropriate base sequence in the messenger RNA, thereby placing the aminoacids in the sequence dictated by the messenger. The formation of the peptide links is mediated by a single (aminoacid non-specific) transfer enzyme, plus a co-factor (guanosine triphosphate) (Fig. 14.5(iii)). It is evident that the transfer RNA molecules correspond precisely with Crick's postulated adaptors.

The nature of the chemical bonds involved in these steps is shown in more detail in Fig. 14.6. The link between AMP and the aminoacid is between the

$aa_1 \cdot RNA_1$

$$
\begin{array}{l}
\text{R}_1 \\
\quad | \\
\text{Amino}\!-\!\alpha\,\text{Carbon}\!-\!\text{Carboxyl}\!-\!{}^{2'}\text{Ribose}\!-\!{}^{5'}\text{Phosphate}\!-\!{}^{3'}\text{Ribose}\!-\!{}^{5'}\text{Phosphate}\!-\!{}^{3'}\text{Ribose}\!-\!{}^{5'}\!\cdots \\
\text{group}\quad | \qquad\quad \text{group} \qquad\quad {}^{1'}| \qquad\qquad\qquad\quad {}^{1'}| \qquad\qquad\qquad\qquad {}^{1'}| \\
\qquad\quad \text{H} \qquad\qquad\qquad\qquad\quad {}^{9}\text{Adenine} \qquad\quad {}^{3}\text{Cytosine} \qquad\qquad {}^{3}\text{Cytosine}
\end{array}
$$

$aa_2 \cdot RNA_2$

$$
\begin{array}{l}
\text{R}_2 \\
\quad | \\
\text{Amino}\!-\!\alpha\,\text{Carbon}\!-\!\text{Carboxyl}\!-\!{}^{2'}\text{Ribose}\!-\!{}^{5'}\text{Phosphate}\!-\!{}^{3'}\text{Ribose}\!-\!{}^{5'}\text{Phosphate}\!-\!{}^{3'}\text{Ribose}\!-\!{}^{5}\!\cdots \\
\text{group}\quad | \qquad\quad \text{group} \qquad\quad {}^{1'}| \qquad\qquad\qquad\quad {}^{1'}| \qquad\qquad\qquad\qquad {}^{1'}| \\
\qquad\quad \text{H} \qquad\qquad\qquad\qquad\quad {}^{9}\text{Adenine} \qquad\quad {}^{3}\text{Cytosine} \qquad\qquad {}^{3}\text{Cytosine}
\end{array}
$$

$aa_1 \cdot aa_2 \cdot RNA_2$

$$
\begin{array}{l}
\text{R}_1 \qquad\qquad\qquad\qquad\qquad\qquad \text{R}_2 \\
\quad | \qquad\qquad\qquad\qquad\qquad\qquad\quad | \\
\text{Amino}\!-\!\alpha\,\text{Carbon}\!-\!\text{Carboxyl}\!-\!\text{Amino}\!-\!\alpha\,\text{Carbon}\!-\!\text{Carboxyl}\!-\!{}^{2'}\text{Ribose}\!-\!{}^{5'}\text{Phosphate}\!-\!{}^{3'}\text{Ribose}\!-\!{}^{5'}\!\cdots \\
\text{group}\quad | \qquad\quad \text{group} \qquad\quad \text{group} \qquad\quad | \qquad\quad \text{group} \qquad\quad {}^{1'}| \qquad\qquad\qquad\qquad {}^{1'}| \\
\qquad\quad \text{H} \underbrace{\qquad\qquad\qquad\qquad}_{\text{Peptide linkage}} \text{H} \qquad\qquad\qquad\qquad {}^{9}\text{Adenine} \qquad\qquad {}^{3}\text{Cytosine}
\end{array}
$$

aa_1

$$\begin{array}{ccc} & R_1 & \\ & | & \\ \text{Amino}-&\alpha\text{ Carbon}-&\text{Carboxyl} \\ \text{group} & | & \text{group} \\ & H & \end{array}$$

Appp

$$\text{Phosphate}-\text{Phosphate}-\text{Phosphate}-^{5'}\text{Ribose}$$
$$^{1'}|$$
$$^{9}\text{Adenine}$$

$aa_1\cdot pA$

$$\begin{array}{ccc} & R_1 & \\ & | & \\ \text{Amino}-&\alpha\text{ Carbon}-&\text{Carboxyl}-\text{Phosphate}-^{5'}\text{Ribose} \\ \text{group} & | & \text{group} \qquad\qquad\qquad {}^{1'}| \\ & H & {}^{9}\text{Adenine} \end{array}$$

RNA_1

$$\text{Ribose}-^{5'}\text{Phosphate}-^{3'}\text{Ribose}-^{5'}\text{Phosphate}-^{3'}\text{Ribose}-^{5'}\text{Phosphate}-\cdots\text{(About 80 nucleotides)}$$
$$^{1'}| \qquad\qquad\qquad {}^{3}| \qquad\qquad\qquad {}^{3}|$$
$$^{9}\text{Adenine} \qquad\qquad \text{Cytosine} \qquad\qquad \text{Cytosine}$$

FIGURE 14.6   The structure of the intermediates in protein synthesis. The link between transfer RNA and aminoacid is shown as arising through the 2′ carbon atom of ribose but this is not yet conclusively established. The symbols in the left hand column have the same meaning as in Fig. 14.5.

phosphate of AMP and the carboxyl group of the aminoacid (—P—O—C—). The transfer RNA molecules each consist of a single nucleotide chain containing about 80 nucleotides (see § 14.9). The end of this chain which becomes linked to the aminoacid has the same structure in all the transfer RNAs. The terminal base is adenine and the next two are both cytosine. The linkage between aminoacid and transfer RNA is between the ribose of this terminal nucleotide (adenylic acid) and the carboxyl group of the aminoacid (—C—O—C—). It is probable, though not yet conclusively established, that the link arises through the 2′ carbon atom of the ribose (cf. Zamecnik 1962). The presence of an oxygen atom at this position in RNA, which is the main distinction between it and DNA, makes this 2′ linkage possible. The peptide linkage is formed by a covalent bond between the carboxyl carbon atom of the first aminoacid and the amino group of the second. The transfer RNA of the first aminoacid is detached from this carboxyl carbon in the process. The aminoacids are added successively in this way, each displacing the transfer RNA of the preceding one. The polypeptide chain therefore grows at its carboxyl end. In other words, the free amino end of the completed chain is where synthesis began and the free carboxyl end where it ended. This was demonstrated by Dintzis (1961) from study of the incorporation of tritium-labelled leucine into the haemo-globin of *Oryctolagus* reticulocytes.

Chapeville, Lipmann, von Ehrenstein, Weisblum, Ray, and Benzer (1962) have demonstrated the truth of the adaptor hypothesis. The amino-acid cysteine was converted into alanine by reduction with nickel hydride after the aminoacid had become attached to the cysteine-specific transfer RNA. It was then found that alanine was incorporated into polypeptides in place of cysteine. This was demonstrated with an *in vitro* protein-synthesizing system with which it has been shown that a synthetic RNA containing uracil and guanine will lead to the incorporation into polypeptides of certain aminoacids including cysteine, but not alanine (see § 14.10). This experiment shows that the messenger RNA code is recognized by the transfer RNA and not by the aminoacid attached to it, and thereby estab-lishes the truth of the Crick-Hoagland adaptor hypothesis. Von Ehrenstein, Weisblum, and Benzer (1963) using *Oryctolagus* reticulocytes, confirmed that in the same way alanine could be incorporated into a peptide of the α-chain of haemoglobin that normally contains cysteine but not alanine.

§ 14.9 The structure of transfer RNA

With the establishment of the adaptor theory, the analysis of the structure of the adaptors, or in other words, of transfer RNA, becomes of paramount importance for understanding how the aminoacid code is translated. Their structure, as far as it is known at present, shows several remarkable features. The base composition from all sources examined appears to be strikingly uniform. According to data tabulated by Brown (1963), the transfer RNA of the bacterium *Escherichia coli*, the alga *Euglena gracilis*, the fungus *Saccharomyces cerevisiae*, the flowering plant *Pisum sativum*, the protozoan *Tetrahymena*

FIGURE 14.7   The structure of (a) uracil ribonucleoside (uridine), and (b) 5-ribosyluracil (pseudouridine).

pyriformis, the insect *Calliphora* sp., the fish *Salmo* sp., and the mammals *Oryctolagus cuniculus, Cavia porcellus, Rattus norvegicus* and *Bos taurus* are all similar, with a molar base composition approximating to 19% adenine, 18% uracil, 30% guanine, 29% cytosine and 4% of unusual bases. Most of this 4% is a nucleotide called pseudouridylic acid, which has uracil as its nitrogenous base, but the linkage to ribose is at position 5 in the uracil molecule instead of at position 3 (see Fig. 14.7). The nucleoside so formed is called 5-ribosyluracil or pseudouridine. Transfer RNA has frequently been found also to contain small quantities of a number of methylated purines. These are listed in Fig. 14.8. There is evidence that transfer RNA is formed by transcription of a nucleotide sequence from DNA (see § 16.1). The methylation of purines is thought to occur subsequently, and the pseudouridylic acid also to be formed subsequent to the transcription, through enzymatic modification of uridylic acid (the ribonucleotide containing uracil).

The close approximation to equality between the quantities of adenine and uracil and of guanine and cytosine in transfer RNA suggests that there is complementary base pairing as in DNA. Physical and chemical studies (cf. review by Brown, 1963) have established that transfer RNA contains only a single nucleotide chain with about 80 nucleotides. For base pairing, it would therefore be necessary for one part of the molecule to be complementary to another part, and for the chain to be folded back upon itself. Spencer, Fuller, Wilkins, and Brown (1962) found the X-ray diffraction patterns of transfer RNA to be strikingly similar to those of DNA and concluded that a substantial fraction of the molecule had a double-stranded helical structure with complementary sequences of bases. They suggested

Purine

| | Position of substituent in purine | | |
	1	2	6
Adenine		methyl	amino amino methylamino dimethylamino
Guanine	methyl	amino amino methylamino dimethylamino	hydroxy hydroxy hydroxy hydroxy

FIGURE 14.8   The methylated purines found in transfer RNA. Adenine and guanine are shown for comparison.

that transfer RNA was a rod-shaped molecule 10 mμ long and 2·5 mμ wide, and composed of a single nucleotide chain folded back on itself in the middle like a hairpin, and with base sequences in one arm complementary to those in the other and forming 3½ turns of an intertwined double helix (Fig. 14.9). From molecular model-building they deduced that the fold at the end of the molecule (middle of the chain) must consist of at least 3 nucleotides with free hydrogen bonding sites on the bases. They suggested that these might be the nucleotides which form hydrogen bonds with messenger RNA. There is evidence that the pseudouridine and the methylated purines are situated in the central part of the chain, or in other words, on the model of Spencer *et al.*, in this coding region with messenger RNA.

From the X-ray data, Spencer *et al.* inferred that, on account of the extra hydroxyl group in the sugar molecule, an RNA double helix, such as they postulated for transfer RNA, has a rather different structure from a DNA double helix. Whereas DNA has the base-pairs set perpendicular to the helix axis, the RNA base-pairs are thought to be tilted about 20°, such that they are lower on the right than on the left (when the axis is vertical and the helices are observed from the side). For a given number of base-pairs, the tilting gives a molecule only about ¾ the length of DNA, and correspondingly

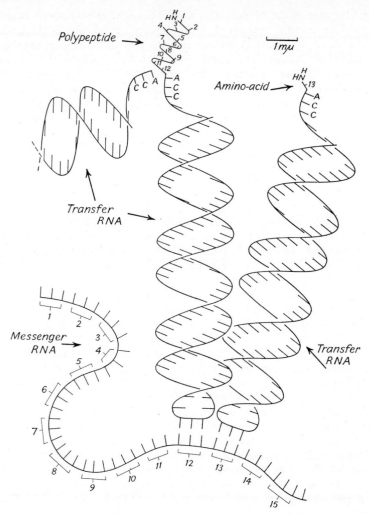

FIGURE 14.9.   Diagram to illustrate the structure for transfer
RNA proposed by Spencer *et al.* (1962), and to
show how the triplet sequence in messenger RNA
is believed to determine which transfer RNA molecules shall succeed one another in taking up position
on the ribosome (not shown), and hence which
aminoacids shall succeed one another in the
polypeptide. The transfer RNA which added
aminoacid no. 11 to the polypeptide has just been
displaced by that which has brought no. 12, while
that bringing no. 13 has just been selected through
its ability to pair with triplet no. 13 in the messenger.

wider. One turn of the RNA double helix is thought to have about 11 nucleotide pairs in $2 \cdot 8$ mμ, compared with 10 pairs in $3 \cdot 4$ mμ in DNA. Bassel, Hayashi and Spiegelman (1964) studied the hybrid molecules, consisting of one nucleotide chain of DNA and one of RNA, formed by RNA synthesis *in vitro* from the single-chain DNA of virus $\phi X174$ of *Escherichia coli*. From electron micrographs, they found that the hybrid molecules were circular in form, and with an average circumference only about $\frac{5}{6}$ of that of the corresponding DNA double-chain molecules (see § 12.7). They suggested that in the RNA synthesis small segments of the DNA template might be omitted, but it seems more likely that the RNA chain is complete, but that it distorts the DNA chain and produces a molecule intermediate in length between the corresponding DNA and RNA double helices.

The part of each transfer RNA molecule which is recognised by the specific aminoacid and its attached specific enzyme (aminoacyl RNA synthetase) is not known, but there is evidence of differences in base sequence in the region adjoining the terminal adenine-cytosine-cytosine- sequence, and also at the other end of the chain. It is therefore tentatively assumed that the aminoacid specificity of each transfer RNA is determined by the base sequence of the two ends of the chain (although the extreme end of one is always adenine-cytosine-cytosine-), and the specificity with messenger RNA by the base sequence of the central region which forms the hairpin bend in the model of Spencer *et al.* It is assumed that the large intervening regions of the nucleotide chain have the same base sequence in all transfer RNA molecules. This would account for their uniformity in total base composition. The functions of the pseudouridine and methylated purines are not known.

Holley *et al.* (1965) have obtained the complete nucleotide sequence of a transfer RNA for alanine in *Saccharomyces cerevisiae*. This was achieved by partial digestion with two different ribonucleases, followed in each case by separation of the various nucleotide fragments by chromatography, and their identification. It was found that this transfer RNA consists of a linear sequence of 77 nucleotides, that the abnormal bases are scattered through the molecule and not grouped together, and that there are no long runs of nucleotides with a complementary sequence in reverse order in the other half of the molecule, such as would be expected with the hairpin model. Indeed, the longest uninterrupted sequences having the inverted complementary sequence elsewhere in the molecule are of 5 nucleotides. The configuration of the molecule therefore remains uncertain, and may be variable depending on the external conditions. If the molecule is hairpin-shaped, there must be many irregularities in its detailed structure. The triplet of nucleotides (*anticodon*), which is presumed to pair with a triplet coding for alanine in messenger RNA, has not been identified with certainty. One possibility is the sequence cytosine-guanine-guanine at positions 19 to 21, numbering the nucleotides from the end of the chain with a free 5′-phosphate. This triplet is flanked on each side by an abnormal base, which might have the function of insulating the anticodon from the influence of neighbouring nucleotides. These abnormal bases are 5, 6-dihydrouracil, which Madison and

Holley (1965) have shown to occur in alanine transfer RNA of *Saccharomyces*.

Gilbert (1963) has suggested that there is only one active site for the synthesis of the peptide bond on each ribosome, and that each transfer RNA molecule takes the place of the preceding one, adding its aminoacid to the chain and ejecting the previous transfer RNA as it does so. In Fig. 14.9, a transfer RNA is supposed just to have added aminoacid no. 12 to a polypeptide chain, displacing the transfer RNA which brought aminoacid no. 11. Gilbert has suggested that this displacement of the previous tenant forces the messenger to move over the ribosome by one reading unit, thereby allowing the next transfer RNA to take up position: in the diagram, this is the transfer RNA carrying aminoacid no. 13. Eventually, the end of the messenger is far enough away to attach a second ribosome. The aggregates of ribosomes which occur when protein synthesis is taking place would arise in this way, as suggested by Gierer (1963) and others, through a series of ribosomes being serviced by one messenger RNA molecule. Each ribosome would move along the messenger as its polypeptide chain is synthesized. Slayter, Warner, Rich, and Hall (1963) have studied the ribosome aggregates in the reticulocytes of *Oryctolagus* under the electron microscope. These cells synthesize haemoglobin predominantly, and so the messenger RNA is expected to be of a uniform length of not less than 150 mμ, assuming 3 nucleotides to every 1 mμ, a coding ratio of 3, and 150 aminoacids per polypeptide. The electron micrographs agreed with this expectation: there were usually 5 ribosomes held together by a thread 1 mμ in width and 170–280 mμ in length (see Fig. 14.10(a)).

Staehelin, Wettstein, Oura and Noll (1964) have found the average length in nucleotides of the segment of messenger RNA between adjacent ribosomes in the ribosomal aggregates of liver cells of *Rattus*. By sedimentation analysis it was found that the molecular weight of the messenger RNA was proportional to the size of the ribosome aggregate, and corresponded to 90 nucleotides per ribosome. On the assumption that the ribosome spacing is the same in *Oryctolagus* reticulocytes synthesizing haemoglobin, there must be approximately 450 nucleotides to the haemoglobin messenger RNA molecule since it usually extends to 5 ribosomes. As the haemoglobin polypeptides synthesized contain about 150 aminoacids, it follows that the coding ratio is 3 (see Fig. 14.10(b)).

Evidence that the aminoacid code was likely to be the same in a wide range of organisms was obtained by von Ehrenstein and Lipmann (1961). They showed that transfer RNA and associated aminoacid-activating enzymes derived from *Escherichia coli*, when mixed with the ribosomes and attached haemoglobin messenger RNA from the reticulocytes of *Oryctolagus*, would bring about the synthesis of haemoglobin. In other words, the bacterial transfer RNA was interpreting the mammalian messenger correctly as judged by the fingerprint of the end-product. However, there is evidence to suggest that the translation of the code can be modified by gene mutation. Brody and Yanofsky (1963) found that a suppressor gene can alter the primary structure of a protein. Mutant $A36$ leads to the insertion of arginine instead of glycine at a particular position in the A protein of tryptophan

(a)

(b)

150
amino-acids

←- - - - 450 *nucleotides*- - - -→

FIGURE 14.10 Ribosomes from reticulocytes of *Oryctolagus cuniculus* (Rabbit). The thread
joining the ribosomes is thought to be
messenger RNA for one of the polypeptide chains of haemoglobin.

(a) Appearance as seen in electron
micrographs prepared by Slayter *et
al.* (1963).

(b) Diagrammatic representation to
show the progressive formation of
the polypeptide chain on the ribosomes as they move along the
messenger RNA (from left to right
in the diagram).

synthetase in *Escherichia coli*. This makes the enzyme non-functional and
hence imposes a requirement for tryptophan on the bacterium. A mutation
of a suppressor gene, which was not linked to the *A* gene, caused mutant *A*36
to become wild-type in phenotype, and it was found that glycine was
inserted again in place of the arginine. Brody and Yanofsky suggested that
the suppressor gene probably interfered with the translation of the *A* gene
messenger RNA into polypeptide, for example, (a) by altering the arginine
activating enzyme so that it activated glycine in addition to arginine, or (b)
by altering the glycine activating enzyme or the arginine transfer RNA so that
they paired with one another in addition to normally, or (c) by altering the
glycine transfer RNA so that it paired with the arginine triplet in the messenger,
as well as pairing normally. This discovery is analogous to that referred to in
§ 13.8, p. 223, where a bacterial mutant is described which modifies the
reading of the messenger RNA for the protein which forms the membrane
of the head of virus *T*4. (See also § 14.10 and § 16.1.)

If the mechanism of protein synthesis outlined in this and the preceding section is correct, the reading of the aminoacid code would be in consecutive non-overlapping triplets of nucleotides in messenger RNA. It is not necessary to assume that there is any recognition of the coding triplets in the transfer of nucleotide sequence from DNA to RNA.

§ 14.10   The deciphering of the code

A major step forward in the understanding of the aminoacid code was taken by Nirenberg and Matthaei (1961) when they discovered a direct method for deciphering it. They had found that a synthetic RNA in which all the bases were uracil would bring about the incorporation of phenyl-alanine into polypeptide chains. This was achieved with an *in vitro* protein-synthesizing system derived from disrupted cells of *Escherichia coli*. After centrifuging the cell contents, the ribosomes were mixed with supernatant solution containing transfer RNA and enzymes, and adenosine triphosphate (ATP) and an ATP-generating system were added. The synthetic RNA was obtained by means of the polynucleotide phosphorylase first isolated by Grunberg-Manago and Ochoa (1955) (see § 14.4). The aminoacid was labelled with ^{14}C and the subsequent presence of the label in polypeptide chains demonstrated.

Lengyel, Speyer, and Ochoa (1961) synthesized an RNA using a mixture of the ribonucleoside diphosphates of uracil (U) and cytosine (C) in the proportion of 5:1. On the assumption that nucleotides are randomly incorporated into the chain in proportion to their abundance, out of every 216 triplets there will be 125 with the sequence UUU, 25 each with UUC, UCU, and CUU, 5 each with UCC, CUC, and CCU and 1 with CCC. Lengyel *et al.* found that when added to the protein-synthesizing system, this RNA led to the incorporation of serine as well as phenylalanine into the polypeptide. There were approximately 4·4 phenylalanine residues to every 1 of serine, and so it was tentatively concluded that, if it is a triplet code, one of the 3 trinucleotides containing 2 uracils and 1 cytosine codes for serine. In the same way, a synthetic RNA containing uracil and adenine in the proportion of 5:1 was found to lead to the incorporation of phenylalanine and tyrosine in the proportion of 4:1, suggesting that the code for tyrosine contained 2 uracils and 1 adenine.

By an extension of this technique, provisional nucleotide triplets were soon assigned to nearly all the aminoacids. A notable feature was that all these triplets contained uracil. This suggested that more than one triplet could code for the same aminoacid, since uracil was not known to occur in such excess in natural messenger RNA. The multiple coding for individual aminoacids was confirmed when Gardner, Wahba, Basilio, Miller, Lengyel, and Speyer (1962) found that most synthetic RNA molecules without uracil will also bring about aminoacid incorporation. Moreover, they showed that an RNA containing only adenine leads to a polypeptide composed of lysine residues. This was first demonstrated with an *in vitro* protein synthe-sizing system derived from liver cells of *Rattus*, and it was subsequently shown with the *E. coli* system. In conjunction with the original discovery that uracil RNA gives a phenylalanine polypeptide, this finding was of particular significance because adenine and uracil are complementary. The implication was that nucleotide sequence is transcribed from one particular chain of the DNA molecule, because the other chain would lead (through a complementary messenger RNA) to the formation of a different polypeptide. Thus an adenine triplet in DNA would give a uracil triplet in messenger RNA and hence phenylalanine in the peptide, while the complementary thymine triplet in the other DNA chain would give rise to an adenine triplet in messenger RNA and hence lysine in the peptide. As indicated in § 14.7, there is experimental evidence that messenger RNA is indeed synthesized only as the complement of one specific chain of the DNA.

In vitro protein synthesizing systems based on components of mammalian cells were found by several authors to show the same code as *E. coli*. This confirmed von Ehrenstein and Lipmann's conclusion (see § 14.9) that at least the greater part of the code was the same.

Wahba, Miller, Basilio, Gardner, Lengyel, and Speyer (1963), in adding further data to previously published results, brought the total number of triplets assigned to aminoacids to 47. All the 64 possible triplets are shown in Fig. 14.11, and the arrows indicate the aminoacid allocations that have been proposed. Triplets with the same overall composition are grouped together since in most instances there is no information about the nucleotide sequences associated with the specific aminoacids*. The data of Fig. 14.11 show two striking features. In the first place, the number of aminoacids allocated to the groups of triplets often equals but rarely exceeds the number of triplets in the group. This suggests that each triplet codes unambiguously for a specific aminoacid. An exception to this is the coding of both phenylalanine and leucine in *E. coli* by RNA containing only uracil (cf. von Ehrenstein and Dais 1963). With this uracil RNA and an *in vitro* protein-synthesizing system derived from *Bacillus stearothermophilus*, Friedman and Weinstein (1964) found that the formation of leucine was favoured at 37°C and of phenylalanine at 65°C. This bacterium is remarkable in its ability to grow at such high temperatures. An increase in the concentration of magnesium ions had a similar effect to lowering the temperature, while the addition of polyamines or streptomycin led to some incorporation of isoleucine, and small amounts of several other aminoacids. Davies, Gilbert and Gorini (1964), using the protein-synthesizing system from *Escherichia coli*, found that streptomycin caused extensive and specific alterations in the coding properties of synthetic RNAs. These results suggest that the translation of the code is capable of some modification through environmental factors. The possibility of genetic modification by suppressor mutations has already been mentioned (see § 14.9). Other phenomena, such as 'polarity mutants', which may also be due to changes in the reading of the code, are discussed in § 16.1.

A second feature of the results in Fig. 14.11 is that there are up to 5 triplets for the same aminoacid, and these usually appear to differ from one another by single nucleotide substitutions only. Two exceptions to this are

* Much information has since been obtained: see p. 262.

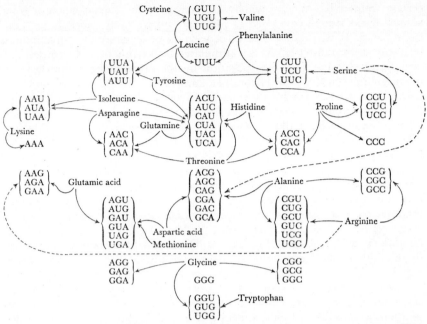

FIGURE 14.11   The triplets of nucleotides in *Escherichia coli* messenger RNA assigned to the various aminoacids, according to the data of Wahba *et al.* (1963). Broken arrows indicate triplets which differ by more than one nucleotide from others coding for the same aminoacid.   A = adenine.   C = cytosine.   G = guanine.   U = uracil.

indicated by broken arrows in the diagram. The close relationship between nearly all the alternative triplets for each aminoacid suggests that they arose from one another by mutation and that initially there was only a single triplet for each. Such multiple coding* would have a selective advantage in buffering the proteins against the effects of mutation. Support for the idea that the alternative coding arose by mutation has come from the work of Nirenberg and associates described below. They have obtained evidence for the nucleotide sequence in 44 codons, and in almost every instance of multiple coding the triplets differ by single nucleotides. A feature of particular interest in their data is the possibility that in the reading of the messenger the two pyrimidines (uracil and cytosine) may not be distinguished when they occur at the 3′ end of the RNA triplet (see p. 262).

In confirmation of this alternative coding for individual aminoacids, Weisblum, Benzer, and Holley (1962) demonstrated the existence in extracts of *Escherichia coli*, of two different transfer RNA molecules each specific for the same aminoacid (leucine). The two leucine transfer RNAs were separated by countercurrent fractionation. This technique depends on the discovery that

---

* Multiple coding for individual aminoacids is often referred to as code *degeneracy*, but, as Tatum (1964) has pointed out, this is a misleading expression, since it has evolutionary implications which may not be valid.

certain transfer RNAs have widely different partition coefficients in a two-phase solvent system composed of pH 6 phosphate buffer, formamide and isopropanol. It was found that incorporation of leucine into polypeptides by one of these transfer RNAs was stimulated by a synthetic RNA containing uracil and cytosine, and incorporation by the other was stimulated by a uracil-guanine RNA. Von Ehrenstein and Dais (1963) isolated a third leucine transfer RNA, which responded to an RNA containing uracil only.

That the aminoacid code should include several alternative coding units for many and perhaps all of the aminoacids provides an explanation for an otherwise puzzling phenomenon, namely, the remarkable diversity in the frequency of each base-pair in the DNA of different organisms, particularly among bacteria (cf. § 11.6). The range is from $\frac{1}{4}$ to $\frac{3}{4}$ of the total. This variation is much greater than could be due to diversity in aminoacid composition of the constituent proteins. The molar percentage of adenine + thymine out of the total bases in the DNA of 59 species of chromosomal organisms and 73 species of bacteria is shown graphically in Fig. 14.12, which is based on the data given by Sueoka (1961*a*). The uniformity in base composition of the more highly evolved organisms compared with fungi, algae and bacteria is apparent. This may reflect the relative length of time that has elapsed (or perhaps the number of generations) since they evolved. With alternative codes for the same aminoacid, considerable change in nucleotide composition is possible without affecting the aminoacid composition of the proteins. It is to be expected, therefore, that if a group of organisms has been in existence for a sufficiently long period of time, the nucleotide composition of its DNA will diverge through the occurrence of successive mutations until it spans the permissible range. As a very approximate indication of this range, the incomplete data for the aminoacid code in Fig. 14.11 would allow variation in adenine-thymine content from 43% to 70% without affecting aminoacid composition. This is on the assumption that all the aminoacids are equally abundant in proteins, which is far from the truth.

Sueoka (1961*b*) has shown that part of the variation in DNA base composition is to be attributed to alterations in the relative proportions of the various aminoacids in the proteins of the different species. He compared the DNA composition of 11 species of bacteria with the aminoacid composition of their total protein. The molar proportion of adenine plus thymine out of the total bases ranged from 28% to 65%. Sueoka found that asparagine and aspartic acid (which were not distinguished from one another), glutamine and glutamic acid (also not distinguished), isoleucine, lysine, phenylalanine, and tyrosine were relatively more abundant in the species with a high proportion of adenine and thymine than in those with a low content of this base-pair. Reference to Fig. 14.11 shows that these aminoacids all have a relatively high adenine-thymine content for their coding nucleotides (upper left-hand half of the diagram). Conversely, Sueoka found that alanine, arginine, glycine, and proline were more abundant in species with a high proportion of the guanine-cytosine base-pair, and from the diagram it is evident that these aminoacids are coded by nucleotides with a high guanine-cytosine content (lower right-hand half of the diagram). The remaining aminoacids

% Adenine and thymine in DNA

FIGURE 14.12   Histograms to show the molar percentage of adenine plus thymine
out of the total bases (adenine, cytosine, guanine and thymine) in
the DNA of 59 species of chromosomal organisms and 73 species
of bacteria, from the data given by Sueoka (1961*a*). The Algae
consist of 3 species of Diatoms (which had 60–64% of adenine
plus thymine) and 6 Green and 1 Brown Alga (34–46% adenine
plus thymine). The two species of Fungi are *Neurospora crassa*
(46% adenine plus thymine) and *Saccharomyces cerevisiae* (64%).
The seed-plants (Spermaphyta) consist of 1 Gymnosperm, 2
Monocotyledons and 8 Dicotyledons. The Invertebrates comprise
1 annelid, 3 crustaceans, 1 orthopteran insect, 1 mollusc and 6
echinoderms, and the Vertebrates consist of 4 species of fish, 1
amphibian, 1 reptile, 1 bird and 7 mammals including man
(60% adenine plus thymine).

(apart from cysteine and tryptophan which were not estimated) showed no
regular variation in frequency with DNA base content, and from Fig. 14.11
it is evident that they are coded predominantly or entirely by triplets containing members of both base-pairs. This comparison of aminoacid and
nucleotide frequencies has thus given independent support to the data on the
aminoacid code obtained with the *in vitro* protein-synthesizing system. It also
suggests that the code worked out for *E. coli* is similar, if not identical, for a
range of bacteria.

Another independent method for obtaining information about the
aminoacid code has been developed by Tsugita and Fraenkel-Conrat (1962)
and Wittmann (1962) using tobacco mosaic virus. Since nitrous acid is

thought to cause mutation by altering cytosine to uracil, and adenine to hypoxanthine which is then expected to pair like guanine (see § 14.2), any changes in the protein of the virus coat caused by mutations induced with nitrous acid will be expected to be the result of one or other of these two nucleotide substitutions. These authors have found that particular amino-acid substitutions, such as phenylalanine in place of serine, and isoleucine in place of threonine, turn up repeatedly with nitrous acid treatment. On the whole, there is good agreement between these substitutions and those predicted by changing cytosine to uracil and adenine to guanine in the code deduced from the results of the protein synthesis *in vitro* using *E. coli* components and synthetic RNA. However, owing to the occurrence of several coding triplets for the individual aminoacids, it has rarely been possible to interpret the nucleotide changes with certainty.

The work with mutants of tobacco mosaic virus has neverthless enabled an important inference to be made concerning the aminoacid code. Assuming the code was the same in a wide variety of organisms, Brenner's analysis (see § 14.1) eliminated all fully overlapping triplet codes, but the possibility that the code might be partially overlapping remained. If *A B C A C D* is a sequence of nucleotides, and if the code is in partially overlapping triplets, *ABC* might stand for the first aminoacid, and *CAC* for the second. The mutants of tobacco mosaic virus with abnormal protein induced by nitrous acid were found always to show only single aminoacid substitutions, or occasionally two substitutions at well-separated positions in the molecule. If the code were partially overlapping, a single nucleotide change would be expected sometimes to cause an alteration of two adjacent aminoacids, but this has not been observed. It is concluded that the code is non-overlapping.

Yanofsky and associates have likewise found that mutational changes affecting the *A* protein of the enzyme tryptophan synthetase of *Escherichia coli* modify single aminoacids at a time (see § 13.8 and Fig. 13.8), and furthermore they have demonstrated that recombination can occur within a coding unit. Henning and Yanofsky (1962) studied the changes due to mutations affecting the aminoacid at a particular position in the polypeptide. No less than 6 different aminoacid substitutions were found at this point (Fig. 14.13(*a*)), and some of the strains yielded recombinants when crossed with one another (Fig. 14.13(*b*)–(*d*)). The hypothetical explanation involving recombination within a codon, which Henning and Yanofsky offered for their results, using the triplets assigned to these aminoacids from the synthetic RNA data, is shown in the diagram. Owing to the existence of more than one triplet for most (perhaps all) the aminoacids (see Fig. 14.11), many alternative explanations of their data are possible, but it is evident that the results are compatible with the existing coding data, and moreover provide information about the relative positions of the nucleotides in the triplets. It seems likely that continued studies along these lines, in conjunction with the results of aminoacid incorporation induced by synthetic poly-ribonucleotides, will ultimately result in the complete deciphering of the code.

As described in § 13.8, so-called amber mutants are known in virus T4 of *E. coli* in which polypeptide synthesis ends prematurely. Weigert and Garen

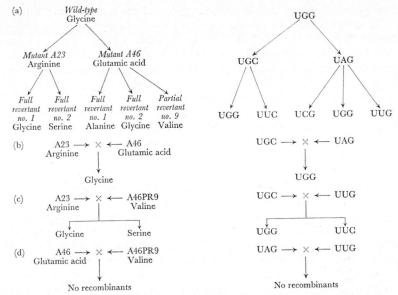

FIGURE 14.13   Changes found by Henning and Yanofsky (1962) in the aminoacid
at a particular position in the polypeptide of the *A* protein of the
enzyme tryptophan synthetase of *Escherichia coli*. The changes observed are shown on the left, and Henning and Yanofsky's explanations are given on the right, expressed in terms of possible RNA
coding triplets (cf. Fig. 14.11) (*a*) Change due to mutation. (*b*)–(*d*)
Changes due to recombination.

(1965) studied the reversion of an amber mutant of *E. coli*. In this mutant,
synthesis of the polypeptide of alkaline phosphatase is incomplete. The
aminoacid at the position in the polypeptide corresponding to its end in the
mutant was identified in 21 revertants, and from the range of aminoacids
found and the known codon assignments for them, it was inferred that there
was an RNA triplet indicating the end of the polypeptide, and that this
triplet was *UAG*.

Brenner, Stretton and Kaplan (1965) have also found that the RNA
nucleotide triplet coding for polypeptide chain termination in amber mutants
is *UAG*. They used mutants of virus *T4* of *E. coli* in which the synthesis of the
protein of the virus head was stopped at specific points in the polypeptide
(see § 13.8), and they identified the aminoacids which occurred at these
points when the virus was grown on a mutant bacterial strain which allowed
the protein synthesis to go to completion. From the codons previously
assigned to these aminoacids, they deduced the codon for polypeptide-end,
since only single nucleotide changes would be expected to distinguish it from
each of these aminoacid codons. They suggested that there is a specific
transfer RNA for *UAG*, and that in bacterial strains where the mutant
character of the virus was suppressed, a transfer RNA carrying a particular
aminoacid can also respond to *UAG*, and so allow some of the polypeptides
to go to completion.

18

Brenner *et al.* found that in another group of mutants of virus *T*4 called 'ochre' mutants, the mutant character of which is suppressed by different strains of *E. coli* from those which suppress amber mutants, the RNA codon for the end of the polypeptide chain was *UAA*. This was shown by study of the production and reversion of *r*II ochre and amber mutants using chemical mutagens, in conjunction with the observation that ochre mutants can be converted into amber mutants by mutation.

Nirenberg and Leder (1964) have described a method using *E. coli* extracts for measuring the interaction of transfer RNAs carrying specific aminoacids with ribosomes carrying messenger RNA. The behaviour of synthetic polyribonucleotides with chains of various lengths and compositions was studied. Trinucleotides with a 5′-terminal phosphate were found to be highly active in binding specific transfer RNAs to ribosomes, whereas similar dinucleotides, and also trinucleotides with 3′-terminal phosphate, were largely or entirely inactive. The trinucleotides with 5′-terminal phosphate containing only uracil (*UUU*), only adenine (*AAA*), and only cytosine (*CCC*) were found to direct the binding to ribosomes of transfer RNAs for phenylalanine, lysine, and proline, respectively, in agreement with earlier work (Fig. 14.11). The continued study (cf. Nirenberg *et al.*, 1965) of the behaviour of trinucleotides of known composition in binding specific amino-acyl transfer RNAs to ribosomes has suggested which aminoacids are coded by 44 different RNA triplets* and, like the work of Yanofsky and associates described above, also promises to elucidate the entire code.

* Glycine	GGU		Leucine	UUG CUG *CUU* *CUC*	Lysine	AAA AAG
Alanine	GCU				Phenylalanine	UUU UUC
Serine	UCG UCU UCC AGC AGU		Isoleucine	AUU AUC	Tyrosine	UAU UAC
			Aspartic acid	GAU GAC	Histidine	CAU CAC
Threonine	ACU ACC ACA ACG		Asparagine	AAU AAC	Tryptophan	*UGA*
Cysteine	UGU		Glutamic acid	GAA	Proline	CCU CCC CCA
Methionine	AUG		Glutamine	CAA CAG	End of polypeptide	UAA UAG
Valine	GUU					
			Arginine	CGC CGA *AGA*		

The triplets shown in italics may not code for any aminoacid when they occur at a terminal as distinct from an internal position in messenger RNA. The orientation of the trinucleotides in these formulae follows the conventional sequence (cf. § 12.5), that is, with 5′-phosphates to the left and 3′-phosphates to the right of the symbols (A, C, G, and U) for the ribonucleosides.

15. The polaron hybrid DNA hypothesis of genetic recombination

§ 15.1 Introduction

When recombination between alleles was first discovered (in *Drosophila* and *Aspergillus*), it was assumed that its mechanism was the same as between different genes. The recombinant individuals, selected because they were wild-type for the character shown by the pair of alleles, usually had one specific new combination of outside marker genes (see § 9.11 and § 13.2), such as is expected with crossing-over. Moreover, reciprocal recombinant genotypes were observed. In *Drosophila* these were from different meioses, but in diploid strains of *Aspergillus*, Pritchard (1955) found several instances of complementary recombinants in the two homologous chromosomes of the diploid, following mitotic recombination between alleles (see § 13.3). These observations appeared to establish that crossing-over could occur between alleles.

This conclusion was supported by theoretical considerations. The discovery that the linkage map of a series of alleles was collinear with the genetic map of the genes in the linkage group (§ 13.2) suggested that there might be no physical discontinuity between successive genes in the chromosome. If cistrons were segments of a DNA molecule, recognisable from one another merely by their characteristic nucleotide sequence, then it might be expected that the recombination process, whatever its mechanism, would bear no relation to the points of junction of one cistron with another and would be the same irrespective of whether the mutant sites happened to be within the same cistron or not. However, later work, notably with fungi belonging to the Ascomycetes, revealed that recombination between alleles can occur by mechanisms other than crossing-over.

§ 15.2 Recombination in Ascomycetes

As described in § 8.6 with reference to *Neurospora*, the products of meiosis in Ascomycetes are held together in a large cell, the ascus. By isolating the spores from individual asci, detailed information about the process of recombination can be obtained, if there is segregation for linked character-differences. It was by this means that Lindegren (1933) showed that crossing-over occurs between chromatids one from each homologue and that the centromeres segregate at the first division of meiosis (§ 8.6). Subsequently

(Lindegren, 1953), he obtained evidence that in *Saccharomyces cerevisiae* a mutant character, such as inability to ferment α-methyl glucoside, sometimes segregated from its normal allele at meiosis so as to give 3 normal and 1 mutant spores in the ascus, or 1 normal and 3 mutant, instead of the expected 2 of each kind. Lindegren followed Winkler (1930) in calling this phenomenon gene *conversion*. This discovery was so unexpected that it did not gain general acceptance until Mitchell (1955) demonstrated its occurrence with pyridoxin-requiring mutants of *Neurospora crassa*. She made use of linked marker genes on either side of the locus under study, such as were not available in *Saccharomyces*, and so was able to show that the 3:1 ratios at the pyridoxin locus were associated with normal 2:2 ratios for both of the linked character-differences. This established that the 3:1 ratios were due to abnormal segregation during meiosis at a particular mutant site in the chromosome, rather than to abnormal behaviour of whole chromosomes or nuclei.

Many examples of conversion have since been discovered. It is most readily detected with spore characters since the abnormal segregation can then be directly observed in the ascus (Pl. 4(*b*)–(*e*)). Indeed, Zickler (1934) saw this using spore-colour mutants of *Bombardia lunata*, but his observations had been neglected. Olive (1959) examined 2700 asci of *Sordaria fimicola* heterozygous for hyaline *versus* normal black ascospore colour and found 6 asci with 6 black and 2 hyaline spores, and 5 asci with 2 black and 6 hyaline spores. A mutant (*g*) with grey spores showed not only 6:2 and 2:6 ratios for spore colour in heterozygous asci but also 5:3 and 3:5 ratios. This was a remarkable discovery, as it implied that segregation of the character-difference had occurred at the mitosis after meiosis (*postmeiotic segregation*).

Kitani, Olive and El-Ani (1962) discovered another class of asci showing postmeiotic segregation. These asci had 4 black and 4 grey spores but the sequence was abnormal, with half the spores not in pairs. Such arrangements in the ascus can arise from the overlapping of two of the spindles at the third division such that the nuclei pass one another (see Table 8.2, p. 102). However, Kitani *et al.* made use of linked marker genes on either side of the grey spore locus, and this enabled them to distinguish between abnormal behaviour of whole nuclei (spindle overlap) and abnormal behaviour at the site of the spore mutant. The method of distinction is shown in Fig. 15.1 by plus and minus signs. These represent the behaviour of a linked character-difference of the mycelium which could be recognised after dissecting the asci and isolating and germinating the spores. With spindle overlap, the linked character will show the same aberrant sequence as the spore character, but with postmeiotic segregation at the mutant spore site it will not. Moreover, the postmeiotic segregation may give spore sequences such as 1 grey, 4 black, 3 grey, which are unlikely to arise from spindle overlap. Kitani *et al.* examined over 200,000 asci segregating for black and grey spores and found that the 5 classes of aberrant asci resulting from abnormal segregation at the *g* site occurred with widely different frequencies. The numbers in each class expected in a sample of 10^5 asci, according to their data, are shown below the

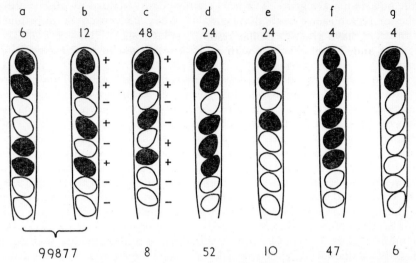

FIGURE 15.1   Asci of *Sordaria fimicola* from a cross between a normal black-spored
strain and a mutant with grey spores. The grey spores are shown
white in the diagram. The figures below the drawings of asci show
the numbers of each kind of ascus expected in a random sample of
100,000 asci, according to counts made by Kitani *et al.* (1962).
These numbers refer not only to the spore sequences shown but
also to any permutations of them which may arise from variation
in the orientation of the appropriate pair of chromosomes on the
spindle at any of the nuclear divisions in the ascus, or from the
presence or absence of crossing-over in the interval of the chromosome between the gene for spore colour and the centromere. The
number of such permutations is shown above the drawings. The
plus and minus signs in (*b*) and (*c*) show how a character-difference
of the mycelium has segregated. This character-difference becomes
evident after the spores germinate, and is due to a gene linked to
that for spore colour.

drawings in Fig. 15.1. These numbers include other spore sequences in
addition to those shown. The other sequences differ in spindle orientations
or in the division of meiosis at which segregation occurred (see § 8.6). The
number of alternative sequences which could arise in these ways is shown
above the drawings.

A notable feature of the data of Kitani *et al.* is that about 36% of the
aberrant asci (classes (*c*)–(*g*) of Fig. 15.1) showed crossing-over between the
marker genes on either side of the *g* site. Since these genes were closely
linked, with only about 4% of recombination, it is evident that the aberrant
segregation at the *g* site shows a highly significant correlation with the
occurrence of crossing-over in the immediate neighbourhood. Furthermore,
in 48 instances out of 52 the two chromatids involved in the crossing-over
were the same as those involved in the aberrant segregation. Nevertheless,
a majority of the aberrant asci (64%) showed the parental combinations of

the outside marker genes. The less extensive data obtained by others, using the more laborious methods needed to study conversion of nutritional instead of spore characters, have given similar results. This is exemplified by the data of Stadler and Towe (1963) with allelic cysteine-requiring mutants of *Neurospora crassa*.

Some further remarkable discoveries concerning recombination were made by Lissouba and Rizet (1960) using *Ascobolus immersus*. This fungus normally has dark brown ascospores, but mutants are known with colourless spores. The spores are forcibly discharged from the asci when mature, and can be collected on a sheet of glass in clusters of 8, corresponding to individual asci. When mutants were crossed pairwise, some were found to be due to mutation at closely-linked sites, since almost all the resulting asci had pale spores only. Five mutants of spontaneous origin identified as *W*, and nos. 46, 63, 88, and 137, respectively, formed one such group, which was called series 46. These mutants were presumed to be allelic. The spores from a total of about 84,000 asci were examined from the 10 pairwise crosses between the mutants and 440 of the octads (groups of 8 spores from individual asci) were found to contain wild-type (dark) spores. Two of these octads had 4 dark and 4 pale spores and the remainder had 2 dark and 6 pale. It was evident that the dark spores were arising through recombination, because a total of nearly 10^6 asci homozygous for individual mutants showed none. The frequencies of recombinants from each of the 10 crosses between the different mutants are shown in Fig. 15.2. The recombination frequencies fit a linear map satisfactorily when the mutants are placed in the sequence shown in the diagram, but the larger frequencies are somewhat irregular and tend to be more than the sum of the appropriate smaller ones.

A total of 120 of those octads which contained 2 dark and 6 pale spores were studied further. The spores were germinated and their genotype determined by crossing each with the parental genotypes. The dark spores were found to be wild-type as expected. The pale ones invariably gave a few wild-type recombinants with one or other parent but not with both. Double mutant spores would have been revealed, if present, because they would have given no recombinants with either parent, but none was found. Thus all the recombinant (wild-type) spores appeared to have arisen by a non-reciprocal event and not by crossing-over.

Furthermore, in each of these octads 4 pale spores always had the genotype of the parent whose mutant site was to the left on the map, as drawn in Fig. 15.2, and the other 2 pale spores had the genotype of the right-hand parent. For example, in a cross between mutants 188 and *W*, each ascus with 2 wild-type spores was found to have 4 spores of the same genotype as 188 and 2 like *W*, while if *W* was crossed with 137, there were 4 like *W* and 2 like 137. In other words, it was as if in every tetrad, instead of 2 products of meiosis with the genotype of the left-hand mutant and 2 like the right-hand mutant, one of the latter had been transformed into wild-type without affecting the others. The agreement with the recombination map implies that a map of the mutant sites based on this difference between left- and right-hand positions (polarity) would place the sites in the same sequence as

FIGURE 15.2   A recombination map of 5 pale-spored mutants belonging
to series 46 in *Ascobolus immersus*, according to the data of
Lissouba and Rizet (1960). The reference letters or numbers
of the mutants are given above the line. The figures below
the line show the frequencies of dark (wild-type) spores per
100,000 progeny ascospores from each pairwise cross.

in Fig. 15.2. Lissouba and Rizet proposed the name *polaron* for a segment of
the hereditary material, such as that revealed by these mutants, within
which recombination appeared to be entirely by a mechanism other than
crossing-over.

Polarity in recombination was observed by Siddiqi (1962) at the *paba*-1
locus in *Aspergillus nidulans* and by Murray (1963) and Stadler and Towe
(1963) at the *me*-2 and *cys* loci, respectively, in *Neurospora crassa*. Direct
comparison between the data for these nutritional mutants and the *Ascobolus*
spore mutant data is not possible, since the techniques for observing recombination differ, but it appears that there are a number of differences of
detail. Such variation is evident also between different genes in *Ascobolus*,
where Lissouba, Mousseau, Rizet, and Rossignol (1962) found that the
pattern of recombination within two other series of spore colour mutants
(nos. 19 and 75) differed in a number of respects from series 46. Diverse
proportions of reciprocal and non-reciprocal recombination were found with
different mutants in the same series. This confirmed the discovery by Case
and Giles (1958) that both reciprocal and non-reciprocal recombination
could occur between a pair of alleles. Their example was at the pantothenic
acid 2 (*pan*-2) locus in *N. crassa*.

A feature of recombination which any hypothesis of its mechanism must
account for is the phenomenon of *negative interference*. A majority of the
adenine-independent progeny obtained by Pritchard (1955) from crosses
between allelic adenine-requiring mutants of *Aspergillus nidulans* had one
specific crossover genotype for linked marker genes on either side of the
adenine locus, for example, $y + + bi$ from the heterozygote $\dfrac{y + 8 +}{+ 11 + bi}$
(see § 13.2). However, a significant minority showed other combinations of
the outside markers ($y + + +$, $+ + + bi$, and $+ + + +$). Giles (1952)

had first described this phenomenon with inositol-requiring alleles of *N. crassa*, and it was observed with alleles at the pyridoxin-1 (*pdx*-1) and nicotinic acid 1 (*nic*-1) loci in this species by Mitchell (1956) and St Lawrence (1956), respectively. Among the recombinant progeny which did not require pyridoxin and nicotinic acid, respectively, for growth, not only were all 4 of the genotypes with respect to linked marker genes represented, but one crossover genotype was not markedly the most frequent class such as it would be expected to be with simple crossing-over between alleles. Thus, Mitchell found that 111 pyridoxin-independent progeny consisted of 43 and 28 with one or other parental genotype, respectively, for the outside markers, and 31 and 9 with one or other crossover genotype, respectively. Thus, less than one third of the recombinants could be attributed to a simple crossover between the alleles. St Lawrence found an even more extreme instance: 72 nicotinic acid-independent progeny from a cross between allelic mutants nos. 1 and 2 consisted of 25 and 14, respectively, with the two parental combinations of the outside marker genes, and 18 and 15, respectively, with the two crossover combinations.

Recombination between alleles thus appeared frequently to be associated with recombination in the neighbouring regions demarcated by the linked marker genes. Later work has confirmed the general occurrence of this negative interference between recombination in closely linked regions. This is in direct contrast to the positive interference found between recombination in longer intervals of the linkage map, where it has been well-established ever since the pioneer work of Muller (1916) that crossing-over in one region frequently reduces the likelihood of its simultaneous occurrence in a neighbouring region (see § 8.7). Pritchard (1955) found that negative interference was strictly localised in extent. However, Calef (1957) showed that it was not confined to alleles. In a cross between adenine-requiring mutant no. 15 and para-aminobenzoic acid requiring mutant no. 1 at the closely-linked *ad*-9 and *paba*-1 loci in *Aspergillus nidulans*, he found that out of 105 recombinants which did not require adenine or *p*-aminobenzoic acid for growth, 49 had additional recombination in one or both neighbouring regions.

§ 15.3   Recombination in bacteria

As indicated in § 10.2, the occurrence of recombination in bacteria was discovered by Lederberg and Tatum (1946) using biochemically deficient mutants of *Escherichia coli*. Two multiple mutants, one having requirements for threonine, leucine and thiamin, and the other for biotin, phenylalanine and cystine, had been obtained by successive treatment with X-rays. The two triple mutants were grown in mixed culture in complete medium containing yeast extract, peptone and glucose, and then suspensions of the washed cells were plated on minimal medium. Wild-type (prototrophic) colonies appeared with a frequency of about 1 per 10^6 cells. This is a much greater frequency than could be attributed to mutation since simultaneous reverse mutation of all three mutants in one or other parent would be required to produce a wild-type colony. Control experiments showed no wild-types when the parents were cultured separately. It was also established by experiment that the prototrophs were not mere mixtures or heterokaryons.

By an extension of the original technique, the recombination of unselected character-differences such as resistance to streptomycin and to particular viruses was studied. Nutritional mutants could be included in the un-selected category by plating on a medium with the appropriate supplements. The colonies which developed on this medium were then scored for the unselected character-differences. In this way data on the relative frequencies of recombination between the various mutants were obtained. The re-combination frequencies were found to be non-random and to fit a single circular linkage map (Jacob and Wollman, 1958a). A similar linkage map has been obtained from recombination experiments with *Salmonella typhimurium*, and with *Streptomyces coelicolor* (Hopwood, 1965).

The mechanism of transfer of genetic material from cell to cell in *E. coli* has been investigated by a number of authors (cf. Hayes 1964). The details of the process are remarkable. It appears that there is sexual differentiation of cells, the two sexes differing in a number of respects. In particular, they are thought to differ in the charge on the cell surface such that cells of opposite sex may stay in contact if they happen to meet. A conjugation tube is then formed. The male cells are inferred to contain a 'sex factor' which evidently carries the genes for the male characters: it is absent from female cells. This sex factor is capable of replication independently of and more rapidly than the chromoneme.* After the formation of the conjugation-tube, one of the editions of the sex factor may be transferred to the female cell, whereupon the latter changes sex and the conjugation-tube breaks down. Alternatively, the circular chromoneme of the male cell may be broken open at a particular point, with the sex factor attached to one specific end of it. The chromoneme and sex factor are then transferred to the female cell, with the free end of the chromoneme leading the way. Very frequently transfer is interrupted before completion as a result of random breakage of the chromoneme during transfer, with the result that the sex factor is rarely transferred since it is at the tail. Jacob and Wollman (1958a) separated conjugating cells by shaking the culture in a high-speed mixer, and they did this at various time intervals after the start of conjugation, which takes about 100 minutes at 37°C. On the basis of the characters of the male parent which appeared in the progeny, it was possible to find the time at which each gene was transferred. The time sequence map of the genes confirmed the map based on recombination frequencies. Strains of *E. coli* were found to arise, apparently by mutation, in which the sex factor was attached at the other end of the chromoneme, the orientation of the latter during conjugation being reversed so that the sex factor was again at the tail. In other mutants, the circular chromoneme was opened at different points in the linkage group, but the point of opening was constant for any particular mutant. The sex factor appears to consist of about $2 \cdot 5 \times 10^5$ nucleotide pairs of DNA, so it could be regarded as a second chromoneme of about $\frac{1}{10}$ the length of the

* Chromoneme = bacterial (or viral) chromosome—see § 11.1.

other. Jacob and Wollman (1958*b*) have coined the term *episome* for structures such as the *E. coli* sex factor and phages, which may exist attached to the chromoneme, whereupon they replicate only when it does, or they may exist unattached, when they replicate independently of and usually more rapidly than the chromoneme.

Two other methods of transfer of hereditary material from cell to cell are known in bacteria, besides conjugation. In genetic transformation, which was discovered by Griffith (1928) in *Diplococcus pneumoniae* (see § 11.2), and has since been shown to occur in *Haemophilus influenzae* and a number of other bacteria, segments of DNA derived from the bacterial cells and equivalent to about $\frac{1}{200}$ of the total hereditary complement, are taken up by other cells of the same or a closely related species. These cells seem to absorb the DNA only during a particular phase of the cycle of cell division.

In *transduction*, which was discovered by Lederberg, Lederberg, Zinder and Lively (1952) in *Salmonella typhimurium*, a virus is responsible for transferring some of the bacterial DNA to another cell along with its own DNA. The length of the bacterial DNA segment transferred in this way averages about $\frac{1}{100}$ of the total complement. Virus *P*22 of *S. typhimurium* will transfer any part of the *Salmonella* linkage group, but virus *lambda* (λ) of *Escherichia coli* will transfer only a particular segment of the *E. coli* chromoneme. Many bacterial viruses can exist in a dormant form called prophage. In this condition their DNA appears to be incorporated at a specific locus of the host chromoneme, and to replicate along with it. The *E. coli* genes transferred by virus lambda are in the immediate vicinity of the locus of the virus when it is incorporated into the bacterial chromoneme.

It is evident that in bacteria the process of transfer of hereditary material from one cell to another, whether it is by conjugation, by transformation, or by transduction, differs fundamentally from the nuclear fusion at fertilisation characteristic of chromosomal organisms, since in bacteria only a part—and usually quite a small part—of the total hereditary complement of DNA is transferred.

The behaviour of the donor's DNA fragment on arrival in the acceptor cell appears to be similar whatever the means of transfer. Observations which any hypothesis of the mechanism of recombination must explain include the following (see Hayes (1964) for fuller discussion and references):

(*a*) A transferred gene from the donor may function at once in the acceptor cell, for example, in conferring resistance to streptomycin on a previously sensitive cell, but it does not follow from this that the progeny of this cell will necessarily inherit the donor character. This phenomenon is particularly well-known with transduction in *Salmonella* and is called *abortive transduction*. It appears that the donor DNA fragment fails to replicate and is therefore inherited by one daughter-cell only. When a donor character does become fixed in the progeny of the acceptor cell, it is evident that recombination has occurred such that the donor allele has become incorporated into the chromoneme of the acceptor cell in place of the acceptor allele.

(*b*) By labelling the donor DNA of conjugating *E. coli* with radioactive phosphorus (^{32}P), Jacob and Wollman (1958*a*) showed that, probably before chromonemal replication and certainly less than an hour after transfer, genetic information in the donor fragment has begun to be conveyed to material free of ^{32}P. This was shown by a slowing down in the rate of loss of recombinants through radioactive breakdown of the ^{32}P.

(*c*) Isolation of the individual cells formed at each division after conjugation has shown that segregation of a parental character-difference may occur as late as the ninth division.

(*d*) Reciprocal differences in recombination frequency, depending on which parent is the donor, have been reported both with transformation and transduction. The data appear to indicate polarity in the recombination process.

(*e*) Isotope labelling experiments have established that both with conjugation and transformation, recombination can involve physical incorporation of part of the donor chromoneme into that of the acceptor cell.

(*f*) The work of Yanofsky and associates discussed in § 14.10 has shown that recombination in *E. coli* can occur between individual nucleotides of DNA. Some further features of their work are discussed in § 15.6.

§ 15.4   Recombination in viruses

As already mentioned (§ 13.4), the occurrence of genetic recombination in bacterial viruses was discovered by Delbrück and Bailey (1947) and by Hershey (1947) with the *T*-even viruses of *Escherichia coli*. Evidence was given in § 11.3 for the belief that only the DNA of the virus enters the host cell, and that it there undergoes replication a number of times prior to the formation of new virus particles, 100 or more of which may be formed per bacterial cell. Opportunity for recombination following mixed infection would appear to be confined to the period of DNA replication. The early data on recombination frequencies obtained with these *T*-even viruses from crosses (mixed infections) such as those described in § 13.4, were found to fit linear linkage maps, and more recently these maps have been shown to be part of a single circular linkage map (Epstein *et al.*, 1964—see Chapter 16.)

Outstanding discoveries which provide information about the mechanism of recombination in bacterial viruses include the following. Hershey and Rotman (1949) found that if the host is simultaneously infected with 3 different strains of virus *T*2, some of the progeny may have characters from all 3 parents. This would be accounted for if opportunities for recombination occurred repeatedly during the successive replications of the DNA. Hershey and Chase (1952*a*) discovered that about 2% of the virus progeny, following mixed infection by strains with clear and with turbid plaques, had mottled plaques. They established that the mottled plaques were initiated by virus heterozygous for the pair of alleles. It appeared that the heterozygous region was quite short. For every locus studied, a similar frequency (about 2%) of such heterozygotes was found. Using several genetic markers simultaneously, Levinthal (1954) found that heterozygosity at a particular locus was usually associated with recombination between markers situated at a distance on either side, suggesting that the origin of the heterozygosity is related to that of the recombinants. Chase and Doermann (1958) found that with closely-linked mutants of virus $T4$, recombination in one interval appeared to favour recombination in a neighbouring one, or in other words, there was 'negative interference' over short intervals of the linkage map, comparable to that known in chromosomal organisms (see § 15.2).

Meselson and Weigle (1961), by an ingenious experiment, showed that recombination in virus *lambda* of *Escherichia coli* could occur independently of replication of the chromoneme. A mixed infection of the host was made using two strains of the virus which differed from one another in two linked mutant characters concerning the morphology and the clarity of the plaque. As a result of multiplication in the host when cultured on appropriate media, the parental viral strains also differed in the atomic weight of their carbon and nitrogen (^{13}C ^{15}N, and the normal ^{12}C ^{14}N, respectively). The progeny virus particles, resulting from inoculation of normal ^{12}C ^{14}N *E. coli* with the mixture, were centrifuged in caesium chloride solution to give a density gradient. The contents of the centrifuge tube were then removed drop by drop from the end, and the number of virus particles in each drop estimated by diluting and plating on the host. The genotype with respect to the two parental character-differences was observed for a random sample of the progeny particles in each drop. It was found that the progeny, whether of parental or recombinant genotypes, were concentrated at three positions in the centrifuge tube corresponding to heavy (^{13}C $^{15}N/^{13}C$ ^{15}N), half-heavy (^{13}C $^{15}N/^{12}C$ ^{14}N), and light (^{12}C $^{14}N/^{12}C$ ^{14}N) DNA, indicating 0, 1 (or more), and 2 (or more) replications of originally heavy DNA, respectively (cf. Fig. 12.5). The significant discovery was the occurrence of recombinants with an unreplicated (^{13}C $^{15}N/^{13}C$ ^{15}N) chromoneme.

Kellenberger, Zichichi and Weigle (1961) obtained similar results using a slightly different technique which did not involve culturing on 'light' or 'heavy' bacteria. As genetic markers they used mutants with abnormal DNA contents, which could be separated by density-gradient centrifugation, and as nucleotide-chain markers they used radiophosphorus (^{32}P) and followed the distribution of its radioactivity.

Meselson (1964), in further experiments with virus *lambda* labelled with heavy isotopes, has found some indication that a small amount of DNA is removed and resynthesized in the formation of recombinant molecules.

§ 15.5   Hypotheses to explain recombination

Several hypotheses have been put forward to explain the remarkable series of discoveries concerning recombination described in the previous sections. Giles (1952) and Pritchard (1955) suggested that multiple crossover events might be responsible for the phenomena they had observed. If crossovers occurred in clusters, this would explain the negative interference within short regions. Pritchard attributed the positive interference over longer intervals to spacing of the regions where pairing of homologous chromosomes was sufficiently effective to allow crossovers to occur. The effective pairing segments would be variable in position, but rarely close together.

By itself, this hypothesis was clearly inadequate to explain non-reciprocal recombination. Lederberg (1955) suggested that recombination in bacteria could be related to the process of replication of the hereditary material, which might be copied first from one parent and then, further along the chain-molecule, from the other parent. Freese (1957) applied this model to chromosomes. It was suggested that if a daughter-chromatid were formed by a 'conservative' replication process, that is, by the copying of the hereditary material of a parent chromosome so as to leave the latter intact, then a process of copy-choice or switch-synthesis might operate when two homologous chromosomes were closely associated with one another. If the synthesis of the two daughter-chromatids, one from each parental chromosome, was not quite synchronised, both might be copied over a short interval from the same parent, thereby giving rise to a 3:1 ratio within a tetrad at a mutant site. This explanation of non-reciprocal recombination was combined with the multiple crossover idea by postulating that the switching back and forth between the parental templates during the synthesis of the daughter-chromatids occurred several times. This hypothesis explained a number of the observations on recombination, but it suffered from several serious defects:

(1) The conservative method of replication of chromosomes was in conflict with the evidence that both DNA and chromosomes replicate semi-conservatively (see Chapter 12). It was therefore incorrect to speak of parent- and daughter-chromatids, since the DNA of each chromatid is half old and half new.

(2) The copy-choice hypothesis predicts that successive crossovers along a chromosome arm will involve the same two chromatids (the daughters, not the parents), but the pair of chromatids involved in each crossover appear to be chosen at random, or nearly so (see § 8.8).

(3) Replication of both the DNA and the protein of the chromosome appears to take place before the homologous chromosomes start to associate at the zygotene stage of meiosis (see § 11.5 and Pl. 2(*a*)).

(4) Isotope labelling experiments have shown that recombinants, both in bacteria and their viruses, may contain parental atoms (§ 15.3 and § 15.4).

(5) Postmeiotic segregation (cf. Pl. 4(*e*)) was unexplained.

(6) The inequality in the frequency of 6:2 and 2:6 ratios of black:grey spores found by Kitani *et al.* with the *g* mutant of *Sordaria fimicola* was unexplained.

(7) Recombination must occur with molecular precision, such that nucleotides are rarely duplicated or omitted*, but it is not clear how this would be achieved with a switching of copying from one template to another.

* Evidence for occasional duplication or omission of nucleotides is discussed in § 15.6.

Most of these defects in the copy-choice hypothesis can be avoided by making suitable modifications or additional postulates, and numerous highly elaborate theories have been put forward. However, to account for both postmeiotic segregation and 6:2 and 2:6 ratios shown by the same mutant, such as Kitani *et al.* have found with the grey-spored mutant of *S. fimicola*, requires an intricate and implausible model. It appears that none of the variants of the copy-choice hypothesis will provide a satisfactory explanation for all the observations, although the model proposed by Stadler and Towe (1963) accommodates a majority of them.

Whitehouse (1963) proposed a model based on breakage and rejoining of chromatids. It was assumed that replication of chromosomes is completed prior to the occurrence of recombination, and that during the zygotene or pachytene stages of meiosis, when the homologous chromosomes are associated in pairs, recombination occurs at a number of points along the length of the chromosome, and that one chromatid from each chromosome, selected at random, is involved each time. It was also assumed that the reconstruction of DNA molecules in new ways, following breakage, took place not by an end-to-end association of broken chains but by a lateral association of complementary segments from homologous regions, to give *hybrid DNA*. End-to-end joining would appear readily to allow deficiencies or duplications of nucleotides to arise, whereas lateral association would automatically give great precision to the recombination process. Furthermore, it has been shown by Marmur and Lane (1960) that complementary nucleotide chains of DNA will associate spontaneously *in vitro* under suitable conditions to give the duplex molecule. It therefore seemed likely that re-assembly of broken molecules might occur *in vivo* in a similar way. If, in the process of crossing-over, the two DNA molecules assumed to be involved were broken one chain at a time, re-association in new ways could occur before the second chains were broken. This might have a selective advantage by reducing the likelihood of complete breakage without rejoining. Failure of rejoining would lead ultimately to loss of the acentric part of the chromosome, with lethal consequences for that cell lineage (cf. § 9.8). If the initial breakage was in homologous regions of complementary chains, one from each molecule, crossing-over could occur by a succession of steps involving chain separation, synthesis of new chain segments, and base pairing of complementary segments from the two molecules (Whitehouse, 1963). On the other hand, if the initial breakage were in chains of the same polarity, crossing-over could occur merely by chain separation, followed by annealing between the complementary chains from the two molecules, without the necessity for synthesis of any new segments (Holliday, 1964). However, it is then necessary to postulate that a nucleotide chain from one molecule, which has broken free at one end, can coil round an unbroken chain from the other one, since this is necessary for the specific hydrogen bonding in complementary base pairing. Without specifying the sequence of events in detail, Meselson (1965) has also suggested that recombination involves pairing between complementary DNA chains of different parentage. He favours a model in which recombination may be associated with the excision of chain segments and their resynthesis along the complementary chain derived from the other parent.

In order to account for polarity in recombination, it appears necessary to postulate the existence of discontinuities at intervals along the chromosome in the pattern of recombination. As already mentioned, Lissouba and Rizet (1960) considered the chromosome to be subdivided into segments called polarons within which recombination was entirely by conversion. Using the copy-choice hypothesis, they suggested that within a polaron the replication that allowed the copying choice always took place in the same direction (from left to right in Fig. 15.2), and that whenever synthesis switched from copying one parent chromosome to copying the other one, it did not switch back again until the end of the polaron was reached. On the other hand, Hastings and Whitehouse (1964), using the hybrid DNA model, suggested that the ends of a polaron were defined by the initial points of breakage of the DNA chains. It was presumed that this breakage was enzymatically controlled and could occur only at these fixed positions which the enzyme could 'recognise'. This recognition of the points of junction of one polaron with the next might be from the base sequence discernible in the small or large groove of the double helix, or it might be from some other feature of the nucleoprotein structure.

The steps in the process of crossing-over according to this *polaron hybrid DNA* model, are illustrated in Fig. 15.3. Only 2 of the 4 chromatids are shown, as the other 2 do not take part (although they may participate in another crossover further along the chromosome). Fig. 15.3(i) shows a polaron in two homologous DNA molecules. The arrow-heads are placed at the junctions of the polaron with neighbouring polarons and show the direction of the phosphate-sugar backbones to the nucleotide-chains. No attempt has been made to show the spiral coiling. The short lines perpendicular to the lines representing the nucleotide-chains are intended to show complementary base pairing. In (ii), breakage of complementary chains has occurred at the left-hand junction, and the chains have uncoiled and separated over the greater part of the length of the polaron. In (iii), synthesis of nucleotide-chains has occurred from the left-hand junction alongside both of the unbroken chains and complementary to them. The newly-synthesised chains are shown by broken lines, and need not be of equal length. In (iv), the newly-synthesised chains have dissociated from their templates, and in (v) they have associated with the complementary broken chains from the other molecule. The final stages of crossing-over involve the filling of any gaps in the duplex crossover molecules with nucleotides complementary to the other chain (Fig. 15.3(vi)), and the breakdown of the unpaired non-crossover chains (vii) to give the completed crossover (viii). It will be noticed that there is no net synthesis of DNA.

There is experimental evidence for the occurrence of a limited amount of DNA synthesis at the pachytene stage of meiosis, such as this hypothesis demands. Hotta and Stern (1961) found that the capacity of pollen-mother-cells of *Trillium erectum* to phosphorylate thymidine rises temporarily at this stage, and it appears that this capacity is directly related to DNA synthesis

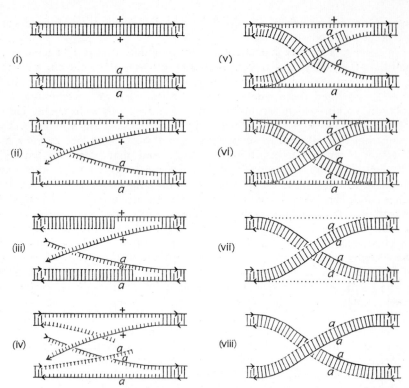

FIGURE 15.3   The mechanism of crossing-over according to the polaron
hybrid DNA model. The lines with arrow-heads represent
nucleotide-chains, with the arrows showing the direction
of the phosphate-sugar backbones. Broken lines represent
newly-synthesised chains, and dotted lines chains which are
breaking down. The arrow-heads are placed at the junction
of a polaron with neighbouring polarons. Transverse lines
extending from one nucleotide-chain to another indicate
hydrogen bonding between complementary bases. The letter
a indicates the site of a mutation, and the plus sign its normal
allele. Mispairing at this site in (v) is corrected in (vi)—see
§ 15.6.

occurring at the time. Wimber and Prensky (1963), using tritiated thymidine,
have shown autoradiographically that some DNA synthesis occurs at this
stage of meiosis in *Triturus viridescens*.

If crossing-over is associated with hybrid DNA formation, as this hypothesis
supposes, the site of a mutation will sometimes happen to lie within the
hybrid region, giving rise to *heterozygous DNA*. The consequences of such
heterozygosity in the molecule are discussed in the next section.

Hybrid DNA formation from fixed points of origin, and as a result of
base-pairing between complementary nucleotide-chains derived from two
different molecules, would also appear to fit many of the observations on
recombination in bacteria and viruses described in § 15.3 and § 15.4 (cf.

Meselson, 1964). Such annealing would likewise give rise to heterozygosity in the DNA at mutant sites.

§ 15.6 Correction of anomalies in DNA

Kelner (1949) showed that the lethal effect of ultraviolet light on the conidia of *Streptomyces griseus* could be reversed by subsequent treatment with visible light. This process of photo-reactivation has since been found to apply to a wide range of organisms, although not to all, and to diverse effects of ultraviolet light on them. Numerous observations pointed to an effect of the ultraviolet light on DNA as the primary source of the changes induced. *Haemophilus influenzae* shows no photoreactivation, but Rupert, Goodgal, and Herriott (1958) demonstrated that a cell-free extract from *Escherichia coli*, which is a photoreactivable species, will reactivate the DNA of *H. influenzae* in the presence of visible light. This was shown by an increased ability of DNA from streptomycin-resistant bacteria to transform strepto-mycin-sensitive cells. The ultraviolet treatment reduced the transforming ability to 1% of the original, and illumination with visible light in the presence of the *E. coli* extract raised it again to between 10 and 50% of the original value. Rupert (1960) isolated an enzyme from *Saccharomyces cerevisiae* which had a similar effect to the *E. coli* extract. It is evident that a number of organisms possess an enzyme system capable of bringing about 'repair' of 'damage' to DNA caused by ultraviolet light.

Beukers and Berends (1960) showed that u.v. irradiation of thymine in a frozen aqueous solution leads to the formation of thymine dimers. It was provisionally suggested that these had carbon–carbon bonds between atom 4 of one thymine and atom 5 of the other, and *vice versa*. Wacker, Dellweg, and Weinblum (1960) studied the effect of ultraviolet irradiation of the DNA from *Streptococcus faecalis* labelled with ^{14}C in the thymine, and concluded that the mutagenic and lethal effects of ultraviolet light on cells were likely to be due to its chemical effect on thymine in DNA.

Setlow and Carrier (1964) and Boyce and Howard-Flanders (1964*a*) have shown that an ultraviolet-resistant strain of *Escherichia coli* has the ability to remove thymine dimers from its DNA, whereas a particular ultraviolet-sensitive strain lacks this capacity. This reaction does not require visible light. It appears that a specific gene is responsible evidently specifying an enzyme controlling dimer excision. Boyce and Howard-Flanders showed that the dimers were extracted as a whole, including the intervening phosphodiester bond, and that nucleotides were then inserted into the excised region by complementary pairing with the intact opposite chain, and the broken phos-phodiester backbone was rejoined. It is of particular significance that the repair mechanism appears to make use of the base sequence of the com-plementary chain. Extending these studies, Boyce and Howard-Flanders (1964*b*) found that in *E. coli* the repair in the dark of ultraviolet-irradiated DNA is controlled by 3 genes which are widely spaced in the chromoneme. Mutation of any one of these genes produced an ultraviolet-sensitive mutant unable to excise thymine dimers, and these mutants showed increased sensitivity to the lethal effects of mitomycin *C*. It was inferred that damage to DNA caused by mitomycin *C* is repaired by the same molecular mechanism as ultraviolet damage, and that the enzymes recognise distortions of the phosphodiester backbones of the nucleotide chains, rather than the precise chemical form of the defective bases.

The repair of a partly single-chain DNA molecule might come about through the action of the DNA polymerase isolated by Kornberg and associates from *E. coli* (see § 12.4), since Richardson, Inman, and Kornberg (1964) have demonstrated the *in vitro* ability of this enzyme to restore the full double-chain structure after limited digestion with exonuclease III. The latter enzyme will act as a phosphatase and hydrolyse 3'-phosphate groups at the end of a DNA nucleotide chain of high molecular weight, and will then act as an exonuclease to bring about stepwise hydrolysis from the 3'-hydroxyl end, releasing 5'-nucleotides (cf. Richardson, Schildkraut, and Kornberg, 1964).

Rasmussen and Painter (1964) have found that tritiated thymidine is incorporated into the chromosomes of human cells in tissue culture following ultraviolet irradiation, and the effect is much enhanced if the thymine of the DNA has been partially replaced by 5-bromouracil. Control experiments without ultraviolet treatment showed no uptake of tritium, except in the fraction of cells undergoing normal DNA replication. It was inferred that a mechanism exists for the repair of ultraviolet damage to DNA, and that thymine is inserted into the DNA in the process.

From study of mutation caused by ultraviolet light in *Ustilago maydis*, Holliday (1962) came to the conclusion that both of the daughter cells arising from the first mitosis after irradiation were often mutant. In order to account for this, he suggested that the radiation modified a nucleotide (or nucleotides) in one chain, and that an enzymatically-controlled repair mechanism, in restoring normal hydrogen bonding, was liable to replace the complementary nucleotide in the other chain, so as to match the mutated one. The overall effect of ultraviolet light and 'repairing' enzyme would then be, either to remove the effect of the ultraviolet light or to extend it to both chains. In other words, if ultraviolet light causes mispairing, that is, heterozygosity in the DNA, the repairing enzyme in restoring homozygosity may make the molecule homozygous mutant instead of homozygous normal. Holliday suggested that a similar process could be responsible for gene conversion if the DNA had become heterozygous at the mutant site through the pairing of complementary homologous chains.

Whitehouse (1965) pointed out that on a hybrid DNA model of recombination, the 5 kinds of aberrant asci found by Kitani *et al.* (1962) with the grey-spored mutant of *Sordaria fimicola* (Fig. 15.1(*c*)–(*g*)) are just what are expected if correction of heterozygosity in the DNA at the mutant site does not always happen, but may occur in either direction, that is, to homozygous normal (black) and to homozygous mutant (grey). If hybrid DNA occurred at the *g* site in both of the chromatids participating in crossing-over, and if there was no correction of the mispairing, asci with 4 black and 4 grey spores and with half of them not in pairs (Fig. 15.1(*c*)) would result. The

5:3 and 3:5 ratios would be the result of correction in one chromatid but not in the other, while the 6:2 and 2:6 ratios would be the consequence of correction in the same direction in both chromatids (see Fig. 15.4). Moreover, the relative frequencies of these asci were in agreement with this explanation. If the frequencies with which hybrid DNA at the mutant site remained heterozygous, became homozygous normal, and became homozygous mutant, were x, y, and z respectively, the expected frequencies of classes (c)–(g) (Fig. 15.1) would be x^2, $2xy$, $2xz$, y^2, and z^2, respectively, assuming that the correction mechanism operates independently in the two chromatids (see Fig. 15.4). If in every 10^5 asci there were 152 with hybrid DNA at this site, and if $x = 0\cdot27$, $y = 0\cdot56$, and $z = 0\cdot17$, the frequencies of classes (c)–(g) per 10^5 asci would be 11, 46, 14, 48, and 4, respectively, in excellent agreement with the observed frequencies of 8, 52, 10, 47, and 6. The difference between y and z, that is, in the frequency of correction of the mispairing in opposite directions, might be related to the nature of the mutation itself, that is, whether a transition $(AT \leftrightarrow GC)$, transversion $(AT \leftrightarrow TA$, $AT \leftrightarrow CG$, or $GC \leftrightarrow CG)$, or an addition (or deletion) of one or more nucleotides (see § 14.2), while postmeiotic segregation, implying the persistence of mispairing through meiosis, might be due to failure of the postulated 'correcting' enzyme to reach its substrate during a critical period of time.

One of the implications of the correction of heterozygosity in DNA as a source of recombination is that it can give rise to reciprocal as well as to non-reciprocal recombination. This is evident from Fig. 15.4, where correction in one direction in one chromatid and in the opposite direction in the other one will lead to normal reciprocal recombination, with asci containing 2 pairs of black and 2 pairs of grey spores. Whitehouse and Hastings (1965) have therefore taken the term conversion to include reciprocal events arising from this cause, and in applying Lissouba and Rizet's polaron concept to the hybrid DNA model, it has been assumed that a polaron is a region within which recombination is entirely by conversion and not by crossing-over, but that such conversion may lead to either reciprocal or non-reciprocal recombination. Reciprocal conversion could simulate a two-strand double crossover and may account for the excess of such crossovers which has been observed (see § 8.8).

The correction of mispairing in DNA at a mutant site would cause recombination simultaneously in two intervals of the chromosome, that is, between the mutant and neighbouring markers on both sides. Moreover, the hybrid DNA segments, where heterozygosity in the DNA arises, can occur only within crossovers and so there will be an association between crossing-over and the correction of mispairing. It is assumed that there may be dissociation of the chains of the DNA molecules on one side of a polaron junction, as illustrated in Fig. 15.3, or on both sides. The latter would give simultaneous crossovers in the same two chromatids in adjacent polarons, with the result that outside markers would remain in parental combinations. This would account for the aberrant asci for the grey-spored mutant of *Sordaria fimicola* with parental combinations of outside markers

(a)

(i)	(ii)	(iii)	(iv)	(v)	(vi)	(vii)	(viii)	(ix)	(x)	(xi)
	+	+	+	+	+	+	+	+	+	+
+	+	+	+	+	+	+	+	+	+	+
+	+	g	+	g	g	g	+	g	g	+
	+	+	+	+	g	+	+	g	g	+
	g	g	g	+	g	g	+	g	+	g
g	g	+	+	+	+	g	+	g	+	g
g	g	g	g	g	g	g	g	g	g	g
g	g	g	g	g	g	g	g	g	g	g

| | | Aberrant 4:4 | 5:3 | | 3:5 | | 6:2 | 2:6 | Normal 4:4 | |

FIGURE 15.4   The diagram shows the origin of aberrant asci of *Sordaria fimicola* heterozygous for black (+) and grey (*g*) ascospore colour, according to the hybrid DNA model of crossing-over. The pairs of horizontal lines represent DNA molecules (chromosomes or chromatids), the individual lines corresponding to nucleotide chains, and the full or broken lines distinguishing their parental origin.

In (*a*) is shown (i) the parental chromosome-pair, (ii) the chromatids derived from them, (iii) the chromatids after a cross-over has occurred such that there is hybrid DNA in the region of *g* in two of the chromatids, and (iv)–(xi) the consequences of correction of the heterozygosity in one or both chromatids. In (ii)–(xi), the 8 nucleotide chains, each carrying either + or *g*, correspond to the 8 spores in the mature ascus. The numbers of spores of each colour in the asci are shown below the 8 symbols, with the number of black (+) spores given first. Asci of classes (iii), (v), (vii), (viii) and (ix) correspond to (*c*)–(*g*), respectively, in Fig. 15.1. The various permutations of spore sequence due to the presence or absence of a proximal cross-over, or to the chromosome orientation at the nuclear divisions in the ascus, are not shown.

(see § 15.2), and the similar results for genes in *Neurospora* and *Aspergillus*. Apart from these 'double crossovers', which are essentially single events in origin, there appears to be no evidence for the existence of negative interference between crossovers. It appears that recombination by correction of heterozygosity in DNA, together with the association between this correction and crossing-over, will account for negative interference. Pontecorvo (1958) pointed out that negative interference could be the result of the proximity to one another of the mutants necessary to detect it, if heterozygosis at one point along a chromosome favours recombination in its immediate vicinity,

FIGURE 15.4   In (*b*) is shown the expected frequency of each class of ascus in
(cont.)   terms of the frequency of correction of heterozygosity, where x is
the frequency of remaining heterozygous, y of correction to homozygous wild-type ($+$), and z to homozygous mutant (g), within
each DNA molecule. It is assumed that correction occurs independently in each molecule (chromatid). The Roman numerals
correspond to those in (*a*).

and in essence this is the explanation of negative interference provided by the
hybrid DNA model.

As already mentioned in § 15.5, according to the model of recombination
proposed by Holliday (1964), the primary breakage is in identical rather
than in complementary chains in the two molecules, and there is no DNA
synthesis. The secondary breakage, necessary to complete the crossover, may
then occur in the same two chains, giving parental combinations for outside
markers, or it may occur in the complementary chains, giving a crossover.

A hypothesis of recombination based on the correction of heterozygosity
in DNA has to account for the fact that recombination frequencies between
closely-linked mutants fit a linear map (cf. Fig. 15.2). The fit is often rather
an approximate one, but nevertheless is well established. If recombination
frequency depended merely on correction frequency, it would bear no
relationship to the distance between sites. However, another factor to be
considered is the frequency with which heterozygosity arises in the first
place. If there is variability in the length of the hybrid DNA segments from
a fixed origin, it is evident that mutant sites near the origin will occur in
hybrid DNA more often than those further away. There will then be a
gradient of decreasing conversion frequency with distance from the origin.
The recombination frequency of a pair of mutants within a polaron will

depend on the frequency with which either site (or both) lies within a hybrid DNA segment. The further the mutants are apart, the nearer they will be to the ends of the polaron, and hence, if hybrid DNA can arise from either end, the greater the recombination frequency. It will therefore be expected that the recombination frequencies will enable the sequence of the sites to be determined, but the frequencies will not be expected to be additive. It is evident that the unit of measurement of distance on a map of closely-linked mutants may not bear a constant relationship to the physical distance between sites. Near the ends of a polaron, where hybrid DNA is most frequent, the map may be relatively extended, and in the middle of the polaron, where hybrid DNA is least frequent, it may be relatively contracted compared with the intervening regions.

A further factor to be considered is the possibility that the heterozygosity itself interferes with the formation of hybrid DNA. This is suggested by the data of Lissouba and Rizet (1960) for series 46 in *Ascobolus immersus*, where mutants show conversion when they are the right-hand member of a pair, but not when the left-hand member (see § 15.2). If these mutants are near the right-hand end of a polaron, such that all the hybrid DNA is formed from the right, it may be that the mutant to the right prevents the hybrid DNA extending to the mutant to the left. Holliday (1964) has pointed out that the widespread occurrence of longer intervals on allele maps which are greater than the sum of the shorter ones (cf. Fig. 15.2) is evidence for interference by the mutations in the recombination process, and moreover indicates that two mutant sites that are close together may prevent hybrid DNA formation to a greater extent than two further apart, with the result that conversion frequencies will be higher with the more loosely-linked sites from this cause alone. Holliday has called this phenomenon *map expansion*. It is the converse of what is found in linkage maps extending over long intervals of the chromosome, where owing to the occurrence of more than one crossover in an interval, the recombination frequency of two widely-spaced mutants is less than the sum of the recombination frequencies of each with an intervening mutant (see § 7.4).

Whitehouse and Hastings (1965) have pointed out that there is another factor which may be responsible for the additivity of recombination frequencies between alleles. Setlow and Carrier (1964) and Howard-Flanders and Boyce (1964) have obtained evidence that from 20 to 50 nucleotides are excised when ultraviolet-induced thymine dimers are removed from the DNA of *Escherichia coli*. If a similar length of chain were removed in the correction of mispairing in hybrid DNA, a second site of heterozygosity might be included in the excised segment. Both sites would then necessarily be corrected to the same parental genotype, and there would be no recombination between the two alleles. Two mutant sites close together in the DNA would be expected to show such linked correction more often than two sites further apart, and so the closer the mutants the lower their recombination frequency.

Evidence in support of the occurrence of recombination by a mechanism dependent on correction of heterozygosity in DNA is provided by the data of

Yanofsky *et al.* (1964) for mutants affecting the *A* protein of tryptophan synthetase in *Escherichia coli* (see § 13.8). Particular mutants were found to show consistently higher recombination frequencies than others, even though their sites were almost identical in position and within the same codon. Moreover, the recombination behaviour was found to be associated with the aminoacid substitution which the mutation induced. Thus, mutants nos. 23, 27, 28, and 36, which led to the replacement of glycine by arginine at a certain position in the polypeptide, gave higher frequencies of recombination with allelic mutants than mutants nos. 46, 95, and 178, which caused the substitution of glutamic acid at the same position. It is inferred that the heterozygosity in the DNA in these two groups of mutants differ in their influence on hybrid DNA formation or on the correction mechanism. In spite of this influence of individual mutants on recombination, it is also evident from the data of Yanofsky and associates that allelic recombination frequencies reflect the physical distance apart of mutant sites, as can be seen from Fig. 13.8.

That genetic recombination can involve the repair of DNA has now been established through the work of Howard-Flanders, Clark, Simson, Theriot and Boyce (1965). These authors have isolated several mutants of *E. coli* that are highly sensitive to both X-rays and ultraviolet light, and have found that these mutants form less than 0.5% of the normal frequency of recombinants. From isotope labelling experiments it appears that these mutants are unable to reconstruct their DNA after radiation-induced breakdown. It is inferred that there are common steps in the enzymic pathways of DNA repair and of genetic recombination.

The idea that crossing-over occurs with such molecular precision that no nucleotide is lost or gained must be qualified in view of the discovery by Magni and von Borstel (1962) that mutation at a number of nutritional loci in *Saccharomyces cerevisiae* is 6 to 20 times as frequent at meiosis as at mitosis and, moreover (Magni 1963), is often associated with crossing-over at or near the site of mutation. The strains used were initially homozygous at the loci where mutation occurred. Demerec (1962) has observed a similar phenomenon in *Salmonella typhimurium*. Magni (1964) has found that nutritional mutants in *Saccharomyces* thought to be due to base substitution (for example, because they were induced by base analogues) show at meiosis the same low rate of reverse mutation to wild-type as at mitosis. He has inferred that the high mutation-rate at crossing-over is exclusively with mutations whose molecular basis is the addition or deletion of one or more nucleotides. Paszewski and Surzycki (1964) have studied what appears to be the same phenomenon using a spore-colour mutant in *Ascobolus immersus*, and have found that back-mutations affect 2 of the 6 spores in the ascus and that, in the one ascus tested, the 6 mutant spores all behaved alike as regards further mutation. It is tentatively concluded that the phenomenon affects only one of the two chromatids taking part in crossing-over.

On the polaron hybrid DNA theory of crossing-over, it is possible that one or more nucleotides might be gained or lost if the synthesis of a new chain (Fig. 15.3(iii)) ended at the position of a run of identical bases, and if the tip of the newly-synthesised chain initiated the contact with the complementary chain from the other molecule (between stages (iv) and (v) in Fig. 15.3). Displaced pairing might then arise. For example, if the newly-synthesised chain ended with a run of thymines, it might begin to associate with the complementary chain displaced by one nucleotide, thus:

```
---C C A C C T T T G G A G G
                            T T T T
     G G T G G A A A C C T C C A A A A T T A C T G A---
```

This might lead to a distorted molecule:

```
---C C A C C T T T G G A G G  T T T
   G G T G G A A A C C T C C  A A A A T T A C T G A---
```

with the possibility of correction of the distortion by the addition of a nucleotide complementary to the unpaired one. Conversely, loss of a nucleotide could arise if the pairing was displaced in the other direction, and if the resulting distortion in the molecule were corrected by removal of the unpaired nucleotide. It is possible that the high spontaneous mutability at certain sites ('hot spots') in the rII region of virus $T4$ of *Escherichia coli* (see § 14.2) might be due to such displaced pairing.

§ 15.7   The one polaron: one cistron hypothesis

Whitehouse and Hastings (1965) have applied the polaron hybrid DNA model of recombination to the extensive data available from Ascomycetes (*Ascobolus immersus, Aspergillus nidulans, Neurospora crassa, Saccharomyces cerevisiae*, and *Sordaria fimicola*). They have found that the data fit the hypothesis satisfactorily, and moreover provide evidence that the polaron may coincide with the cistron. Polarity in recombination appears to be of general occurrence. Furthermore, it appears that near the proximal end of the gene proximal sites show conversion more frequently than distal, and near the distal end the converse is true. In other words, conversion is of maximum frequency at each end of the cistron. This is what would be expected if the polaron coincides with the cistron and the hybrid DNA may originate at either end of it. In most of the genes that have been studied, conversion appears to be more frequent at one end than the other. Extreme instances of this are the spore mutants of series 46 in *Ascobolus immersus* studied by Lissouba *et al.* (1960, 1962), and *me*-2 (methionine 2) in *Neurospora crassa* studied by Murray (1963). In both of these genes, it appears that most of the hybrid DNA, and perhaps all of it, orignates from one end only, thus making an exception to the generalisation given above.

In order to explain the remarkable diversity in the recombination data both within and between species, and also between alleles, it is evident that there must be considerable variability in the recombination process. This variation can arise from differences in the frequency of chain breakage at different polaron junctions (see above), from variation in the proportion of single and double crossovers (see § 15.6), and from diversity in the degree of interference in hybrid DNA formation and in the pattern of correction, due to the nature of the mutation (see § 15.6). Another source of variation in the crossover mechanism may arise from variability in the length of the hybrid DNA segments. In Fig. 15.3(v), hybrid DNA is shown extending to a mutant site in one chromatid and not in the other. Depending on the direction of the correction of heterozygosity, either non-recombinant 4:4 segregation or a 6:2 ratio will arise. The significant point is that with hybrid DNA at a mutant site in only one chromatid, all recombination will be non-reciprocal (cf. Fig. 15.3(vi)). Whitehouse and Hastings have suggested that when recombination between two mutants appears to be more or less exclusively non-reciprocal (cf. § 15.2), the DNA synthesis has occurred unequally in the two chromatids such that it has not reached either mutant site in one of them. It may be significant that DNA synthesis along the two chromatids in the same physical direction will necessarily mean synthesis in opposite directions chemically, with the consequence that the times of initiation in the two chromatids might be unequal. More nearly equal synthesis in the two chromatids is postulated to account for the frequently reciprocal recombination between alleles in *Aspergillus nidulans*.

Whitehouse and Hastings found that the data available from study of recombination between mutants in different but closely-linked cistrons, such as *ad*-9 and *paba*-1 in *A. nidulans*, appear to be consistent with the existence of a polaron junction between the genes. The evidence for this is as follows. If *ad*-9 and *paba*-1 are adjacent cistrons with a polaron junction between them, and if hybrid DNA forms in one direction only from the junction, conversion can occur either in *ad*-9 or *paba*-1, but not in both, and outside markers will show crossing-over. On the other hand, if hybrid DNA extends in both directions from the junction to give a double crossover, mutants in both cistrons may show conversion. This would account for the negative interference which Calef found to extend from *ad*-9 to *paba*-1 (see § 15.2), but owing to the double crossover, outside markers will show parental combinations. Thus, if there is an intervening junction, it should not be possible for two mutants each to show conversion when outside markers show crossing-over. It appears significant that no such progeny were found, when allowance had been made for crossovers elsewhere between the outside markers. The data were thus in agreement with the one polaron: one cistron hypothesis.

Jessop and Catcheside (1965) have discovered in *Neurospora crassa* a recessive mutant, *rec* (recombination), which brings about a more than tenfold increase in the frequency of recombination between alleles at the *his*-1 (histidine-1) locus, with little or no effect on recombination between the nearby genes *amination* and *inositol* on each side. They suggest that the *rec* gene determines the structure either of an enzyme which catalyses one of the events in recombination, or of a regulator of such an enzyme. That the action of *rec* appears on present evidence to be specific to *his*-1 points tentatively to the existence of a unit of recombination coinciding with the cistron.

If the polaron coincides with the cistron, crossing-over can be initiated only between genes and not within them. This represents a step back towards the old bead hypothesis of the gene, but with a significant difference. The old idea (§ 9.9) was that crossing-over was confined to the links between genes, but it is now suggested that crossing-over is merely initiated between the genes, and then extends into the gene on one or other side. Moreover, there is a secondary process of recombination, namely, the correction of heterozygosity, which occurs only when a heterozygous gene lies within a crossover. This accounts for the two units of recombination: the *polaron* as the smallest element into which the chromosome is divisible by crossing-over, and the *recon* as the smallest element into which it is divisible by the correction of heterozygosity.

Hastings and Whitehouse (1964) suggested that if the polaron coincides with the cistron, it is possible that some of the steps in crossing-over are mediated by the same enzymes as in messenger RNA formation. It is not known how messenger RNA is formed and the steps suggested are hypothetical. Both processes would appear to involve (*a*) recognition of the end of the gene, (*b*) breakage of one of the DNA chains at this point, (*c*) separation of the chains over the length of the gene, (*d*) synthesis of a nucleotide chain complementary to one of the two DNA chains, (*e*) separation of the new chain from its template, and (*f*) formation of a duplex DNA molecule (that is, hybrid DNA in crossing-over, and restoration of the original condition of the DNA after messenger RNA formation).

A re-formulation of the one polaron: one cistron hypothesis, which makes the resemblance between the postulated steps in crossing-over and in messenger RNA formation look even more significant, is discussed in the next chapter.

16. The theory of the operon

§ 16.1 The operon

Demerec and associates (1955) obtained large numbers of nutritionally-deficient mutants of *Salmonella typhimurium*. Initially, ultraviolet light was used as mutagen, but subsequently it was found that the spontaneous mutation-rate was adequate, since mutants were readily selected from large populations of cells. The selection technique involved incubating the bacteria in minimal medium containing penicillin, which is lethal to growing cells but harmless to auxotrophic mutants, which were not metabolising because they were unable to grow on minimal medium.

When two mutants were grown in mixed culture, recombinants were often obtained. It was established that these were occurring as a result of transduction, that is, transfer of small fragments of the hereditary material from one cell to another by a virus (*P*22) (cf. § 15.3). By means of this recombination, detailed mapping of mutant sites was possible. It was found that there were numerous linearly-arranged sites of mutation within each functional unit (cistron). This was comparable to results with *Aspergillus nidulans* and the *T*-even viruses of *Escherichia coli* discussed in Chapter 13. However, an unexpected discovery made by Demerec and Demerec (1956) with tryptophan-requiring mutants, and by Hartman (1956) with histidine-requiring mutants, was that cistrons concerned with successive steps in the synthesis of these aminoacids were closely linked, and moreover were arranged on the linear linkage map in the same order as the steps which they control in the biosynthetic pathway. This was in complete contrast to the results with chromosomal organisms, where, for example in *Neurospora*, the genes concerned with the various steps in the synthesis of specific aminoacids appeared to be scattered more or less at random through the linkage-groups.

Series of closely-linked genes arranged in the same order as the steps which they control in a biochemical sequence have since been found to be of frequent occurrence in bacteria, including the Actinomycete *Streptomyces coelicolor* (Hopwood and Sermonti, 1962). Such linkage, however, is not found for all the steps in every pathway, and appears to be lacking in *Pseudomonas aeruginosa* (Fargie and Holloway, 1965).

Ames and Garry (1959) discovered that the amount of each of the enzymes concerned in histidine synthesis in *Salmonella* could vary over a wide range depending on the growth conditions, but the ratio of the activity of one enzyme to that of another was constant. They suggested that the cluster of genes acted as a unit of regulation. The rate of production of the enzymes decreased (repression) as the amount of the final end-product, histidine, increased, and the integrated action of histidine on the group of enzymes has been called *co-ordinate repression*.

Jacob, Monod and associates (see Jacob and Monod 1961, 1962) found that mutants of *Escherichia coli* unable to make use of lactose were due to mutations in one or other of a series of 3 closely-linked cistrons, each concerned with the production of a different enzyme (β-galactosidase, a permease, and a transacetylase—see Fig. 16.1(*a*)). These enzymes are normally produced only in response to an inducer (lactose or other β-galactoside). In addition to mutants deficient in the ability to synthesise one of these enzymes, other mutants were found which formed all the lactose enzymes constitutively, that is, without the need of inducer. These mutants were found to be of two kinds.

One class of constitutive mutants was due to mutation at sites placed at one end of the series of lactose genes. Jacob *et al* (1960) called this region an *operator* and the neighbouring group of genes which it affected in an integrated way they called an *operon*. Jacob and Monod (1961) found that the rate of production of the three enzymes was much increased by lactose, but that the ratio of the activities of the different enzymes was constant. This *co-ordinate induction* was attributed to control by the operator. The co-ordinate repression, for example, of the histidine enzymes in *Salmonella* by histidine, was similarly

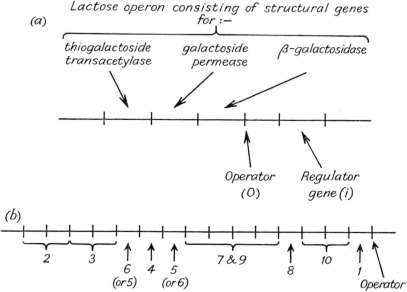

FIGURE 16.1   Linkage maps of (*a*) the lactose operon and its regulator gene in *Escherichia coli*, and (*b*) the histidine operon in *Salmonella typhimurium*. The numbers in (*b*) show the sequence of action in the biosynthetic pathway leading to histidine of the 10 enzymes determined by the 15 cistrons composing this operon.

explained. By study of heterozygotes for both an operator and an operon mutant in the *E. coli* lactose system, Jacob and Monod found that the operator directly influenced the genes of the neighbouring operon. Mutation in one particular cistron of this operon causes a failure of formation of the enzyme β-galactosidase, and as already mentioned, mutation in the operator causes the lactose enzymes to be formed constitutively (operator constitutive, O^c) instead of only in response to inducer. In cells heterozygous for these mutants (partial heterozygotes occur following conjugation—see § 15.3), the operator mutant was found to affect the lactose operon in its own chromoneme*, but not that in the homologue. Denoting the β-galactosidase-deficient mutant by z, they found that the cis configuration $\left(\dfrac{z\ O^c}{+\ +}\right)$ was normal, that is β-galactosidase was formed only in response to inducer, but in the trans configuration $\left(\dfrac{+\ O^c}{z\ +}\right)$ β-galactosidase was formed constitutively.

The second class of constitutive mutants was found by Pardee, Jacob and Monod (1959) to be due to mutation at a gene locus called i (inducer) which was also closely linked to the lactose operon. Double heterozygotes for i and z mutants were found to be normal, that is, they formed β-galactosidase only in response to inducer, whether the mutants were in the cis $\left(\dfrac{z\ i}{+\ +}\right)$ or the trans $\left(\dfrac{+\ i}{z\ +}\right)$ configuration.

A feature of the operon hypothesis of fundamental importance is that it postulates the existence of two kinds of genes: *structural genes*, responsible for specifying the aminoacid sequence in polypeptides, and *regulator genes*, which control the functioning of the structural genes. The inducer (i) locus in the *E. coli* lactose system is an example of a regulator gene.

Jacob and Monod (1962) found that some β-galactosidase-deficient mutants were associated with reduced quantities of the other two lactose enzymes, and some permease mutants had a reduced level of transacetylase, but β-galactosidase was unaffected. From the linkage map (Fig. 16.1(*a*)), it is evident that these mutants are polarised in their effects, only enzymes made by genes on the distal side of the mutant site with respect to the operator being reduced in amount. They have therefore been called polarity mutants. Beckwith (1964) has shown that a class of mutants which Jacob and Monod had called operator zero (O^0) mutations, because they prevent the formation of all the enzymes of the operon, appear to be polarity mutants with the mutant site situated in the β-galactosidase structural gene near the operator.

The histidine operon in *Salmonella* has been intensively studied by Hartman, Ames and associates (see particularly Hartman *et al* (1960) and Smith and Ames (1964)). Over 1,000 histidine-requiring mutants have been isolated. The operon has been found to consist of 15 cistrons specifying 10 enzymes (Fig. 16.1(b)). There are several instances of pairs of cistrons determining one enzyme, and one group of 4 cistrons specifies two enzymes, a dehydrase (no. 7) and a phosphatase (no. 9). It appears that different parts of the

* Chromoneme = bacterial (or viral) chromosome—see § 11.1.

same protein molecule catalyse different reactions (see § 13.7). As can be seen from Fig. 16.1(*b*), the gene sequence on the linkage map does not correspond precisely with the sequence in which the enzymes act in the biosynthetic pathway. In particular, the cistron specifying the enzyme catalysing the first step in histidine synthesis appears out of place, being next to those which determine the enzyme for the last step. Numerous polarity mutations have been found, and the operator appears to be at the right-hand end of the operon in Fig. 16.1(*b*), that is, next to the gene controlling step no. 1.

Jacob and Monod (1961) regarded the operator as the point of initiation of the formation of messenger RNA. They considered the possibility that separate messenger RNA molecules were synthesised from each cistron, but they favoured the idea that a single messenger was formed corresponding to the entire operon, because this would provide a neat explanation of the coordinate induction or repression of the enzymes of an operon.

Attardi *et al.* (1964) isolated the messenger RNA corresponding to the lactose operon of *E. coli* by means of the technique developed by Hall and Spiegelman (1961), whereby messenger RNA forms hybrid molecules with homologous DNA when a heated mixture is slowly cooled (see § 14.6). Attardi and associates found the sedimentation rate of the messenger RNA was such as to suggest that it corresponded to the entire operon. Martin (1964), using differential labelling with ^{14}C and ^{3}H to distinguish the RNA of a mutant deficient for the *Salmonella* histidine operon from that of a non-deficient strain, has found by chromatography on a methyl albumin column, followed by centrifuging in a sucrose gradient, that the histidine operon messenger RNA had a sedimentation rate of 34 *S*. This would correspond to a molecular weight equivalent to about 10,000 nucleotides, which would be reasonable for 15 cistrons. Martin's results therefore suggest that the messenger is derived from the entire histidine operon.

Ames and Hartman (1964) postulated that, at or near the junctions between cistrons in the messenger RNA from an operon, there may be a special triplet of nucleotides which they called a *modulating triplet*, and that this may cause the reading of the message to slow down or stop at this point, through association with a *modulator transfer RNA*. If the reading of messenger RNA begins at the operator end, the effect of the modulating triplets will be that genes near the operator will give rise to relatively large numbers of enzyme molecules and genes at the other end of the operon to relatively few. These authors suggest that the sequence of cistrons in an operon corresponds to that of the efficiency of the associated enzymes. The least efficient enzyme will require most molecules, and hence would be expected to be coded by the gene nearest the operator. On this hypothesis, the sequence of genes in the operon need not correspond to that of the action of the enzymes in the biosynthetic pathway. Some exceptions to such correspondence are known, as, for example, in the *Salmonella* histidine operon (see above). Ames and Hartman suggested that polarity mutants are due to mutation of a normal triplet to give a modulating triplet.

Jacob and Monod (1961) postulated that the lactose regulator gene, *i*, acted by forming a specific repressor substance which interacted with the operator and prevented the formation of messenger RNA. The inducer (such as lactose) was considered to interact with the repressor substance, and so prevent it from functioning. The i and O^c constitutive mutants were thought to be defective in the production and receipt, respectively, of the repressor substance, with the result that the enzymes of the operon were formed in the absence of inducer. An essential feature of this hypothesis for the control of enzyme activity is that messenger RNA should be extremely unstable, such that enzyme synthesis stops within 2 or 3 minutes of stopping the synthesis of the messenger. The instability would presumably be on account of rapid breakdown by the enzyme ribonuclease. For the *E. coli* lactose operon, there is evidence from the work of Hayashi *et al.* (1963), Attardi *et al.* (1964) and others, that the amount of messenger RNA present can vary, depending on the presence of inducer or other conditions. The messenger RNA was isolated by the technique described above of hybridisation with homologous DNA. These results suggest, but do not conclusively establish, that there is modification of the rate of messenger RNA production, as Jacob and Monod have postulated.

An alternative hypothesis to account for the regulation of protein synthesis was proposed by Ames and Hartman (1964). They suggested that the control might be, not in the transcription of DNA into messenger RNA, but in the translation of messenger RNA into polypeptide. They consider that repression might be due to the presence of a modulating triplet in the operator region, and that O^c mutants might be the result of mutation of this triplet to a normal one.

Even if, as appears likely on present evidence, Jacob and Monod's repressor model is found to be essentially correct as an explanation of their results with the *E. coli* lactose operon, there is evidence that this method of control of protein synthesis is not the only one. McFall and Mandelstam (1963), from study of the inhibition of the synthesis of β-galactosidase and other enzymes in *E. coli* by glucose, came to the conclusion that β-galactosidase production is controlled not only by the regulator gene, i, but also by a second specific repressor which was effective even in i mutants. This second repressor appeared to be the immediate end-product (galactose) of the reaction, or some closely related substance. The end-products of other reactions similarly acted as specific repressors for the enzymes of those reactions. Furthermore, Harris and Sabath (1964), from study of the synthesis of the enzyme penicillinase in *Bacillus cereus* in response to inducer (cephalosporin C), found that the antibiotic actinomycin D inhibited RNA synthesis within 1 or 2 minutes of its addition to the culture, but that synthesis of the enzyme continued for the cell generation-time (about 20 minutes). It was inferred that the messenger RNA for penicillinase was stable, and that in consequence the regulation of the synthesis of the enzyme could not occur by controlling messenger RNA formation.

These results suggest that a mechanism exists for the regulation of enzyme synthesis acting at the level of the translation of messenger RNA into polypeptide, and moreover that this mechanism does not require the activity of regulator genes such as i in the *E. coli* lactose system.

The operon concept originated from experimental results obtained with bacteria, but it appears likely also to apply to bacterial viruses. Epstein *et al.* (1964) have discovered two classes of conditional lethal mutants in virus *T*4 of *E. coli*: temperature-sensitive mutants which form plaques at 25°C but not at 42°C, and ambivalent (amber) mutants which form plaques on one strain of the host (*CR*63) but not on another (*B*) (see § 13.8 and § 14.10). Both classes of mutations can occur in numerous genes, and have enabled the map position and function of the genes to be established. Many of the temperature-sensitive and host-sensitive mutations occur in the same genes. In a few instances, the phenotypes of such mutants differ, and from the nature of the differences it has been inferred that the temperature-sensitive mutants make defective protein at 42°C, while the host-sensitive mutants make no protein on strain *B*. Using these conditional lethal mutants, 47 genes, possibly representing about half the total number of genes in the *T*4 chromoneme, have been mapped, with the results shown in Fig. 16.2. It is evident that the genes are not randomly distributed on the circular map, but that those with related functions are grouped together. Epstein *et al.* tentatively suggested that the chromoneme may be organised into 10–20 operons, but they emphasise that the clustering of genes of like function is the only evidence for this.

As a derivative of the idea of interactions between regulators and operators in the control of gene action, Jacob and Brenner (1963) have made comparable postulates to account for the control of DNA replication. They suggest that replication is controlled in such a way that it occurs independently in each unit or *replicon*. Bacterial and viral chromonemes appear to be single replicons, but a chromosome contains a number of them (see § 12.7). Jacob, Brenner and Cuzin (1964), in elaborating the replicon concept, pointed out that the enzymes which make DNA and RNA copies from a DNA primer function in an uncontrolled way *in vitro*, but that *in vivo* both replication and transcription appear to be controlled with such precision and specificity that they cannot be regulated by the flow of their precursors. Jacob *et al.* postulated that DNA replication required, first, a structural gene controlling the synthesis of a specific *initiator*, which might be a specific DNA polymerase or a priming enzyme able to separate the chains of the double helix, and secondly, an operator of replication, or *replicator*, which would be a recognition site upon which the initiator would act, allowing the replication of the DNA attached to the replicator. This model for control of replication is based on the repressor model for the control of gene action, but with the essential difference that positive regulation of replication is postulated instead of the negative regulation, by removal of a repressor, proposed for protein synthesis. The initiator and replicator were considered to be specific for each replicon, so that, for instance, the initiator for a bacterial virus would not recognise the replicator for its host. This hypothesis would account for the observation that chromonemal fragments, introduced into a bacterial cell by conjugation, transformation, or transduction, fail to replicate unless incorporated into the chromoneme of the acceptor cell (see § 15.3), since the fragments would be unlikely to include the replicator.

Evidence that bacterial nuclear material is not composed only of structural genes specifying aminoacid sequence in polypeptides has been obtained by several authors. Yankofsky and Spiegelman (1962) showed that ribosomal RNA from *Escherichia coli* when mixed with heated *E. coli* DNA and slowly

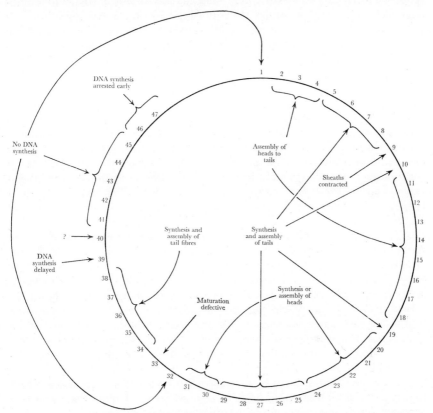

FIGURE 16.2   The circular linkage map of virus *T*4 of *Escherichia coli* obtained by Epstein *et al.* (1964). The genes are numbered consecutively according to their position on the map. Genes which act early in the development of the virus are labelled on the outside of the circle, and the late-acting genes are labelled within the circle.

cooled formed hybrid DNA-RNA molecules. It was inferred that there are base sequences in the DNA complementary to those in ribosomal RNA. Evidence was obtained (Yankofsky and Spiegelman, 1963) that in *Bacillus megaterium* the two RNA components of the ribosomes, which have sedimentation rates of 23 *S* and 16 *S*, respectively, do not compete with one another in forming hybrid molecules with DNA. It was concluded that the two RNA components are derived from different cistrons in the DNA. Evidence has since been obtained pointing to a similar relationship between DNA and ribosomal RNA in chromosomal organisms (see § 16.4).

Goodman and Rich (1962) and Giacomoni and Spiegelman (1962) obtained comparable results for *E. coli* transfer RNA, where over 20 cistrons appear to be involved, as expected with multiple coding (see Chapter 14).

It thus appears that some genes are concerned in specifying nucleotide sequence in RNA for its own sake, rather than as an intermediary to amino-acid sequence in polypeptides. It is possible that the repressor substances postulated by Jacob and Monod and discussed above, and the controlling elements and controlling episomes to be discussed in § 16.3, are also composed of nucleic acid, although latterly protein has been favoured for the repressor substances.

The operon concept was developed by Jacob, Monod and associates to explain the integrated control of the action of genes in a biosynthetic pathway in bacteria. In chromosomal organisms, the genes concerned with successive steps in reaction chains appear, in general, to be scattered through the linkage groups. This is well-established for *Neurospora crassa* and *Aspergillus nidulans*, and is indicated, for instance, by the frequency of $9:3:3:1$ ratios (or modifications such as $9:7$) in the F_2 generation in studies on the inheritance of anthocyanin pigmentation in flowering plants. The histidine-3 (*his*-3) region in linkage group I in *N. crassa*, however, appears to control two or three different steps in the synthesis of histidine. Giles (1965) has suggested that *his*-3 may be an operon containing 2 or 3 cistrons, but according to the analysis of the recombination and complementation data for 124 *his*-3 mutants made by Catcheside (1965), it is more probable that the different enzymic functions are to be attributed to a single polypeptide. The recombination data also suggest that the *his*-3 mutants are all in one polaron. In view of this uncertainty whether *his*-3 in *Neurospora* contains more than one cistron or not, there appears to be no well-established instance of the occurrence in chromosomal organisms of an operon in the sense of a group of closely-linked cistrons under integrated control and concerned with different steps in a biosynthetic pathway.

On the other hand, there is some evidence from chromosomal organisms that genes of similar function occur near together more often than might be expected by chance, although without any evidence of integrated control of their activity. This is exemplified by the cistrons *ad*-3*A* and *ad*-3*B* in linkage group I of *N. crassa*. These genes are closely linked but according to de Serres (1964) not quite adjacent, and mutants at either locus are similar, needing adenine or hypoxanthine for growth and accumulating a purple pigment. Another example from *N. crassa* is provided by the genes *cys*-1 and *cys*-2 in linkage group VI (Stadler, 1956), mutation of either of which produces a requirement for cysteine. It is possible that the nucleolar organizer may represent a number of genes of similar function in close proximity (see § 16.4).

From study of mutants of *Aspergillus nidulans* able to use nitrite but not nitrate as a nitrogen source, Pateman *et al.* (1964) have put forward the hypothesis that 5 genetic loci are concerned with the synthesis of a common co-factor necessary for the normal functioning of the enzymes nitrate reductase and xanthine dehydrogenase, and that this co-factor also functions as a regulator of nitrate reductase synthesis. These enzymes are known to be flavoproteins which also contain iron and molybdenum as prosthetic groups. It is suggested that the co-factor in question might be that associated with molybdenum. These ideas, if confirmed, would imply that structural genes and regulator genes may not be so sharply differentiated as Jacob and Monod had originally supposed.

Monod and Jacob (1962) have suggested that if the hypothesis of one operon—one messenger is found to be correct, this allows the operon to be redefined as the unit of transcription. They point out that this definition would remain valid and useful irrespective of the number of cistrons in an operon. Using operon in this sense, it is evident that one of the fundamental differences between bacteria and chromosomal organisms appears to be that in bacteria the operons generally include a number of cistrons, the maximum recorded being 15, while in chromosomal organisms they appear usually, and perhaps always, to contain only one.

If the process of crossing-over has features in common with messenger RNA formation, as was suggested in § 15.7, the polaron would be expected to coincide with the operon defined as the unit of transcription. The recombination data from chromosomal organisms appear to agree with this expectation, and so the idea that polarons correspond with cistrons can be tentatively re-formulated as the one polaron—one operon hypothesis.

An incidental consequence of the difference between bacteria and chromosomal organisms in operon size is that inversion of a segment of DNA will less often be lethal with a smaller operon. This is because messenger RNA is formed from one specific DNA chain only (see § 14.7), which means that inversions involving only a part of an operon would cause mutation, since they would lead to the coding of defective protein from any cistrons so involved. Before discussing the significance of operon size in relation to the control of gene action and cell differentiation, it is necessary to consider the structure of the chromosome.

§ 16.2 Chromosome structure

One of the most striking features of chromosomes in many organisms is that certain parts of them stain differently from other parts. Heitz (1928), after studying the mitotic chromosomes of the liverwort *Pellia fabbroniana*, introduced the term *heterochromatin* to describe segments which stained more deeply than the majority (*euchromatin*). Subsequently, the use of the term heterochromatin was extended to include regions which stain differently from the rest, since it was found that the same region may stain more deeply at one period of the nuclear cycle and less deeply at another. Heterochromatic regions lack chromomeres, such as the euchromatic parts of a chromosome show in early prophase I of meiosis. Corresponding to this, the heterochromatic segments of the salivary gland chromosomes of *Drosophila* show an amorphous appearance without transverse bands. Small segments of heterochromatin occur at numerous points in the chromosomes, and are revealed by cold treatment prior to fixation. In addition, there are usually extensive heterochromatic regions near the centromere of each chromosome. These centromere regions form an aggregate in the *Drosophila* salivary gland chromosomes (see Fig. 9.1), apparently as a result of a general attraction between the heterochromatin of the different chromosomes. Non-homologous pairing between heterochromatic segments has been observed at the pachytene stage of meiosis in *Zea*, and may be responsible for an association in inheritance between genes in different linkage groups observed by Longley (1945) in *Zea* (female side only), by Michie and Wallace (1953) in *Mus*, and by Shult and Lindegren (1958) in *Saccharomyces*. Another feature of heterochromatin is that it appears to replicate after euchromatin. Thus, Schmid (1963) has shown by tritium labelling that the late replicating regions of human chromosomes in tissue culture correspond to secondary constrictions.

In many organisms, chromosomes composed wholly of heterochromatin occur (review: Müntzing 1959). They have been called supernumerary or *B*-chromosomes, and they usually vary in number in different individuals or populations of the species.

The heterochromatic regions appear to correspond with parts of the linkage maps without genes. Examples of this in *Drosophila* are the *Y*-chromosome and the centromere regions of the other chromosomes. The viability of individuals lacking a *Y*-chromosome, or lacking *B*-chromosomes, contrasts with the lethality of even small deficiencies from the normal or *A*-chromosomes. On the other hand, the heterochromatic regions are evidently not devoid of function even though they appear to lack normal genes. This is shown by the necessity for a *Y*-chromosome if male *Drosophila* is to be fertile, and by the existence of adaptations in the haploid generation of flowering plants favouring an increase in the number of *B*-chromosomes. The means by which such increase is brought about include failure of *B*-chromosomes to segregate normally at mitoses in the pollen or embryo sac, such that daughter nuclei in the germ-line receive more of them than do other nuclei. Selective fertilization by gamete nuclei with the larger numbers may also occur (for references, see Müntzing 1959). Likewise, Rhoades (1942) found that in *Zea* heterozygous for a terminal heterochromatic knob in chromosome no. 10 the homologue with the knob reached the functional embryo-sac in 70% of meioses instead of the 50% expected if the orientation of the chromosome-pair on the meiotic spindle were at random.

From study of the number of sternopleural chaetae in stocks of *Drosophila melanogaster* differing only in their Y-chromosome, Mather (1944) found evidence for the occurrence in this chromosome of a number of genes having small and more or less additive effects on bristle number. It was inferred that heterochromatin is not inert but contains genes which are qualitatively different from those occurring in euchromatin. Other genetical phenomena associated with heterochromatin are discussed in § 16.3 and § 16.4.

Ris (1957) obtained electron micrographs of thin sections through heterochromatin in the nuclei of amphibians and found that its structure did not differ from that of euchromatin, except in the degree of packing of the fine threads seen. He also found that the chromomeres in leptotene chromosomes of *Lilium longiflorum* differ from the interchromomeric segments merely in the density of the folded and coiled threads. That heterochromatin should differ from euchromatin merely in the way its material is arranged is in keeping with some observations which suggest that under certain circumstances euchromatin can become heterochromatic (see § 16.3 and § 16.4).

From study of electron micrographs of chromosomes from a number of different plants and animals at various stages of mitosis and meiosis, Ris (1957) came to the conclusion that a chromosome is multistranded in the sense that it is built like a cable with numerous identical sub-units. Kaufmann and McDonald (1957) reached similar conclusions. However, the possibility that the chromosome is single-stranded does not appear to be excluded by these observations because the multiple strands observed with the electron microscope might represent a single strand folded back and forth upon itself a number of times.

The nuclei of closely-related species with the same chromosome number may differ appreciably in their DNA content. For example, Schrader and Hughes-Schrader (1956) found by measurement of the density of Feulgen staining at prophase I of meiosis in males of the hemipterous insects *Thyanta antiguensis* and *T. perditor* that the amount of DNA per nucleus was, in arbitrary units, 0.89 ± 0.02 and 1.10 ± 0.03, respectively. Both species have 12 autosomes and, in the male, an X- and a Y-chromosome. Some authors have inferred from such results that there are specific differences in the number of strands making up the chromosomes. However, the diversity in total DNA might be due to differences in content of heterochromatin. It is known that, even within a species, populations may differ in the number of B-chromosomes which they possess, so it would not be surprising if there was also considerable variation in the amount of heterochromatin in the A-chromosomes.

The chromosomes at diplotene of meiosis in female newts show a remarkable feature which has earned them the name of lampbrush chromosomes (review: Callan, 1963; see § 8.13) (cf. Pl. 3(*a*) and (*b*)). The chromosomes at this stage are very long (up to 800 μ) and have hundreds of loops projecting laterally for 10–15 μ or more, giving a fuzzy or lampbrush appearance. The loops arise in pairs from chromomeres (Fig. 16.3(*d*)), and are thought to be associated with the functioning of some of the genes, since RNA and protein synthesis have been demonstrated autoradiographically as occurring alongside them (see § 16.4). This synthesis is no doubt related to the considerable growth of the oocytes which occurs during the period of at least 200 days that the nucleus remains at the diplotene stage. The nucleus itself increases greatly in size during this period. Callan found that when a lampbrush chromosome is stretched, the chromomeres break transversely and a pair of lateral loops span the break (see Fig. 16.3(*e*)). He inferred that the loops may have an axis which is continuous with the very fine thread which joins the chromomeres, and forms the main axis of the chromosome. From electron micrographs of lampbrush chromosomes after pepsin digestion, Gall (1956) confirmed that there is an axis to the lateral loops, and moreover showed that it was resistant to the enzyme. His interpretation of the structure of a lampbrush chromosome is shown in Fig. 16.3(*f*). Callan and Macgregor (1958)

FIGURE 16.3   Drawings to illustrate the appearance of
the chromosomes at the diplotene stage
of meiosis in oocytes of *Triturus*.
(*a*) One chromosome-pair with three
chiasmata.
(*b*) Part of one chromosome, to show the
lampbrush appearance in more detail.
(*c*) Diagrammatic representation of (*b*) to
illustrate how the loops arise in pairs
from the chromomeres.
(*d*) One such pair of loops in more detail.
(*e*) The appearance of such a loop-pair
after stretching (from Callan).
(*f*) The structure of a loop-pair, according
to Gall (1956).

transferred unfixed *Triturus* lampbrush chromosomes to physiological
saline, and studied the effect of enzymes on them. They found that pepsin
and trypsin, which split peptide linkages near free acidic and basic groups
respectively, and ribonuclease, which breaks down RNA, did not destroy the
linear integrity of the chromosomes, whereas deoxyribonuclease (DNase)
which breaks down DNA, had a dramatically different action: the lateral
loops and the thread joining the chromomeres rapidly disintegrated. They
inferred that DNA runs throughout the length of the chromosome, including

the axis of the lateral loops. Dutt and Kaufmann (1959) observed no disruption of meiotic chromosomes in males of the grasshoppers *Trimerotropis maritima* and *Melanoplus femur-rubrum* when unfixed material was treated with DNase, but Macgregor and Callan (1962) attribute this to the relatively compact condition of the chromosomes at the time of treatment, compared with the remarkably extended diplotene chromosomes in female *Triturus*. Macgregor and Callan have found that much contracted parts of these amphibian chromosomes, such as the chromomeres, also fail to show breakage by DNase.

Gall (1963) studied the kinetics of the DNase breakage of *Triturus* lampbrush chromosomes. Unfixed chromosomes were photographed at intervals over a period of one hour after placing in the enzyme solution. From the photographs the number of breaks was counted and plotted against the time. Breaks in the lateral loops were scored separately from breaks in the main axis. It was assumed that the chromosome consists of n longitudinal sub-units, that each is attacked independently and with equal probability by the enzyme, and that all of them have to be digested at approximately corresponding positions in order to cause a break in the chromosome. The number of breaks will then be directly proportional to the time if there is one sub-unit, proportional to the square of the time if there are two sub-units, to the time cubed if there are three, and so on. Gall obtained the values $n = 2.6 \pm 0.2$ for the loops, and $n = 4.8 \pm 0.4$ for the main axis. He considered the true sub-unit numbers to be 2 and 4, respectively, because delay in penetration of the enzyme through the nuclear sap, and delay in observing a break after it had occurred, would both tend to raise the observed values of n above the true one. That there should be twice as many sub-units in the main axis as in the loops is in keeping with his earlier interpretation of the structure of lampbrush chromosomes (Fig. 16.3(f)), according to which the loops are parts of the axis of individual chromatids, while the main axis consists of a pair of sister chromatids in close association with one another. From *in vitro* studies, Thomas (1956) found evidence that DNase cleaves the phosphorus-ester links in the two nucleotide chains of DNA independently and at random, and that breakage of the molecule occurs only when the two chains are severed less than about 3 nucleotide-pairs apart. Gall inferred that the two sub-units of the chromatid were the two nucleotide chains, and that the chromatid contains either one very long DNA molecule or a series of DNA molecules connected end-to-end. This conclusion is in agreement with the results of Taylor's experiments with plant chromosomes labelled with tritiated thymidine (see § 12.2).

It has been apparent for many years that mutation and recombination are phenomena that are normally shown by chromatids rather than by sub-units within the chromatid. For recombination, this is manifest from the results of tetrad analysis (cf. § 8.6), although postmeiotic segregation (see § 15.2) constitutes an exception. With the acceptance of the DNA theory of the molecular basis of heredity, it appeared most improbable that several DNA molecules carried the same genetic information within one chromatid. If a mutation can represent a change in only one nucleotide-pair, and if, as would

appear, recombination normally occurs with such precision that no nucleotide is lost, added or changed*, the simultaneous occurrence of any particular
gene in more than one DNA molecule in a chromatid is exceedingly unlikely. This argument applies only to the germ-line, and it is evident that in
certain differentiated cells the chromosomes are multistranded (*polytene*),
for example, in the salivary gland nuclei of *Drosophila*. As indicated in § 15.7,
Whitehouse and Hastings (1965) have found that published data on recombination are in agreement with a theory of crossing-over based on the assumption that a chromatid can be looked upon as one DNA molecule (or as a
number joined end-to-end). The recombination data contradict hypotheses
of chromatid structure which postulate a multistranded condition, since
these would require exceedingly elaborate and implausible models to account
for crossing-over. It is evident that the genetic data confirm the cytological
observations of Taylor with *Vicia* and *Bellevalia* root-tips, and of Callan and
Gall with *Triturus* oocytes, and establish that a chromatid is a single-stranded
structure in the sense that each gene is represented in only one DNA molecule.

   The simplest hypothesis of chromosome structure which fits the data is
that the whole of the DNA of a chromosome is contained in one giant DNA
molecule. Gall (1956) has estimated that the 12 chromosomes in the haploid
set of *Rana pipiens* contain an average of 20 cm of DNA if it were straightened
out, and the 11 chromosomes of *Triturus viridescens* an average of 90 cm. There
appears to be no evidence at present for the occurrence of more than one
DNA molecule in a normal chromosome. If more than one is present, the
cytological and genetical data require them to be joined end-to-end.

   If the central axis of a chromosome is a single DNA molecule, how does the
protein fit into its construction? The unequal spacing of the two nucleotide
chains about the DNA helix axis leaves two spiral grooves. Atoms nos. 2 and
3 of the purines and pyrimidines lie at the bottom of the smaller groove, and
atoms nos. 5 and 6 at the bottom of the deep groove (cf. Fig. 11.5). Watson
and Crick (1953b) pointed out that the molecular dimensions of DNA were
such that a fully extended polypeptide chain could be wound round the same
helix axis as the nucleotide chains. Feughelman *et al.* (1955) confirmed this
for nucleoprotamine, the nucleoprotein found in the sperm of some animals.
Protamine appears to consist of one polypeptide chain in which about two-
thirds of the aminoacid residues are arginine. Feughelman and associates
showed from X-ray crystallographic evidence that the polypeptide chain
lies in the smaller groove. The spacing is such that the basic end-groups of
the arginine side-chains of the polypeptide can combine with the phosphate
groups of the DNA, while non-basic aminoacid residues probably occur in
pairs at folds in the polypeptide chain.

   Wilkins (1957) tentatively suggested that in nucleohistone, which appears
to occur universally in chromosomes except in the sperm of some animals,
there might be a polypeptide chain in both grooves of the DNA. However,

* The rare occurrence of mutation in association with recombination is discussed in
§ 15.6.

the *X*-ray diagrams were much less clear than for nucleoprotamine, and the structure of nucleohistone remains uncertain (cf. Wilkins and Zubay, 1963).

Kellenberger (1961) has discussed the process of condensation of DNA in the formation of the head in bacterial viruses. The DNA of the head occupies only about one-fifteenth of its previous volume, through removal of water molecules. The condensation process does not occur in the presence of chloramphenicol, which is an inhibitor of protein synthesis. When virus *T*2 of *Escherichia coli* is ruptured by osmotic shock, small quantities of proteins and polyamines are released, in addition to the DNA. It is inferred that protein plays a part in the condensation process. It appears that the polyamines may have a similar function, since Kaiser, Tabor and Tabor (1963) found that the polyamine spermine protects DNA from breakage by hydrodynamic shear. Spermine has the chemical formula:

$$NH_2 . (CH_2)_3 . NH . (CH_2)_4 . NH . (CH_2)_3 . NH_2$$

These authors found that if an aqueous suspension of DNA obtained from virus *lambda* of *E. coli* is stirred, genes placed well apart on the linkage map are inherited independently, indicating that the DNA has been broken. The marker genes were found often to stay together in the progeny if spermine was added before stirring the DNA. Only a minute quantity of spermine was required. It was suggested that the spermine might make the DNA more resistant to shear, either by alignment of the aliphatic chains along the helix, or by pulling together phosphate groups from different parts of the molecule to give a more compact configuration.

It is possible that the basic proteins (protamine or histones) in chromosomes have a similar function to the polyamines and protein in the heads of bacterial viruses. The protein part of the chromosome may be responsible for its characteristic morphological features, such as chromomeres and spiral coiling, since bacterial chromonemes, which lack these features, also lack protein in association with their DNA. That protamine should occur in association with the chromosomes in the sperm of some animals, instead of the histones found in other nuclei, may be related to the smaller size of the protamine molecule allowing the chromosomes to become more compact. For sperm, small size means greater mobility and hence has a selective advantage.

The histones of the chromosomes are known to show species specificity, and this suggests that their function is not merely to protect the DNA from breakage, and to allow it to fold into condensed configurations. It is possible that the histones play a part in chromosome pairing at meiosis. Moses and Coleman (1964) have found that the pairing cores seen under the electron microscope at meiotic prophase I (see § 8.20) are composed of protein, and it may be that the close pairing of homologous chromosomes comes about through some sort of interaction between the histones and the protein of the pairing core. Another possible function for the histones, namely, that they are concerned in the control of gene action in cell-differentiation, is discussed in § 16.4. Information about this control has been obtained from study of the causes of instability in gene expression, such as gives rise to mottled colouring or other kinds of variegation.

302 Mechanism of Heredity

§ 16.3 Unstable phenotypes

§ 16.3 Unstable phenotypes

Emerson (1914) was the first to show that a variable or unstable phenotype may be caused by mutations occurring with abnormally high frequency. He studied the variegated pigmentation of the pericarp found in some strains of *Zea mays* and established that the coloured stripes were due to mutation to a dominant allele of a gene affecting the pigment, for he found that the coloured condition was sometimes inherited. This was evidently when the mutation had occurred in the germ-line.

An outstanding example of a variegated phenotype resulting from mutation is due to the work of Rhoades (1936, 1938), also with *Zea*. The production of red or purple anthocyanin pigment in the aleurone layer of the endosperm of the maize grain requires the simultaneous presence of four dominant genes called A_1, A_2, C, and R, and situated in chromosomes nos. 3, 5, 9, and 10, respectively. After self-pollination of a maize plant homozygous for all these dominant factors, Rhoades (1936) found an ear with grains in the proportion of 12 with coloured aleurone: 3 dotted: 1 with colourless aleurone, instead of all the grains coloured as expected. The dotted aleurone character, which had not been observed previously, consisted of small spots of colour of fairly uniform size distributed apparently at random over the aleurone layer (see Fig. 16.4(a)). The 12:3:1 ratio was evidently a modified 9:3:3:1 ratio, and implied that the dotted character was due to a dominant gene inherited independently of that responsible for the otherwise colourless aleurone. Further breeding work confirmed this conclusion. The dominant gene responsible was called Dotted, Dt. It was found that a mutation had occurred at the A_1 locus to the recessive allele a_1 giving colourless aleurone, and that Dt interacted specifically with a_1 to give the dots, provided the genes A_2, C and R were also present. Dt was found to have no effect on recessive alleles at these other loci. It was found that Dt had been segregating previously in the strain of maize in which the mutation from A_1 to a_1 took place, but it had not been detected owing to the homozygosity for A_1.

The A_1 gene causes anthocyanin pigment to form in various other parts of the plant, provided the genotype is appropriate. These parts are the leaf-sheaths, the bracts surrounding the female inflorescence ('husks'), the stems ('culms'), the male inflorescence ('tassel'), the anthers and the pericarp. Rhoades (1938) found that Dt in the presence of a_1 and also of whatever other genes were necessary, caused small and narrow longitudinal stripes on the husks and culms; numerous small spots on the anthers or occasionally an entire anther coloured; and fine streaks or sectors on the pericarp. By making crosses with pollen from the rare wholly purple anthers, he showed that the purple character was sometimes inherited and that it was quite stable and was due to the presence of the A_1 gene. It was evident that the dots or stripes in potentially coloured parts of Dt a_1 maize were arising as a result of mutation from a_1 to A_1. Rhoades found that Dt also stepped up the rate of mutation of a_1 to another allele called $a_1{}^p$ which gives a paler anthocyanin than A_1. However, the rate of mutation from colourless to pale was much lower than from colourless to the normal dark pigmentation. Out of

80,955 aleurone dots on 2426 grains, 80 were pale and the remainder dark, implying that about 1 mutation in 1,000 was to the pale allele.

A striking feature of Rhoades' observations was that the mutations of a_1 induced by Dt apparently occurred only at the time when the A_1 gene might be expected to be functioning, that is, at a late stage of the development of each tissue. This was indicated by the small and relatively uniform size of

FIGURE 16.4   (a) A *Dotted* grain of *Zea mays*. The spots represent regions of
                   purple anthocyanin pigment in the otherwise colourless aleurone
                   layer of the endosperm.
              (b) Flower-buds of *Oenothera blandina* showing the uniformly
                   coloured calyx of a normal plant (left), and the mottled
                   appearance (right) of an individual heterozygous for a pair of
                   alleles affecting sepal pigmentation and with a structural change
                   in this particular chromosome in the neighbourhood of that
                   gene (from Catcheside, 1947).

the dots in the anthers and aleurone and of the stripes in the husks, culms and pericarp. Mutation at an earlier stage would be expected to give rise to whole regions or sectors pigmented, but these were rare or absent.

From studies of its linkage with other character-differences, Rhoades (1945) established that Dt was situated in the region of the knob at the end of the short arm of chromosome 9 (see Fig. 7.5). This knob is composed of heterochromatin.

Muller (1930a) found that a new dominant mutation at the notched-wing locus in the X-chromosome of *Drosophila* had appeared following X-ray treatment. In order to test whether it represented a deficiency of a small chromosome segment, like some previous Notch mutants, he crossed it with white-eyed flies, since the gene for white eye-colour was known to be only about 1.5 map units from that for notched wings. Most unexpectedly, the notched-winged offspring had mottled eyes, with lighter and darker areas of diverse size and ranging in colour over the whole series of colours known for alleles of white eye. Muller found that the mottled character was inherited as an allele of white. He also found that the notching of the wings was irregular in its manifestation, both within and between individuals, and that the behaviour of the wing and eye characters was to some extent correlated, as though there was some peculiarity in a chromosome segment rather than in just one gene. Moreover, Muller found from study of linkage with other mutants that the notched-winged mottled-eyed flies had a structural change in the X-chromosome, such that the part of it containing the notched-wing and white-eye loci had been removed and attached to chromosome no. III. Four other independent occurrences of alleles at the white-eye locus giving mottled eyes were found following irradiation of sperm. Although these had normal wings, linkage studies revealed that in every instance there was a structural change involving the X-chromosome. These observations suggested that there might be a causal connection between the mottling and the structural change.

Such a connection was subsequently demonstrated with the white-eye alleles and a number of other genes in *Drosophila*. One of the clearest demonstrations was by Catcheside (1939, 1947) in *Oenothera blandina*. A plant homozygous for a gene giving light red sepals was self-pollinated using pollen treated with X-rays. One of the progeny was found to have irregular patches of light red on otherwise green sepals. By examination of the chromosomes at meiosis, it was found that in this plant an interchange had occurred between segments of two of the chromosomes, and that one of these chromosomes was that which carried the gene for sepal colour. Through crossing-over in the interval between gene and point of interchange (recombination frequency about 1.7%), the sepal colour gene was subsequently transferred to a plant with normal chromosomes. This plant was found to show no variegation. It was inferred that the mottling of the calyx was due to a position effect and not to mutation.

Catcheside (1947) confirmed the position effect when he showed that an allele giving a uniformly deep red sepal colour also gave rise to a variegated calyx, this time of dark red patches on a green background, when transferred through crossing-over to plants carrying the interchange (see Fig. 16.4(b)). Moreover, a gene giving paler petal-colour than normal, which was linked to the sepal-colour gene (recombination frequency 8·5%), gave rise to variegated petals consisting of a mosaic of patches of the two shades of yellow when similarly transferred to plants with the interchange. Both sepal and petal colours became uniform again in progeny in which the genes concerned were restored to the normal chromosome configuration.

These experimental results, and similar data obtained by several authors from studies of variegated phenotypes in *Drosophila*, have usually been interpreted as evidence that the variegation was due to instability in the functioning of the gene and not to a mutational change of the gene itself. An alternative explanation is that mutations occur with high frequency in the tissues where the gene produces its specific effect, but that in other tissues, including the reproductive cell-lineage, the gene is stable.

Schultz (1936) studied the salivary gland chromosomes of a number of mutants of *Drosophila* showing mottled phenotypes, and found that in every instance the euchromatic region containing the genes in question had been transferred, as a result of a structural change, to the neighbourhood of heterochromatin. Moreover, Caspersson and Schultz (1938) found that this euchromatic region bordering on heterochromatin tended to acquire the appearance of heterochromatin, the transverse bands being lost. According to Schultz (1948) it appeared as if in some cells the heterochromatin modified the neighbouring euchromatin so that it resembled heterochromatin both in appearance and in lack of genetical activity, while in other cells there was no such modification, thus accounting for the mottled phenotype. The cytological observations thus appear to confirm the inference from the genetic data and suggest that the mottling results from the genes in question having been rendered inactive in some of the cells, the appropriate part of the chromosome having at the same time become heterochromatic in appearance.

McClintock (1950) discovered an interaction in *Zea* between mutable loci and the variegated phenotypes caused by position effect. A dominant gene which she had called Activator (*Ac*) appeared to cause mutation of certain other genes not linked to it. McClintock had established that *Ac* acted through an unlinked gene called Dissociation (*Ds*). In the presence of *Ac*, genes situated within about 5 map units on either side of *Ds* gave rise to a variegated phenotype similar to the effect of structural changes in *Drosophila* (described above) which bring euchromatin into proximity to heterochromatin. Moreover, in the presence of *Ac*, strains arose with different patterns of variegation, apparently as a result of mutation of *Ds* to new alleles.

A further remarkable feature of these genes such as *Dt*, *Ac*, and *Ds* which cause variability in the manifestation of other genes is that they occasionally become transferred to new positions either in the same or a different linkage group. This was shown for *Ac* and *Ds* by McClintock (1950), and for *Dt* by Nuffer (1955), who found *Dt* was situated in chromosomes nos. 6 and 7, respectively, in two South American strains of *Zea*, instead of in no. 9. With *Ac* and *Dt* such transposition does not affect the phenotype, but this is not true of *Ds*, since it is genes in proximity to *Ds* which give rise to variegation. The regions which *Ac*, *Ds*, and *Dt* occupy in the chromosomes appear to be heterochromatic.

Through the transfer of *Ds* to new positions, McClintock was able to confirm that on removal of *Ds*, the original phenotype was restored. As with the mottled phenotypes associated with transfer of euchromatin to the neighbourhood of heterochromatin described above, the effect of *Ds* on neighbouring genes is therefore usually interpreted as influencing gene action rather than as causing mutation. However, McClintock (1950) has put forward the view that these position effect variegations and those due to mutable loci are essentially one phenomenon, and she has given a striking series of parallels between them (McClintock, 1952). However, it is not clear how far the resemblances are due to the fact that both phenomena are associated with heterochromatin.

Another feature of *Ds* is that it is frequently associated with chromosome breakage or other structural changes at its locus. Alleles of *Ds* differ in the frequency of occurrence of such aberrations. Many of these structural changes could be the consequence of non-homologous crossing-over between different chromosomes or different parts of the same chromosome (cf. § 9.8).

In view of the evidence that *Ac*, *Ds*, *Dt*, and other factors like them (cf. Brink, 1960) are not normal genes, but appear to be abnormal states of a system affecting the manifestation of particular characters at a certain stage of development, McClintock (1957) has proposed the name *controlling element* for them. The characteristic features of such an element are that it does not occupy a fixed position in the chromosome complement, and that it appears to act only within the nucleus, serving as a gene mutator, or modifying or suppressing gene action.

Dawson and Smith-Keary (1963) have studied instability in the suppression of leucine requirement in *Salmonella typhimurium* and found similarities to the mutable loci of chromosomal organisms. They have postulated that *controlling episomes*, having many of the properties of McClintock's controlling elements, are responsible for the genic instability which they have observed. As mentioned in § 15.3, the term *episome* was introduced by Jacob and Wollman (1958b) for genetic particles that can exist either free in the cytoplasm or integrated into the chromoneme. When free, such particles replicate independently of and usually more rapidly than the chromoneme. Examples of episomes include many bacterial viruses, and the sex factor in *Escherichia coli*. Dawson and Smith-Keary found from transduction experiments that certain mutants having a requirement for leucine could become leucine independent as a result of mutation at a neighbouring locus. Some of these mutants which suppressed the leucine requirement were found to give colonies on minimal medium showing great diversity in size. Evidence was found that this instability was due to genetic factors capable of undergoing transduction, and that in any particular unstable mutant, the instability was probably confined to a particular site within the suppressor locus. They suggested that a controlling episome became attached at this site within the gene and was retained there through successive backward and forward mutations which it caused. Loss of the controlling episome would restore stability. This hypothesis was supported by the discovery of a correlation of instability at the leucine-suppressor locus with stability of suppressors for proline requirement, and *vice versa*. It was suggested that the leucine and proline suppressors often competed for a single controlling episome.

A two-element system, such as *Ac* and *Ds*, or *Dt* and a_1, in *Zea*, has not been found in *Salmonella*, nor is there any evidence from *Salmonella* of a modification of gene expression, either of the gene to which the controlling episome becomes attached, or of neighbouring genes such as *Ds* affects in *Zea*. The mutability in the presence of *Dt* of genes such as a_1 when they occur in specific tissues, and the stability of the same genes when in other cells, would be accounted for on Dawson and Smith-Keary's hypothesis if in the development

of the tissues where the mutation occurs, a controlling episome was transferred from Dt to a_1, while in other tissues there was no such transfer.
If the episome contained a nucleotide sequence, the association between
gene and episome might be through complementary base pairing. If there
was a difference between them in nucleotide sequence, this would lead to
mispairing, and if there was correction of heterozygosity in the DNA, a
mutation might arise (cf. § 15.6). The high mutability would then be a
consequence of a failure of the base sequence in the episome precisely to
match that of the gene (or a part of it).

Both the hypothesis of mutation caused by controlling episomes, and of
gene inactivation caused by proximity to heterochromatin (or to a controlling
element within the heterochromatin) are discussed further in § 16.4, since
they appear to have relevance to the control of differentiation.

§ 16.4 The control of differentiation

One of the fundamental problems in biology is how a diversity of types of
cell can develop from a single cell, such as a fertilized egg. At one time it was
thought that cell differentiation must be controlled from the cytoplasm,
since mitosis ensures that daughter-nuclei are identical. However, this
inference was based on the assumption that all the genes were active in every
cell. This assumption is clearly no longer justified in view of the demonstration by Monod, Jacob, and collaborators that the synthesis of β-galactosidase
in *Escherichia coli* is under the control of a regulator gene (see § 16.1).
Differentiation could therefore reflect the control of gene action.

Accepting that the specificity of the enzymes of an organism is inherited in
the structural genes in its nuclei, enzyme activity might be controlled at any
of 3 stages:

1. Control of enzyme synthesis at transcription, that is, messenger RNA
   formation from DNA.
2. Control of enzyme synthesis at translation, that is, polypeptide formation from messenger RNA.
3. Direct control of enzyme activity after synthesis.

Regulation at all these levels is known in bacteria. The mechanism of
control, through induction and repression of enzyme formation, is not fully
understood, but control at transcription is the likely explanation of the action
of the regulator gene, i, in the synthesis of β-galactosidase in *Escherichia coli*,
while control at the level of translation appears likely in Harris and Sabath's
experiments with penicillinase in *Bacillus cereus* (see § 16.1). Control of
enzyme activity, as distinct from synthesis, appears to be restricted to the
first enzyme of a sequence, or if the biosynthetic pathway is branched, to the
first enzyme of each branch, and to be brought about by the end-product of
the reaction chain (cf. Umbarger 1962). Monod and Jacob (1962) proposed
the name *allosteric inhibition* for this phenomenon, because the inhibitor is not a
steric analogue of the substrate, and because, theoretically at least, there is no
reason why substances other than the end-product of the reaction chain

should not act as inhibitors. They pointed out that if the end-product of each of two independent biosynthetic pathways acted as an inhibitor of the enzyme activity for the first step in the other pathway, this would provide a basis for alternative stable states. However, they consider that a steady state would be insufficient to account for differentiation, which appears to require controlled changes in the capacity of individual cells to synthesize specific proteins.

In chromosomal organisms, little is known in biochemical terms of the control of enzyme activity. If, as Monod and Jacob suppose, differentiation implies differential enzyme synthesis, there is the possibility, as in bacteria, of control at transcription or at translation. Control at transcription might be organized differently in chromosomal organisms compared with bacteria, owing to the occurrence of histones in association with the DNA.

A controlling mechanism implies a signal, and a transmitter and receiver. Control of gene action at the level of the transcription of DNA into messenger RNA requires the receiver of a signal to be in the nucleus. On the other hand, much of the protein synthesis of the cell occurs in the cytoplasm, so that control at the level of the translation of messenger RNA into polypeptide might occur in the cytoplasm. Equally, the transmitter might be either nuclear or cytoplasmic. Four possibilities are evident: intranuclear signals; extranuclear signals; and signals from nucleus to cytoplasm, and *vice versa*.

The occurrence of intranuclear signals in the control of gene action is exemplified by the regulator gene for β-galactosidase synthesis in *Escherichia coli* (see § 16.1), and by the evidence for controlling episomes in *Salmonella* and controlling elements in *Zea* (see § 16.3). In particular, Dawson and Smith-Keary's hypothesis of controlling episomes not only offers a possible explanation for mutable genes (see § 16.3), but it also suggests a mechanism for the control of differentiation. It appears significant that mutable genes often show mutation only at the time of development when the gene may be expected to be functioning. This suggests that the normal function of the episome might be to act as a signal for the formation of messenger RNA from that particular operon. If there is any truth in the suggestion that the mutability is due to the correction of heterozygosity in DNA (see § 16.3), in normal development the nucleotide sequences of gene and episome would presumably correspond, with the result that the gene would be stable. The hypothesis of Pateman *et al.* (1964) of a regulatory as well as a catalytic function for an enzyme co-factor (see § 16.1), if confirmed, would suggest that the activity of different operons might be integrated through the occurrence within them of nucleotide sequences with regulatory functions as well as sequences specifying one or more polypeptides with catalytic functions. The regulatory function might be direct, through an episome containing a nucleotide sequence, or it might be indirect through a polypeptide derived from such a sequence.

Schultz (1948), using strains of *Drosophila* having chromosomal structural changes which brought genes into proximity to heterochromatin, found that the extent of the resulting variegated phenotypes associated with position effect (see § 16.3) was easily modified by genetic factors. In the presence of an extra Y-chromosome the development of a variegated phenotype did not occur and the chromosome region brought into proximity to heterochromatin by the structural change remained euchromatic. The influence of the relative numbers of the different chromosomes on development was referred to in § 6.8 with reference to the abnormality of trisomics. Some genes, for example, *Dt* in *Zea* (Rhoades 1936) and *w* in *Drosophila* (see § 9.1), show a dosage effect, that is, their action is dependent on the number of copies present in the nucleus, and so a trisomic individual will be expected to have a modified phenotype. However, the mechanism by which an extra Y-chromosome, which is more or less entirely heterochromatic, can modify the phenotype, is unknown.

A number of further observations indicate the receipt within the nucleus of signals affecting gene action, although their source (whether intra- or extra-nuclear) is usually not known. King and Briggs (1955) transplanted nuclei from *Rana pipiens* embryos at various stages of development into enucleated eggs. They found that the nuclei from certain tissues had lost certain potentialities of expression possessed by the original nucleus of the egg. It appeared that progressive and stable nuclear changes occurred during differentiation, even though, as later studies showed, there were no visible changes in the chromosomes.

Gall and Callan (1962) studied the incorporation of tritiated uridine (the ribonucleoside of uracil containing ^{3}H) into RNA, and of tritiated phenyl-alanine into protein, in association with *Triturus* lampbrush chromosomes (the diplotene stage of meiosis in oocytes), and they found that RNA and protein synthesis occur on the lateral loops, but not on the chromomeres. There was marked variation in intensity of labelling from one pair of loops to another, each of which has a characteristic morphology. It was inferred that in the oocytes there is localized activity of small regions of the chromosomes. The size of the functional units is uncertain pending a fuller understanding of the significance of a remarkable polarity within each loop in the accumulation of protein (see Callan 1963). Edström and Beermann (1962) have shown that the RNA associated with diffuse areas or puffs at specific points in the giant chromosomes of the salivary glands of *Chironomus tentans* has a base composition which is characteristic for each puff. Beermann (1961) has shown that in *C. pallidivittatus* granules are secreted from particular cells in the salivary gland, and that in these cells but not in others, puffing occurs at the position in the appropriate chromosome of a gene concerned with production of the granules (see Fig. 9.1(*b*) and (*c*)). In hybrids with *C. tentans*, which lacks the granules, the *C. pallidivittatus* chromosome alone shows the puff. The inference from these experiments is that loop-formation in lamp-brush chromosomes, and puffing in salivary gland chromosomes are associated with the activity of specific genes. Since there is evidence for characteristic patterns of puffing which vary with the stage of development and with the tissue, Beermann's findings constitute good evidence that differentiation is associated with differential gene activity. Moreover, Clever (1961) has shown with *Chironomus* larvae that injection of ecdysone, which causes premature pupation, initiates within a few minutes puffing at a specific locus in one of the salivary gland chromosomes, to be followed by a whole series of puffs corresponding in position and time sequence to those occurring at normal pupation.

It is probable that the nucleolus represents visible evidence of the activity of a specific gene or group of genes, since the base composition of its RNA agrees with that of the ribosomes and has led to the suggestion that the nucleolus is the site of ribosome formation. Elsdale, Fischberg and Smith (1958) discovered a female *Xenopus laevis* (Clawed Toad) in which half the offspring possessed only one nucleolus in each nucleus instead of the normal two. These heterozygotes for the nucleolar deficiency were of normal pheno-type and on intercrossing gave a 1:2:1 ratio of individuals with 2, 1, and 0 nucleoli, respectively, per nucleus. The homozygotes lacking nucleoli died as young larvae. Brown and Gurdon (1964) showed that the embryos lacking nucleoli were unable to synthesize both of the RNA molecules which occur in ribosomes. These have sedimentation rates of 18 S and 28 S. The survival of the homozygotes to the tadpole stage appeared to depend on the use made of ribosomes inherited cytoplasmically from the mother. It thus appears that the nucleolus is concerned with the synthesis of ribosomal RNA, and that both RNA components are determined by a single gene situated at the nucleolar organizer. Brown and Gurdon favour an alternative possibility, namely, that more than one gene is involved, but that these are under com-mon control, such that the single mutation causing the nucleolar deficiency has prevented all the genes from functioning.

Ritossa and Spiegelman (1965) have hybridized *Drosophila* ribosomal RNA with the DNA of strains of *Drosophila* having from 1 to 4 doses of the nucleolar-organizer region, which is in the X- and Y-chromosomes. The abnormal doses were from stocks which had either a duplication or a deletion of the nucleolar-organizer region of the X-chromosome. The hybridization was achieved by incubating the denatured (single chain) DNA with the RNA for 7–10 hours at 65°C. It was found that the amount of DNA which would hybridize with ribosomal RNA was proportional to the number of nucleolar organizers present. It was inferred that all the DNA which specifies nucleo-tide sequence in ribosomal RNA is situated in the region of the nucleolar organizer. This supports the notion that the nucleolus is the site of ribosomal RNA synthesis. It was found that no less than 0.27% of the DNA of a normal fly could be hybridized with ribosomal RNA. Yankofsky and Spiegelman (1962, 1963) had obtained a similar figure for bacteria. Ritossa and Spiegel-man favoured the idea that the genes for ribosomal RNA are repeated consecutively along the chromosome 100 or more times. Another possibility would seem to be that only one gene is present, but that its DNA is replicated many times when ribosomal RNA is being synthesized. It may be significant that McLeish (1964) has found a considerable amount of DNA in the nucleoli of various flowering plants.

Lyon (1961, 1962) has postulated that in female mammals one of the two X-chromosomes is inactive. She has suggested that in the human embryo inactivation occurs at about the 12th day after fertilization, and that the choice is made independently in each cell, but once made is maintained indefinitely not only in these nuclei but also in all nuclei derived from them during later development. The inactive X-chromosome is more tightly coiled that the active one, and has been shown by tritium labelling to repli-cate later than the other. As a consequence of the random imposition of inactivity, female mammals will be mosaics for any sex-linked characters with local gene action for which they are heterozygous. This is exemplified by a number of mottled phenotypes known in mice (*Mus musculus*), and by the tortoiseshell cat (*Felis catus*). Beutler *et al.* (1962) have shown the presence in some cells and absence in others of the enzyme glucose-6-phosphate dehydro-genase in the erythrocytes of human females heterozygous for the gene affecting this character, which happens to be sex-linked.

A feature of Lyon's hypothesis of great interest is that the inactive X-chromosome shows all the pecularities of heterochromatin, that is, differential staining properties, late replication, and genetical inertness. Evidence was given in § 16.3 that the variegated phenotypes which occur when genes are transferred, as a result of a structural change, to the neighborhood of hetero-chromatin, are associated with a change in the appearance of the euchro-matic segments so as to resemble heterochromatin. These observations naturally raise the question of whether heterochromatin is always to be regarded merely as inactive (or largely inactive) euchromatin. Whatever the nature of heterochromatin, it is evident that, if Lyon's hypothesis is correct, a controlling mechanism must exist whereby the whole X-chromosome is integrated and all its genes are rendered inactive together.

Henderson (1964), using tritiated uridine, studied RNA synthesis in association with the meiotic chromosomes of males of the locusts *Schistocerca gregaria* and *Cyrtacanthacris tartarica* and the grasshopper *Chorthippus brunneus*. He found that with the autosomes RNA synthesis occurs at all stages except when the chromosomes are strongly contracted (metaphase and anaphase, I and II) and that the meiotic prophase I chromosomes, and probably all prophase chromosomes, are lampbrush in nature (cf. Pl. 3(*a*) and (*b*)). The single X-chromosome was found to remain tightly coiled and heavily staining throughout meiosis, and to show no RNA synthesis, indicating that the activity of its genes is under generalized control (see Pl. 2(*f*)).

That histones may play a part in the control of gene action is suggested by the discovery of Izawa, Allfrey, and Mirsky (1963) that the addition of arginine-rich histones to *Triturus* lampbrush chromomeres stops the forma-tion of RNA in association with the lateral loops, and leads to their retraction into the chromosomes. Bonner, Huang, and Gilden (1964) have found that nucleoprotein extracted from *Pisum sativum* will bring about the synthesis of proteins *in vitro*, using the protein synthesizing system derived from *Escherichia coli* and developed by Nirenberg and Matthaei (see § 14.10). Bonner *et al.* have discovered that the proteins synthesized with this system, using nucleoprotein from the developing cotyledons as primer, includes a globulin characteristic of the cotyledons. The nucleoprotein from pea buds, which do not produce this globulin *in vivo*, failed to lead to its synthesis *in vitro* unless the histone had first been removed from the DNA. Barr and

Butler (1963) made similar studies using DNA and histones from *Bos* and a protein-synthesizing system from *Bacillus megaterium*. The histone was fractionated by chromatography and other means, and appeared to consist of a limited number of characteristically different proteins, one, for instance, being rich in lysine and another in arginine. Barr and Butler found that complexes of the DNA with each histone fraction had a much reduced ability to promote RNA synthesis compared with DNA without histones. Although each fraction formed only 20–30% of the total histone, it reduced the activity of the DNA as primer to a much greater extent. Moreover, the artificial peptide poly-*l*-lysine was found to be an extremely effective inhibitor of RNA synthesis. Barr and Butler inferred that the effect of histone in inhibiting the priming activity of DNA was unspecific. They suggested that if there is only a limited number of histone types, there could be proteolytic enzymes or endopeptidases which act specifically on each type to remove them from the DNA. If the segments of histone of each type were of larger extent than the operons, this might account for the lengths of the loops of lampbrush chromosomes, and of the chromosome region affected by abnormal proximity to heterochromatin (or to specific factors within it, such as *Ds*).

In spite of these diverse pieces of evidence, which point to differential gene activity in the chromosomes as the basis of differentiation, there are cogent reasons for believing that such action forms only one aspect of the process. Thus, Spencer and Harris (1964), working with *Acetabularia crenulata*, found that synthesis of enzymes took place in enucleated cells during regeneration of the cap, and moreover that synthesis of one of the enzymes was specifically associated with the formation of the cap. The whole process of regeneration took 6–8 weeks. It was evident that enzyme synthesis can be regulated over long periods in the absence of the nucleus. A number of other observations support the belief that wholly cytoplasmic control of enzyme synthesis is of widespread occurrence in chromosomal organisms. Thus, Reich *et al.* (1962) showed that actinomycin *D* inhibited the formation of RNA in fibroblasts of *Mus* in tissue culture, but that protein synthesis, revealed by incorporation of tritiated leucine, continued for many hours, and Sokoloff *et al.* (1964) found that the addition of thyroxine to cell-free preparations of the liver of *Rattus* stimulated the incorporation of aminoacids into protein in the absence of any synthesis of RNA. Actinomycin *D* or deoxyribonuclease were used to prevent RNA synthesis.

That differential activity at the level of operon transcription cannot form more than a part of the mechanism of differentiation is also evident from study of the development of unicellular (or acellular) organisms such as *Acetabularia* or *Paramecium*, and from the embryology of multicellular organisms. From such studies it is apparent that differentiation occurs within cells as well as between one cell and another. Intracellular differentiation implies a spatial organization within the cell, and this presumably arises through interaction between molecules in the cytoplasm and physical or chemical factors in the external environment. In multicellular structures, this external environment would include other cells or tissues of the organism. How far the molecular configuration of the cytoplasm may be regarded as ultimately determined by the nucleus is a question of fundamental importance to which no precise answer can be given.

Differentiation within cells includes the differentiation of the organelles which it contains. Clues as to how such differentiation may take place are provided by the development of virus *T*4 of *Escherichia coli*. Epstein *et al.* (1964) found that mutants which are defective in DNA synthesis (nos. 1, 32, and 39–47 in Fig. 16.2) fail to show synthesis and assembly either of the head or the tail components. It thus appears that the mutants affecting DNA synthesis also prevent development proceeding past an early stage. This functional interaction defines what they have called early- and late-acting genes, which (with one or two exceptions) are also grouped together physically in the chromoneme. A further point of great interest is that it appears unlikely that there are more than 20 different proteins in the virus, and so Epstein *et al.* imagine that many of the genes are 'morphogenetic' in function, that is, are involved in the assembly of the many components of the mature virus, rather than in the synthesis of protein sub-units. The differentiation of cytoplasmic organelles in chromosomal organisms may perhaps follow a similar pattern, with, first, the activity of structural genes for the enzymes catalysing the formation of the essential components, to be followed later by the activity of morphogenetic genes controlling component assembly. As already mentioned, however, in chromosomal organisms there is little evidence of the grouping together in the DNA of genes concerned with related steps, and much of the control of enzyme synthesis might be at translation rather than at transcription.

It is inferred from Spencer and Harris' results described above that messenger RNA can persist for long periods in the cytoplasm of *Acetabularia*, and such persistence could also account for the examples of delayed Mendelian inheritance described in Chapter 5. On the other hand, the occurrence of cytoplasmic inheritance, also discussed in Chapter 5, indicates that some features of the cytoplasm are self-replicating rather than merely persistent. Many RNA viruses are known to be self-replicating. August, Cooper, Shapiro and Zinder (1964) have demonstrated the existence of an RNA polymerase which is induced in *Escherichia coli* after infection by the RNA virus *f*2, and which uses the triphosphates of the 4 ribonucleosides as substrate, and leads to the production of replicas of the viral RNA without involving DNA. So one possible explanation of cytoplasmic inheritance would be to postulate an RNA genetic system in the cytoplasm supplementary to the DNA system in the nucleus. There appears to be no evidence at present for the existence of such a system. However, it has recently been discovered that DNA apparently occurs in the chloroplasts and mitochondria. Chun, Vaughan and Rich (1963) have obtained evidence that the chloroplasts of *Spinacia*, *Beta*, *Chlamydomonas* and *Chlorella* contain small quantities of DNA with a different base composition from that of the nucleus. Sager and Ishida (1963) found that the chloroplast DNA in *Chlamydomonas* contained 61% adenine plus thymine compared with 38% in the nuclear DNA. Gibor and Izawa (1963) estimated there were 90,000 nucleotide-pairs of DNA per chloroplast in *Acetabularia*. Nass and Nass (1963) have studied the mitochondria of *Gallus domesticus* embryos with the electron microscope, and have observed fibrous areas within them which resemble in appearance and in staining properties the nuclear material of bacteria, and which, moreover, are digested by deoxyribonuclease. They inferred that these areas contain DNA. Bell and Mühlethaler (1964) have obtained autoradiographs of thin sections of the egg-cells of *Pteridium aquilinum* after supplying the gametophytes with tritiated thymidine, and have found evidence of DNA in mitochondria and proplastids. It is not known whether the cytoplasmic inheritance of some plastid characters in flowering plants and some mitochondrial characters in fungi (see Chapter 5) is related in any way to the presence of DNA in these organelles.

It has long been realised that cytoplasmic inheritance does not necessarily imply the existence of self-perpetuating particles such as DNA or RNA might provide. Cytoplasmic mutant phenotypes might result from alteration of a self-perpetuating metabolic system from one steady state to another. This is exemplified by Monod and Jacob's hypothetical system described above where each of two alternative reaction-chains is inhibited by the end-product of the other. It would be necessary, in addition, to postulate that each chain contained features which made it self-perpetuating when once established. However, on present evidence the steps in the reaction-chains would be expected to depend on nuclear gene activity.

It seems possible that an appreciable part of the cytoplasmic organization of a cell at any particular time may be a reflection of the previous nuclear activity. This is supported by studies of the development of, for example, echinoderms and *Acetabularia* (see Chapter 5). On the other hand, the occurrence of cytoplasmic inheritance demonstrates that the organisation cannot all be so explained, and that parts of the cytoplasm constitute self-perpetuating particles or reaction-chains. Until more is known biochemically about the nature of cytoplasmic inheritance, and about how species differ from one another cytoplasmically, the relative importance of Mendelian and non-Mendelian heredity cannot be judged with any precision, and likewise of nucleus and cytoplasm in the control of differentiation.

An important aspect of differentiation is the influence of the external environment, which can frequently modify profoundly the development of an organism. This is particularly evident in plants, where individuals growing in different habitats may differ greatly and yet when cultivated under similar conditions appear alike. An example of environmental influence is provided by sun red *Zea mays*, which has the genotype *A B pl pl*, that is, with the dominant genes *A* (anthocyanin pigment) and *B* (booster of 'plant colour'), and homozygous for the recessive gene *pl* (plant colour). In sun red maize, anthocyanin is formed only in those parts of the plant which are exposed to sunlight. Another example of the influence of the environment is provided by the number of facets to the eye in Bar-eyed *Drosophila melanogaster*. As indicated in § 9.10, the facet number is greatly influenced by the temperature during development: there are 4 or 5 times as many facets at 15°C than at 30°C. In general, to give precision to an account of the effect of a particular gene on an organism, the genotype and the environmental conditions must be specified. Many genes show *incomplete penetrance*, that is to say, they are not expressed in some individuals. Incomplete penetrance reflects variability of genotype or environment. If a gene acts at an early stage of development, it may affect many different characters of the organism, but the various parts may differ in their sensitivity to modification by other genetic factors and by the external environment. This gives rise to *variable expressivity* of the gene, that is, variation in the way in which a gene is expressed in different individuals. The plants of *Antirrhinum majus* found by Darwin to be intermediate in appearance between the normal and peloric forms (see Fig. 2.4) are likely to have arisen in this way.

How the environment influences gene activity is not understood. However, it appears significant that the variegated phenotypes associated both with position effect and with mutable genes show great variability of expression depending on environmental factors. Harrison and Fincham (1964) have shown that the frequency of mutation to a magenta colour in the stems and petals of *A. majus*, which occurs with high frequency in strains of a particular genotype, is much influenced by the temperature when the tissue in question is developing. Many similar instances are known of sensitivity of mutable genes to the temperature at the stage of development when the gene is acting. According to the hypothesis discussed earlier, these observations would suggest that environmental factors which modify development may act by influencing the production, transmission or receipt of controlling episomes.

These speculations concerning the control of differentiation serve to illustrate how little is known about such control mechanisms. It may be significant that operons containing many cistrons appear to be restricted to the relatively undifferentiated bacteria and their viruses. The occurrence of only one cistron per operon may allow greater precision in the regulation of gene action in relation to differentiation, for instance, by allowing the successive steps in a biosynthetic pathway to take place at different times or places in the cell. A single messenger for all the enzymes of the pathway would appear less adaptable in this respect. However, the occurrence of only one cistron per operon would appear to require an elaborate system of signals even within each biosynthetic pathway to bring the genes into activity.

It may be tentatively concluded that the primary basis of differentiation is the controlled activity of specific operons, leading to the formation of the appropriate messenger RNA molecules. The nature of the signal which initiates messenger RNA formation from an operon is unknown. A secondary control mechanism appears to occur at the translation of messenger into polypeptide. Genetic and environmental factors could influence either the primary or the secondary mechanism. How far the influence of the cytoplasm on differentiation is autonomous, and how far it is to be related to previous nuclear activity, is uncertain.

From the evidence outlined in this and earlier chapters, it is apparent that the chromosome is remarkable both in structure and organization. It appears that its axis is either a single DNA molecule, or a series of DNA molecules placed end-to-end, and with a total length which may be many centimetres. The smallest units of mutation and recombination (the *muton* and the *recon*) appear to be individual nucleotide-pairs, of which over 10^9 may occur in a large chromosome. The nucleotides are organized into larger units of various kinds; *cistrons* (genes), usually of several hundred nucleotide-pairs, as the functional units specifying the aminoacid sequence in specific polypeptides; *cistrons* (genes) specifying nucleotide sequences for their own sake, and having diverse functions which possibly include the regulation of gene activity; *operons*, as units of transcription of DNA into messenger RNA, and including one or more cistrons; *polarons* as units of subdivision of the chromosome in terms of the points where crossing-over can be initiated, and possibly coincident with operons; and *replicons* as units of replication and possibly containing a considerable number of operons. The whole chromosome may also behave as a unit, as when the activity of an entire X-chromosome is suppressed.

Appendix 1. Organisms mentioned in the text

I. CHROMONEMAL KINGDOM

The term 'chromoneme' is used for 'bacterial chromosome' (see § 11.1). Chromonemal organisms differ from chromosomal in having no basic proteins (histones or protamines) associated with their DNA, no mitotic apparatus, no nuclear membrane, no mitochondria, and no plastids. The cell-walls have a distinctive composition containing mucopeptides, and the flagella, where present, are of a different construction from those of chromosomal organisms. For a detailed account of the characteristic features of chromonemal organisms, see Stanier (1964). The relationship between bacteria and blue-green algae has been discussed by Echlin and Morris (1965).

A. BACTERIA

Photosynthesis absent, or, if present, without evolution of oxygen.

(i) EUBACTERIALES

a   Pseudomonadaceae
       Pseudomonas aeruginosa

b   Azotobacteriaceae
       Azotobacter vinelandii

c   Micrococcaceae
       Micrococcus pyogenes

d   Parvobacteriaceae
       Haemophilus influenzae

e   Lactobacteriaceae
       Diplococcus pneumoniae (Pneumococcus)
       Streptococcus faecalis

f   Enterobacteriaceae
       Aerobacter aerogenes
       Escherichia coli (Colon bacillus) and its viruses $T1$ to $T7$, λ, ϕX174 and $f2$.
       Salmonella typhimurium (Mouse typhoid bacillus) and its virus $P22$.

    g Bacillaceae
       Bacillus cereus
       —megaterium
       —stearothermophilus
       —subtilis

(ii) ACTINOMYCETALES
    a Mycobacteriaceae
       Mycobacterium phlei
       —tuberculosis avium (Avian tubercle bacillus)
    b Streptomycetaceae
       Streptomyces coelicolor
       —griseus

B. CYANOPHYCEAE
(Myxophyceae, Blue-green Algae)

Photosynthesis with evolution of oxygen

II. CHROMOSOMAL KINGDOM

A. PLANTS
other than bacteria and blue-green algae

(i) ALGAE, other than blue-greens
    a Chlorophyceae (Green Algae)
       Acetabularia crenulata
       —mediterranea
       Chlamydomonas reinhardi
       *—*sp.
       Chlorella sp.
    b Bacillariophyceae (Diatoms)
    c Euglenophyceae
       Euglena gracilis (including *Astasia longa*)
    d Phaeophyceae (Brown Seaweeds)
    e Rhodophyceae (Red Seaweeds)

(ii) FUNGI
    a Phycomycetes
    b Ascomycetes
       1 Endomycetales
         Saccharomyces cerevisiae (Yeast)
       2 Plectomycetes
         Aspergillus nidulans
         —niger
         Penicillium notatum
       3 Discomycetes
         Ascobolus immersus

4 Pyrenomycetes
  Bombardia lunata
  Neurospora crassa
  —sitophila (Red Bread Mould)
  Sordaria brevicollis
  —fimicola
c Basidiomycetes
  Puccinia glumarum (Yellow Rust)
  Ustilago maydis (Maize Smut)

(iii) BRYOPHYTA
a Musci (Mosses)
b Hepaticae (Liverworts)
  Pellia fabbroniana
  Sphaerocarpos donnellii

(iv) PTERIDOPHYTA (Ferns, etc.)
  Ophioglossum petiolaris (Adder's-tongue Fern)
  Pteridium aquilinum (Bracken)

(v) GYMNOSPERMAE (Conifers, Cycads, etc.)

(vi) ANGIOSPERMAE (Flowering Plants)
a Monocotyledones
  1 Gramineae (Grasses)
    Avena sativa (Oats)
    Hordeum vulgare (Barley)
    Oryza sativa (Rice)
    Triticum aestivum (Wheat)
    Zea mays (Maize)
  2 Commelinaceae
    Tradescantia paludosa
    —sp.
  3 Juncaceae (Rushes)
    Luzula sp. (Wood-rush)
  4 Liliaceae (Lilies, etc.)
    Allium fistulosum
    Aloe purpurascens
    Bellevalia romana
    Disporum sessile
    Fritillaria sp.
    Hyacinthus orientalis (Hyacinth)
    Lilium formosanum
    —henryi
    —japonicum
    —longiflorum
    —maximowiczii
    —regale
    Paris verticillata
    Scilla scilloides
    Trillium erectum
    Tulipa sp. (Tulip)

    5 Amaryllidaceae
      Clivia cytranthiflora
      Haemanthus katharinae
    6 Iridaceae *Crocus balansae*
    7 Orchidaceae (Orchids)
b Dicotyledones
    1 Urticaceae
      Urtica pilulifera (Roman Nettle)
    2 Chenopodiaceae
      Beta sp. (Beet)
      Spinacia sp. (Spinach)
    3 Nyctaginaceae
      Mirabilis jalapa (Marvel of Peru)
    4 Caryophyllaceae
      Agrostemma githago (Corn Cockle)
      Silene alba (White Campion)
      —*dioica* (Red Campion)
    5 Papaveraceae
      Chelidonium majus (Greater Celandine)
      Papaver somniferum (Opium Poppy)
    6 Cruciferae
      Lunaria annua (Honesty)
    7 Leguminosae
      Lathyrus odoratus (Sweet Pea)
      Phaseolus vulgaris (Dwarf Bean)
      Pisum sativum (Edible Pea)
      Trifolium pratense (Red Clover)
      Vicia faba (Broad Bean)
    8 Geraniaceae
      Pelargonium zonale (Geranium)
    9 Linaceae
      Linum usitatissimum (Flax)
  10 Violaceae
      Viola cornuta
  11 Caricaceae
      Carica papaya (Papaw)
  12 Onagraceae
      Epilobium hirsutum (Hairy Willow-herb)
      —*luteum*
      Oenothera blandina
      —*hookeri*
      —*lamarckiana* (Evening Primrose)
      —*muricata*
  13 Primulaceae
      Primula sinensis
  14 Labiatae
      Salvia horminum

15 Solanaceae
   Datura tatula
   —*stramonium* (Thorn Apple)
   Hyoscyamus niger (Henbane)
   Nicotiana sp.
   —*tabacum* (Tobacco) and tobacco mosaic virus
   Solanum nigrum (Black Nightshade)
16 Scrophulariaceae
   Antirrhinum glutinosum
   —*majus* (Snapdragon)
   Veronica longifolia
17 Plantaginaceae
   Plantago lanceolata (Ribwort Plantain) and ribgrass virus
18 Compositae
   Aster tripolium (Sea Aster)
   Chrysanthemum roxburghi
   Coreopsis tinctoria
   Haplopappus gracilis

B. ANIMALS

(i) PROTOZOA
   Paramecium aurelia
   Tetrahymena pyriformis
(ii) PORIFERA (Sponges, etc.)
(iii) COELENTERATA (Jelly-fish, etc.)
(iv) PLATYHELMINTHES (Flatworms)
(v) NEMATODA (Threadworms)
   Parascaris equorum (*Ascaris megalocephala*) (Horse Threadworm)
(vi) ANNELIDA (Worms)
(vii) ARTHROPODA
  a Crustacea (Shrimps, Crabs, etc.)
   Procambarus clarkii (Crayfish)
  b Myriapoda (Centipedes)
  c Insecta (Insects)
   1 Orthoptera (Grasshoppers)
    Acrida lata
    Arphia simplex
    Brachystola magna
    Calliptamus palaestinensis
    Chorthippus brunneus
    —*parallelus*
    Cyrtacanthacris tartarica (Locust)
    Melanoplus femur-rubrum
    Phrynotettix tschivavensis (*P. magnus*)
    Schistocerca gregaria (Locust)
    Stauroderus bicolor
    Trimerotropis maritima

2 Hemiptera (Bugs)
Euschistus variolarius
Lygaeus turcicus
Protenor belfragei
Pyrrhocoris apterus
Thyanta antiguensis
—*perditor*

3 Lepidoptera (Butterflies, Moths)
Abraxas grossulariata (Magpie Moth)
Ephestia kuhniella

4 Coleoptera (Beetles)
Tenebrio molitor (Meal worm)

5 Hymenoptera (Ants, Bees, Wasps)

6 Diptera (Flies)
Calliphora sp. (Blow-fly)
Chironomus pallidivittatus
—*tentans*
Drosophila melanogaster (Fruit Fly)
—*pseudo-obscura*
—*subobscura*

d   Arachnida (Scorpions, Spiders)

(viii)   MOLLUSCA
a   Lamellibranchiata (Oysters, etc.)
b   Gasteropoda (Snails, Slugs)
Helix hortensis (Garden Snail)
—*nemoralis*
Limnaea peregra (Freshwater Snail)
c   Cephalopoda (Octopus, etc.)

(ix)   ECHINODERMATA (Sea Urchins, etc.)
Lytechinus variegatus
Paracentrotus lividus
Psammechinus microtuberculatus
Sphaerechinus granularis
Strongylocentrotus purpuratus

(x)   CHORDATA (Vertebrates, etc.)
a   Pisces (Fish)
Alosa sp. (Shad)
Salmo sp. (Salmon)
Salmo sp. (Trout)
b   Amphibia (Amphibians)
1 Anura (Frogs, Toads)
Rana pipiens (American Frog)
—*temporaria* (European Frog)
Xenopus laevis (Clawed Toad)

2 Urodela (Newts, Salamanders)
    Amblystoma sp. (Salamander)
    Batrachoseps attenuatus (Slender Salamander)
    Salamandra maculosa (Spotted Salamander)
    Triturus cristatus (European Crested Newt)
    —*viridescens* (American Newt)
c Reptilia (Reptiles)
    Crotalus adamanteus (Diamond-back Rattlesnake)
d Aves (Birds)
    Gallus domesticus (Domestic Fowl)
e Mammalia (Mammals)
  1 Lagomorpha (Rabbits, Hares)
    Oryctolagus cuniculus (Rabbit)
  2 Rodentia (Rodents)
    Cavia porcellus (Guinea pig)
    Mesocricetus auratus (Golden Hamster)
    Mus musculus (Mouse)
    Rattus norvegicus (Rat)
  3 Cetacea (Whales)
    Balaenoptera borealis (Sei Whale)
  4 Carnivora (Carnivores)
    Canis familiaris (Dog)
    Felis catus (Cat)
  5 Perissodactyla (Odd-toed Ungulates)
    Equus caballus (Horse)
  6 Artiodactyla (Even-toed Ungulates)
    Bos taurus (Domestic Cattle)
    Ovis aries (Sheep)
    Sus domesticus (Pig)
  7 Primates
    Homo sapiens (Man)
    Macacus mulatta (Rhesus Monkey)

Appendix 2. Glossary of genetical terms used in the text

Acentric Applied to a chromatid or a chromosome when it lacks a centromere. This condition may arise in an inversion heterozygote as a result of crossing-over between a normal and an inverted segment that does not include the centromere.

Allele (allelomorph) The term coined by Bateson and Saunders (1902) for characters which are alternative to one another in Mendelian inheritance (Gk. *allelon*, one another; *morphe*, form). The term is also applied to the wild-type and mutant forms of a gene responsible for such a character-difference.

Anaphase Strasburger (1884) originally introduced this term for the stage of nuclear division when the contents of the nuclei were going back (Gk. *ana*) to their normal appearance, but from about 1905 he used the term in the now universally adopted sense of the stage of mitosis or of meiosis I or II when the daughter-chromosomes (or homologous chromosomes at meiosis I) move towards opposite poles of the spindle.

Anticodon The triplet of nucleotides in transfer RNA which is presumed to associate by complementary base pairing with a specific triplet (codon) in messenger RNA during protein synthesis.

Autosomes A term coined by Montgomery (1906) for the chromosomes other than the X- and Y-chromosomes (which he called allosomes) by which the sexes differ.

Back-cross A cross between a parental strain and its progeny from a previous cross.

Centromere The term introduced by Darlington (1936a) for the point on a chromosome which reacts to the spindle at nuclear division, and to which a spindle-fibre appears to be attached at the times when the spindle is evident (metaphase and anaphase) (Gk. *centron*, centre; *meros*, part). The chromosome is usually constricted and often bent at the centromere. In a few organisms the centromeric properties are distributed over the entire length of the chromosome (diffuse centromere).

Chiasma The term which Janssens (1909) introduced for the nodes (Gk. *chiasma*, cross) where the individual chromosomes making up each pair remain in contact during the diplotene and diakinetic stages of prophase I and during metaphase I of meiosis. It is now established that a chiasma arises as a consequence of crossing-over. In some organisms the chiasmata move towards the ends of the chromosome arms during late diplotene and diakinesis (terminalization of chiasmata). The position of the chiasma will then no longer correspond to that of the cross-over. The expression 'terminal chiasma' was coined by Newton and Darlington (1929) for the end-to-end association of homologous chromosome arms as a result of chiasma movement to the end.

Chromatid The term which McClung (1900) proposed for each of the four threads making up a chromosome-pair at meiosis (Gk. *chroma*, colour; for the derivation of *id*, see Diploid). The use of the term was subsequently extended to mitosis, and is now applied to the individual daughter-chromosomes into which each chromosome is divided in all nuclear divisions. The term chromatid is used so long as the daughter centromeres remain in contact with one another. As soon as they separate (anaphase of mitosis and anaphase II of meiosis), the expression daughter-chromosome is substituted for chromatid.

Chromomere The term applied by Wilson (1896) to each of the serially aligned granules of a chromosome, best seen when the thread is relatively elongated as in early prophase I of meiosis (Gk. *chroma*, colour; *meros*, part).

Chromoneme The term used in this book for the DNA thread of bacteria and their viruses (see § 11.1 and Appendix 1) (Gk. *chroma*, colour; *nema*, thread).

Chromosome The term proposed by Waldeyer (1888) for the individual threads within the cell nucleus (Gk. *chroma*, colour; *soma*, body). The expression lampbrush chromosome describes the appearance of the chromosomes at the diplotene stage of meiosis in the oocytes of some amphibia, when the chromatids extend from each chromomere to form lateral loops. Wilson (1909) proposed that a chromosome which is represented twice (the normal diploid condition) in the nuclei of one sex, but is present only once per nucleus in the other sex, should be called an *X*-chromosome, while the dissimilar chromosome which may also be present as a single chromosome in the latter sex, but is absent from the sex with two *X*-chromosomes, he called a *Y*-chromosome. The normal chromosomes were called by Randolph (1928) *A*-chromosomes to distinguish them from supernumerary or *B*-chromosomes which occur in some individuals or populations of certain species, and are composed wholly of heterochromatin.

Cis The term proposed by Haldane (1941), by analogy with chemical isomerism, to describe a double heterozygote in coupling phase, that is, with the two dominant factors derived from one parent and the two recessives from the other. The term is used chiefly for closely linked mutants, to which it was first applied by Pontecorvo (1950). The cis configuration for two recessive mutants, 1 and 2, is $\dfrac{+\ +}{1\ 2}$, where $+$ stands for the wild-type, and the line separates the contributions from the two parents. (Cf. Trans.)

Cistron The term which Benzer (1957) introduced, derived from cis and trans, for the functional unit of the hereditary material defined by the phenotype of the trans (repulsion) heterokaryon or heterozygote for two recessive mutations: if this phenotype is mutant, the mutations are said to be alleles and to belong to the same cistron; if the phenotype is normal (wild-type), the mutations are said to be non-allelic and to belong to different cistrons. Benzer's definition has since been modified to accommodate allelic complementation, and a cistron is now defined (Fincham 1959*a*) as a segment of the hereditary material within which pairs of mutations in the trans configuration are either deficient for a particular enzyme, or give rise to that enzyme in a structurally abnormal form. There is a good case for equating Fincham's definition of a cistron with the term gene.

Codon   The term proposed by Crick (1963) for the sequence of nucleotides in DNA or RNA which is responsible for determining that a specific aminoacid shall be inserted into a polypeptide chain. There appears to be more than one codon for most (perhaps all) aminoacids, and there is evidence that the codons are triplets of nucleotides.

Complementation   The process by which two recessive mutants can supply each other's deficiency, such that a heterokaryon or diploid derived from them and having the trans (repulsion) configuration is phenotypically normal (wild-type) or nearly so. Allelic complementation appears to be due to the formation of hybrid protein molecules.

Conversion   The term proposed by Winkler (1930) for a process of interaction between alleles at meiosis. The term was re-introduced by Lindegren (1953) to account for aberrant ratios in the products of meiosis, apparently arising from such interaction. Whitehouse and Hastings (1965) have suggested that if gene conversion is due to the correction of mispairing of bases in DNA, it may give rise to reciprocal as well as non-reciprocal recombination.

Coupling   The term introduced by Bateson, Saunders and Punnett (1905) for the condition (phase) of a heterozygote for two linked character-differences in which the two dominant factors were derived from one parent and the two recessive factors from the other. This condition may be represented as $\dfrac{A\,B}{a\,b}$, where A/a and B/b represent the two character-differences and the capital letters indicate the dominants. The horizontal line separates the contribution from each parent. (Cf. Repulsion.)

Crossing-over   The term coined by Morgan and Cattell (1912) for the occurrence of new combinations of linked characters. With the acceptance of the chromosome theory, the term is also applied to the process of exchange between homologous chromosomes which gives rise to the new character-combinations.

Deficiency ⎫
Deletion ⎬   Loss of a segment of a chromosome.

Diakinesis   The term coined by Häcker (1897) for the stage of late prophase I of meiosis when the chromosomes are well separated from one another (Gk. *kinesis*, movement; *dia*, apart). This stage is recognized by the highly condensed condition of the chromosomes, the homologous pairs of which are held together by chiasmata. In some organisms, just before or during diakinesis the chiasmata move to the ends of the chromosome arms (terminalization of chiasmata). When there are interstitial chiasmata, the successive loops into which the chromosome-pair is divided are set in planes at right angles to one another.

Dicentric Applied to a chromatid or chromosome with two centromeres, such as arises in an inversion heterozygote as a result of crossing-over between a normal and an inverted segment that does not include the centromere.

Diploid With two homologous sets of chromosomes, such as arise at fertilization. The term was introduced by Strasburger (1905), and is derived from the Greek *diploos* meaning double, and *id*, which was Weismann's term for hypothetical structural units of the nucleus assumed to be represented by the chromomeres. The term *id* was derived from Nägeli's term idioplasm (Gk. *idion*, peculiar).

Diplotene The term proposed by von Winiwarter (1900), originally as an adjective, to describe the nuclei at a particular stage of prophase I of meiosis when the two chromosomes making up each homologous pair have separated from one another except at nodes (chiasmata) distributed along their length. The successive loops between the chiasmata all lie in one plane. (Gk. *diploos*, double; *taenia*, ribbon.)

Dominant The term which Mendel (1866) introduced for a character which is manifest in all the members of the first filial (F_1) generation from a cross between two pure-breeding strains differing in respect of this character, and which is evident in three quarters of the individuals of the second filial (F_2) generation. (Cf. Recessive.)

Duplication The repetition of a sequence of chromomeres or other chromosome segment, usually in linear juxtaposition to the original.

Episome The term introduced by Jacob and Wollman (1958b) for a particle which may at some time exist attached to and apparently integrated with the hereditary material of a cell, and which may at other times occur free from such attachment. When attached, episomes replicate along with the hereditary material, but when free they usually replicate independently of it and more rapidly. Examples of episomes are many bacterial viruses and the male sex factor in *Escherichia coli*. (Gk. *epi*, upon; *soma*, body.)

Euchromatin Parts of chromosomes showing the normal cycle of condensation and normal staining properties at nuclear divisions. (Gk. *eu*, true.) (Cf. Heterochromatin.)

Gene The term coined by Johannsen (1909) for the unit of heredity, that is, the hypothetical entity which determines the development of a particular character. The word gene was derived from De Vries' term pangen, itself a derivative of the word pangenesis which Darwin (1868) had coined. At one time it was assumed that the hereditary units defined by mutation, recombination, and function were the same, but with the discovery that they are not, the term gene is now usually applied to the unit of function, that is, the cistron.

Genetics The term which Bateson (1907*a*) coined for the science of heredity and variation. (Gk. *genesis*, descent.)

Genotype The term proposed by Johannsen (1909) for the hereditary constitution of an individual, or of particular nuclei within its cells.

Haploid With a single set of chromosomes, such as occurs in gamete nuclei (Strasburger, 1905). (Gk. *haploos*, single; for the derivation of *id*, see Diploid.)

Heterochromatin The term proposed by Heitz (1928) for parts of chromosomes with an abnormal degree of contraction or of staining properties at nuclear divisions. (Gk. *heteros*, different; chromatin was Flemming's term for the material of which the chromosomes are composed.) (Cf. Euchromatin.)

Heterokaryon A multinucleate cell containing nuclei of more than one genotype, such as are of widespread occurrence in fungi (Gk. *heteros*, different; *karyon*, nut, nucleus).

Heterozygote The term coined by Bateson and Saunders (1902) for a zygote, or a diploid individual derived from it, which carries both members (Gk. *heteros*, different) of a pair of alleles. This might be as a result of fusion of dissimilar gametes, or from mutation.

Homokaryon A multinucleate cell containing nuclei of only one genotype. (Gk. *homos*, alike; *karyon*, nut, nucleus.)

Homozygote The term coined by Bateson and Saunders (1902) for a zygote, or a diploid individual derived from it, which carries only one member of a pair of alleles, that is, a zygote derived from the union of gametes identical (Gk. *homos*, alike) in respect of a particular gene.

Interchange An exchange of segments between non-homologous chromosomes. In an interchange heterozygote, the chromosomes contributed by one parent have the normal configuration and those contributed by the other parent have the interchange of segments.

Interference The term proposed by Muller (1916) for the interaction between crossovers such that the occurrence of one exchange between homologous chromosomes reduces the likelihood of another in its vicinity. Chromatid interference is the expression which Mather (1933*a*) introduced for a non-random distribution between the chromatids involved in successive crossovers.

Inversion The term introduced by Sturtevant (1926) for the reversal of the linear sequence of the genes in a segment of a chromosome. In an inversion heterozygote one of the chromosomes contributed by one parent has an inverted segment while the homologous chromosome contributed by the other parent has the normal gene sequence.

Leptotene The term proposed by von Winiwarter (1900), originally as an adjective, to describe the nuclei at the earliest stage of prophase I of meiosis, when the chromosomes first become visible as fine threads and have not yet associated in pairs. (Gk. *leptos*, thin; *taenia*, ribbon.)

Linkage An association in inheritance between characters such that the parental character-combinations appear among the progeny more often than the non-parental. Thus, if the parental combinations were *AB* and *ab*, where *A/a* and *B/b* are two pairs of contrasting characters, then linkage is shown if *AB* and *ab* are significantly more frequent than *Ab* and *aB* among the progeny.

Locus The position occupied by a gene in the chromosome. (Cf. Site.)

Meiosis The term coined by Farmer and Moore (1905) to describe the special nuclear divisions associated with the halving (Gk. *meion*, smaller) of the chromosome number in compensation for the doubling at fertilization. Two successive nuclear divisions occur, with no intervening chromosome replication. Grégoire (1904) proposed that the two divisions be denoted by the appropriate Roman numerals I and II. At the first division of meiosis, homologous chromosomes, already divided into chromatids, associate, undergo crossing-over at certain points along their length, and subsequently separate towards opposite poles of the spindle. At the second division, their chromatids separate, leading to four haploid nuclei.

Metaphase Strasburger (1884) originally introduced this term for the stage of nuclear division after (Gk. *meta*) the chromosomes have divided into chromatids, but from about 1905, with the realization that the chromosomes are already double when nuclear division begins, he used the term in the now universally adopted sense of the stage of mitosis or of meiosis I or II when the chromosomes lie on the equatorial plate of the spindle.

Mispairing The presence in one nucleotide chain of a DNA molecule of a nucleotide which is not the complement of that at the corresponding position in the other chain.

Mitosis The term proposed by Flemming (1882) for the process of nuclear division, during which the chromosomes become evident as they shorten and thicken (prophase), and then take up position on the equatorial plate of the spindle (metaphase), to be followed by separation of the two daughter-chromosomes of which each is composed to opposite poles of the spindle (anaphase), and their gradual return to a slender elongated condition (telophase). (Gk. *mitos*, thread.)

Mutation The term which De Vries introduced into biological literature for an abrupt change of phenotype which is inherited. Mutation may be due to a molecular change within a gene, or to the loss or duplication of one or more entire genes.

Muton Within the one-dimensional array of mutant sites in the hereditary material, the muton was defined by Benzer (1957) as the smallest element that, when altered, can give rise to a mutant form of the organism.

Nucleolus The more or less spherical structure which occurs in association with a particular point (the nucleolar organizer) on a specific chromosome in the nucleus. At nuclear divisions, the nucleoli disappear in late prophase, are absent at metaphase and anaphase, and reappear during telophase.

Nucleus   The term proposed by Brown (1833) for the more or less spherical structure which occurs in cells and stains deeply with basic dyes.

Operon   The term which Jacob, Perrin, Sanchez and Monod (1960) introduced for a group of closely-linked genes which appear to affect different steps in a single biosynthetic pathway and which appear to function as an integrated unit. Monod and Jacob (1962) suggested that if the hypothesis of one operon—one messenger RNA molecule is confirmed, the operon could be redefined as the unit of transcription.

Pachytene   The term proposed by von Winiwarter (1900), originally as an adjective, to describe the nuclei at a particular stage of prophase I of meiosis when homologous chromosomes are associated throughout their length. (Gk. *pachys*, thick; *taenia*, ribon.)

Phenotype   The term coined by Johannsen (1909) for the appearance (Gk. *phainein*, to appear) of an organism with respect to a particular character or group of characters, as a result of its genotype and its environment.

Polaron   The term which Lissouba and Rizet (1960) proposed for a segment of the hereditary material within which recombination is polarized and entirely by gene conversion, that is, by a mechanism other than crossing-over. According to Whitehouse and Hastings (1965), reciprocal as well as non-reciprocal recombination may result from the gene conversion within a polaron.

Polyploid   Having three or more (Gk. *polys*, many) sets of homologous chromosomes. The term was introduced by Winkler (1916) by analogy with Strasburger's terms haploid and diploid.

Polytene   The term proposed by Koller (1935) to describe the multistranded condition (Gk. *polys*, many; *taenia*, ribbon) of the chromosomes found in certain specialized tissues such as the salivary glands of *Drosophila*.

Prophase   Strasburger (1884) originally introduced this term for the early stage of nuclear division before (Gk. *pro*) the chromosomes divide into two chromatids, but from about 1905, with the realization that the chromosomes are double from the beginning of nuclear division, he used the term in the now universally adopted sense of the stage of mitosis or of meiosis I or II before breakdown of the nuclear membrane.

Recessive   The term which Mendel (1866) proposed for a character which was not evident in the first filial generation (F_1) of a cross between two pure-breeding strains differing in respect of this character, and which re-appeared in one quarter of the second filial generation (F_2). (Cf. Dominant.)

Recombination   The process by which new combinations of parental characters may arise in the progeny. Recombination may come about through random orientation of non-homologous chromosome-pairs on the meiotic spindles, from crossing-over between homologous chromosomes, from gene conversion, or by other means.

Recon   Benzer (1957) proposed the term recon as the smallest element that is interchangeable (but not divisible) by genetic recombination in the one-dimensional array of mutant sites within the hereditary material.

Replicon The term proposed by Jacob and Brenner (1963) for a unit of replication of the hereditary material, that is, a segment within which replication occurs in a unified way from a pre-determined origin in a fixed direction to a pre-determined end-point.

Repulsion The term introduced by Punnett and Bateson (1908) for the condition (phase) of a heterozygote for two linked character-differences in which the two dominant factors were derived one from each parent of the individual, and likewise with the two recessive factors. This condition may be represented as $\dfrac{A\ b}{a\ B}$, where A/a and B/b represent two pairs of alleles, and the capital letters represent the dominants. The horizontal line separates the contribution from each parent. (Cf. Coupling.)

Ribosome The term proposed by Roberts (1958) for the *ribo*nucleoprotein particles (Gk. *soma*, body) associated with protein synthesis.

Segregation The separation of allelic differences from one another. Segregation may occur at the first or second division of meiosis, or at the first mitosis after meiosis (postmeiotic segregation).

Semi-conservative The term proposed by Delbrück and Stent (1957) to describe the method of replication of DNA postulated by Watson and Crick (1953*b*) in which the molecule divides longitudinally, each half being conserved and acting as a template for the formation of a new half.

Site The position occupied by a mutation within the gene. (Cf. Locus.)

Structural change A general term for a deletion, duplication, or inversion of a chromosome segment, or an interchange of segments which may be between non-homologous chromosomes.

Telophase The last stage (Gk. *telos*, end) of mitosis, or of either division of meiosis, during which the chromosomes become progressively thinner and more elongated (Heidenhain, 1894). Telophase is said to begin with the formation of a nuclear membrane round each group of daughter-chromosomes.

Test-cross A cross between a heterozygote and the corresponding homozygous recessive, for example, $\dfrac{A\ b\ C}{a\ B\ c} \times \dfrac{a\ b\ c}{a\ b\ c}$, where A/a, B/b and C/c represent three pairs of alleles, and the horizontal lines separate the contributions from the two parents of each individual.

Tetrad The four haploid cells formed at the end of meiosis. The term was formerly used for the four chromatids making up a chromosome-pair at the first division of meiosis.

Trans The term proposed by Haldane (1941), by analogy with chemical isomerism, to describe a double heterozygote in repulsion phase, that is, with the dominant factors derived from opposite parents. The term is used chiefly for closely-linked mutants, to which it was first applied by Pontecorvo (1950). The trans configuration for two recessive mutants, 1 and 2, is $\dfrac{+\ 2}{1\ +}$, where $+$ stands for the wild-type, and the line separates the contributions from the two parents. (Cf. Cis.)

Transcription   The transfer of information in the form of nucleotide sequence from DNA to RNA.

Transduction   Gene transfer from one cell to another brought about by a virus. The phenomenon was first described by Lederberg, Lederberg, Zinder and Lively (1952) with reference to *Salmonella typhimurium*, fragments of the hereditary material of which may be transferred by virus *P*22.

Transformation   Gene transfer from one cell to another brought about by fragments of the hereditary material of a cell persisting after its breakdown and subsequently entering another cell. The phenomenon was first described by Griffith (1928) in *Diplococcus pneumoniae*.

Transition   The term proposed by Freese (1959) for a mutation caused by the substitution in DNA or RNA of one purine by the other, and similarly with the pyrimidines. (Cf. Transversion.)

Translation   The transfer of information in the form of nucleotide sequence in DNA or RNA into aminoacid sequence in a polypeptide.

Transversion   The term proposed by Freese (1959) for a mutation caused by the substitution of a purine for a pyrimidine, and *vice versa*, in DNA or RNA. (Cf. Transition.)

Trisomic   The term proposed by Blakeslee (1922) to describe an otherwise diploid individual which has one of the chromosomes represented three times instead of twice.

Wild-type   The normal condition, either with regard to a whole organism (wild-type strain), or with reference to a particular mutation (wild-type at that locus or site, denoted by a plus sign).

Zygotene   The term proposed by Grégoire (1907) to describe the nuclei at a particular stage of prophase I of meiosis when the homologous chromosomes are associating side by side. (Gk. *zygon*, yoke; *taenia*, ribbon.)

References—Author index

References within the text are indicated by italic figures in parentheses.

ADLER, J., LEHMAN, I. R., BESSMAN, M. J., SIMMS, E. S. and KORNBERG, A. (1958). Enzymatic synthesis of deoxyribonucleic acid. IV. Linkage of single deoxy-nucleotides to the deoxynucleoside ends of deoxyribonucleic acid. *Proc. natn. Acad. Sci. U.S.A.*, **44**, 641–647. (*192*)

ALLISON, A. C. (1954). Protection afforded by sickle cell trait against sub-tertian malarial infection. *Br. med. J.*, **1**, 290–292. (*14*)

AMES, B. N. and GARRY, B. (1959). Coordinate repression of the synthesis of four histidine biosynthetic enzymes by histidine. *Proc. natn. Acad. Sci. U.S.A.*, **45**, 1453–1461. (*287*)

AMES, B. N. and HARTMAN, P. E. (1964). The histidine operon. *Cold Spring Harb. Symp. quant. Biol.*, **28**, 349–356. (*290, 291*)

ANDERSON, E. G. (1923). Maternal inheritance of chlorophyll in maize. *Bot. Gaz.*, **76**, 411–418. (*53, 54*)

ANDERSON, E. G. (1925). Crossing over in a case of attached X chromosomes in *Drosophila melanogaster*. *Genetics, Princeton*, **10**, 403–417. (*97–100, 105–110*)

ANDERSON, E. G. (1936). Induced chromosomal alterations in maize. In *Biological Effects of Radiation* edited by B. M. DUGGAR, New York, McGraw-Hill, pp. 1297–1310. (*145–151*)

ARISTOTLE (ca. 350 B.C.) *The Reproduction of Animals* (*De Generatione Animalium*), especially book 1, chapters 17–23. (English translation by A. PLATT, Oxford, Clarendon Press, 1910.) (*1*)

ARLETT, C. F., GRINDLE, M. and JINKS, J. L. (1962). The "red" cytoplasmic variant of *Aspergillus nidulans*. *Heredity*, **17**, 197–209. (*55*)

ASTBURY, W. T. and BELL, F. O. (1938). X-ray study of thymonucleic acid. *Nature, Lond.*, **141**, 747–748. (*178, 227, 228*)

ATTARDI, G., NAONO, S., ROUVIÈRE, J., JACOB, F. and GROS, F. (1964). Production of messenger RNA and regulation of protein synthesis. *Cold Spring Harb. Symp. quant. Biol.*, **28**, 363–372. (*290, 291*)

AUERBACH, C. and ROBSON, J. M. (1947). The production of mutations by chemical substances. *Proc. R. Soc. Edinb. B*, **62**, 271–283. (*141, 144*)

AUGUST, J. T., COOPER, S., SHAPIRO, L. and ZINDER, N. D. (1964). RNA phage induced RNA polymerase. *Cold Spring Harb. Symp. quant. Biol.*, **28**, 95–97. (*313*)

AVERY, O. T., MACLEOD, C. M. and MC CARTY, M. (1944). Studies on the chemical nature of the substance inducing transformation of pneumococcal types. Induction of transformation by a desoxyribonucleic acid fraction isolated from pneumococcus Type III. *J. exp. Med.*, **79**, 137–158. (*168, 171, 180*)

BAGLIONI, C. and INGRAM, V. M. (1961). Four adult haemoglobin types in one person. *Nature, Lond.*, **189**, 465–467. (*219*)

BAILEY, N. T. J. (1959). *Statistical Methods in Biology.* London, English Universities Press.   (*23*)

BAJER, A. (1957–58). Ciné-micrographic studies on mitosis in endosperm. *Expl Cell Res.*, **13**, 493–502; **14**, 245–256; **15**, 370–383.   (*59*)

BARR, G. C. and BUTLER, J. A. V. (1963). Histones and gene function. *Nature, Lond.*, **199**, 1170–1172.   (*311–312*)

BASSEL, A., HAYASHI, M. and SPIEGELMAN, S. (1964). The enzymatic synthesis of a circular DNA-RNA hybrid. *Proc. natn. Acad. Sci. U.S.A.*, **52**, 796–804.   (*252*)

BATESON, W. (1907a). The progress of genetic research. *R. hort. Soc. Rep. 3rd int. Conf. Genet.*, pp. 90–97.   (*328*)

BATESON, W. (1907b). Facts limiting the theory of heredity. *Science, N.Y.*, **26**, 649–660.   (*160*)

BATESON, W. (1909). *Mendel's Principles of Heredity.* Cambridge Univ. Press, 396 pp.   (*3, 13, 45, 159, 350*)

BATESON, W. and SAUNDERS, E. R. (1902). Experimental studies in the physiology of heredity. *Rep. Evol. Comm. R. Soc.*, **1**, 1–160.   (*9, 11, 18, 31, 159, 324, 328*)

BATESON, W., SAUNDERS, E. R. and PUNNETT, R. C. (1905). Experimental studies in the physiology of heredity. *Rep. Evol. Comm. R. Soc.*, **2**, 1–55 and 80–99.   (*12, 18, 44, 78, 83, 159, 160, 326*)

BAUR, E. (1909). Das Wesen und die Erblichkeitsverhältnisse der "varietates albomarginatae" von *Pelargonium zonale*. *Z. VererbLehre*, **1**, 330–351.   (*51–4*)

BAUR, E. (1912). Ein Fall von geschlechtsbegrenzter Vererbung bei *Melandrium album*. *Z. VererbLehre*, **8**, 335–336.   (*72*)

BAUTZ, E. K. F. and HALL, B. D. (1962). The isolation of T4-specific RNA on a DNA-cellulose column. *Proc. natn. Acad. Sci. U.S.A.*, **48**, 400–408.   (*239, 242*)

BEADLE, G. W. (1945). Genetics and metabolism in *Neurospora*. *Physiol. Rev.*, **25**, 643–663.   (*163*)

BEADLE, G. W. and COONRADT, V. L. (1944). Heterocaryosis in *Neurospora crassa*. *Genetics, Princeton*, **29**, 291–308.   (*161*)

BEADLE, G. W. and TATUM, E. L. (1941). Genetic control of biochemical reactions in *Neurospora*. *Proc. natn. Acad. Sci. U.S.A.*, **27**, 499–506.   (*160, 203*)

BECKWITH, J. (1964). A deletion analysis of the *lac* operator region in *Escherichia coli*. *J. molec. Biol.*, **8**, 427–430.   (*289*)

BEERMANN, W. (1961). Ein Balbiani-Ring als Locus einer Speicheldrüsenmutation. *Chromosoma*, **12**, 1–25.   (*143, 309*)

BELL, P. R. and MÜHLETHALER, K. (1964). Evidence for the presence of deoxyribonucleic acid in the organelles of the egg cells of *Pteridium aquilinum*. *J. molec. Biol.*, **8**, 853–862.   (*314*)

BELLING, J. (1927). The attachments of chromosomes at the reduction division in flowering plants. *J. Genet.*, **18**, 177–205.   (*146*)

BELLING, J. (1928a). A working hypothesis for segmental interchange between homologous chromosomes in flowering plants. *Univ. Calif. Publs Bot.*, **14**, 283–291.   (*114, 131*)

BELLING, J. (1928b). The ultimate chromomeres of *Lilium* and *Aloë* with regard to the numbers of genes. *Univ. Calif. Publs Bot.*, **14**, 307–318.   (*152*)

BELLING, J. (1928c). Contraction of chromosomes during maturation divisions in *Lilium* and other plants. *Univ. Calif. Publs Bot.*, **14**, 335–343.   (*116*)

BELLING, J. (1929). Nodes and internodes of trivalents of *Hyacinthus*. *Univ. Calif. Publs Bot.*, **14**, 379–388.   (*64, 114, 120*)

BENEDEN, E. VAN (1875). La maturation de l'oeuf, la fécondation, et les premières phases du développement embryonnaire des mammifères d'après des recherches faites chez le Lapin. *Bull. Acad. r. Belg., Cl. Sci.*, 2me Sèr., **40**, 686–736. *(40)*

BENEDEN, E. VAN (1883). Recherches sur la maturation de l'oeuf et la fécondation. *Archs Biol., Paris*, **4**, 265–638. *(58, 61)*

BENZER, S. (1955). Fine structure of a genetic region in bacteriophage. *Proc. natn. Acad. Sci. U.S.A.*, **41**, 344–354. *(207–208)*

BENZER, S. (1957). The elementary units of heredity. In *The Chemical Basis of Heredity* edited by W. D. MCELROY and B. GLASS, Baltimore, Johns Hopkins Press, pp. 70–93. *(208–210, 325, 329, 330)*

BENZER, S. (1961). On the topography of the genetic fine structure. *Proc. natn. Acad. Sci. U.S.A.*, **47**, 403–415. *(210, 229, 230)*

BENZER, S. and FREESE, E. (1958). Induction of specific mutations with 5-bromouracil. *Proc. natn. Acad. Sci. U.S.A.*, **44**, 112–119. *(228)*

BERNSTEIN, F. (1925). Zusammenfassende Betrachtungen über die erblichen Blutstrukturen des Menschen. *Z. VererbLehre*, **37**, 237–270. *(134)*

BESSMAN, M. J., LEHMAN, I. R., ADLER, J., ZIMMERMAN, S. B., SIMMS, E. S. and KORNBERG, A. (1958). Enzymatic synthesis of deoxyribonucleic acid. III. The incorporation of pyrimidine and purine analogues into deoxyribonucleic acid. *Proc. nat. Acad. Sci. U.S.A.* **44**, 633–640. *(192)*

BESSMAN, M. J., LEHMAN, I. R., SIMMS, E. S. and KORNBERG, A. (1958). Enzymatic synthesis of deoxyribonucleic acid. II. General properties of the reaction. *J. biol. Chem.*, **233**, 171–177. *(190)*

BEUKERS, R. and BERENDS, W. (1960). Isolation and identification of the irradiation product of thymine. *Biochim. biophys. Acta.*, **41**, 550–551. *(277)*

BEUTLER, E., YEH, M. and FAIRBANKS, V. F. (1962). The normal human female as a mosaic of X-chromosome activity: studies using the gene for g-6-pd-deficiency as a marker. *Proc. natn. Acad. Sci. U.S.A.*, **48**, 9–16. *(311)*

BLAKESLEE, A. F. (1922). Variations in *Datura* due to changes in chromosome number. *Am. Nat.*, **56**, 16–31. *(67, 332)*

BOIVIN, A., VENDRELY, R. and VENDRELY, C. (1948). L'acide désoxyribonucléique du noyau cellulaire, dépositaire des caractères héréditaires; arguments d'ordre analytique. *C.r. hebd. Séanc. Acad. Sci., Paris*, **226**, 1061–1063. *(171)*

BOLE-GOWDA, B. N., PERKINS, D. D. and STRICKLAND, W. N. (1962). Crossing-over and interference in the centromere region of linkage group I of *Neurospora*. *Genetics, Princeton*, **47**, 1243–1252. *(110)*

BOLLUM, F. J. (1959). Thermal conversion of nonpriming deoxyribonucleic acid to primer. *J. biol. Chem.*, **234**, 2733–2734. *(192)*

BONHOEFFER, F. and GIERER, A. (1963). On the growth mechanism of the bacterial chromosome. *J. molec. Biol.*, **7**, 534–540. *(199)*

BONNER, D. M., SUYAMA, Y. and DE MOSS, J. A. (1960). Genetic fine structure and enzyme formation. *Fedn Proc. Fedn Am. Socs exp. Biol.*, **19**, 926–930. *(220)*

BONNER, J., HUANG, R. C. and GILDEN, R. V. (1963). Chromosomally directed protein synthesis. *Proc. natn. Acad. Sci. U.S.A.* **50**, 893–900. *(311)*

BOVERI, T. (1888). Zellen-Studien. *Jena. Z. Naturw.*, **22**, 685–882. *(59)*

BOVERI, T. (1889). Ein geschlechtlich erzeugter Organismus ohne mütterliche Eigenschaften. *Gesell. für Morph. Physiol. Münch.* (English translation entitled 'An organism produced sexually without characteristics of the mother.' *Am. Nat.*, 1893, **27**, 222–232.) *(41–42, 44)*

BOVERI, T. (1902). Uber mehrpolige Mitosen als Mittel zur Analyse des Zellkerns. *Verh. phys.-med. Ges. Würzb. N.F.*, **35**, 67–90. *(67)*

BOYCE, R. P. and HOWARD-FLANDERS, P. (1964a). Release of ultraviolet light-induced thymine dimers from DNA in *E. coli* K12. *Proc. natn. Acad. Sci. U.S.A.*, **51**, 293–300. *(277)*

BOYCE, R. P. and HOWARD-FLANDERS, P. (1964b). Genetic control of DNA breakdown and repair in *E. coli* K-12 treated with mitomycin C or ultraviolet light. *Z. VererbLehre*, **95**, 345–350. *(277)*

BOYCOTT, A. E. and DIVER, C. (1923). On the inheritance of sinistrality in *Limnaea peregra*. *Proc. R. Soc. B.*, **95**, 207–213. *(47)*

BOYCOTT, A. E., DIVER, C., GARSTANG, S. L. and TURNER, F. M. (1930). The inheritance of sinistrality in *Limnaea peregra* (Mollusca, Pulmonata). *Phil. Trans. R. Soc.*, **219**, 51–131. *(48)*

BRACHET, J. (1957). *Biochemical Cytology*. New York, Academic Press, 516 pp. *(235)*

BREGGER, T. (1918). Linkage in maize: the C aleurone factor and waxy endosperm. *Am. Nat.*, **52**, 57–61. *(84)*

BRENNER, S. (1957). On the impossibility of all overlapping triplet codes in information transfer from nucleic acid to proteins. *Proc. natn. Acad. Sci. U.S.A.*, **43**, 687–694. *(227–8, 260)*

BRENNER, S., BARNETT, L., CRICK, F. H. C. and ORGEL, A. (1961). The theory of mutagenesis. *J. molec. Biol.*, **3**, 121–124. *(232)*

BRENNER, S., BENZER, S. and BARNETT, L. (1958). Distribution of proflavin-induced mutations in the genetic fine structure. *Nature, Lond.*, **182**, 983–985. *(229)*

BRENNER, S., JACOB, F. and MESELSON, M. (1961). An unstable intermediate carrying information from genes to ribosomes for protein synthesis. *Nature, Lond.*, **190**, 576–581. *(241)*

BRENNER, S., STREISINGER, G., HORNE, R. W., CHAMPE, S. P., BARNETT, L., BENZER, S. and REES, M. W. (1959). Structural components of bacteriophage. *J. molec. Biol.*, **1**, 281–292. *(169–170)*

BRENNER, S., STRETTON, A. O. W. and KAPLAN, S. (1965). Genetic code: 'nonsense' triplets for chain termination and their suppression. *Nature, Lond.*, **206**, 994–998. *(261–2)*

BRIDGES, C. B. (1914). Direct proof through non-disjunction that the sex-linked genes of *Drosophila* are borne by the X-chromosome. *Science, N.Y.*, **40**, 107–109. *(73)*

BRIDGES, C. B. (1916). Non-disjunction as proof of the chromosome theory of heredity. *Genetics, Princeton*, **1**, 1–52 and 107–163. *(73–75, 96, 98, 100)*

BRIDGES, C. B. (1922). The origin of variations in sexual and sex-limited characters. *Am. Nat.*, **56**, 51–63. *(75)*

BRIDGES, C. B. (1936). The bar "gene" a duplication. *Science, N.Y.*, **83**, 210–211. *(154)*

BRIDGES, C. B. and ANDERSON, E. G. (1925). Crossing over in the X chromosomes of triploid females of *Drosophila melanogaster*. *Genetics, Princeton*, **10**, 418–441. *(98, 100, 105, 115)*

BRINK, R. A. (1960). Paramutation and chromosome organization. *Q. Rev. Biol.*, **35**, 120–137. *(306)*

BRINK, R. A. and MAC GILLIVRAY, J. H. (1924). Segregation for the waxy character in maize pollen and differential development of the male gametophyte. *Am. J. Bot.*, **11**, 465–469. *(46)*

BRODY, S. and YANOFSKY, C. (1963). Suppressor gene alteration of protein primary structure. *Proc. natn. Acad. Sci. U.S.A.* **50**, 9–16. *(253–254)*

BROWN, D. D. and GURDON, J. B. (1964). Absence of ribosomal RNA synthesis in the anucleolate mutant of *Xenopus laevis. Proc. natn. Acad. Sci. U.S.A.*, **51**, 139–146. *(310)*

BROWN, G. L. (1963). Preparation, fractionation and properties of sRNA. *Prog. Nucleic Acid Res.*, **2**, 259–310. *(248–9)*

BROWN, R. (1833). On the organs and mode of fecundation in Orchideae and Asclepiadeae. *Trans. Linn. Soc. Lond.*, **16**, 685–745. *(40, 330)*

BROWN, S. W. and ZOHARY, D. (1955). The relationship of chiasmata and crossing over in *Lilium formosanum. Genetics, Princeton*, **40**, 850–873. *(111, 118, 122, 124–5)*

CAIRNS, J. (1961). An estimate of the length of the DNA molecule of T2 bacteriophage by autoradiography. *J. molec. Biol.*, **3**, 756–761. *(200)*

CAIRNS, J. (1963). The bacterial chromosome and its manner of replication as seen by autoradiography. *J. molec. Biol.*, **6**, 208–213. *(196–8, 200)*

CAIRNS, J. (1964). The chromsome of *Escherichia coli. Cold Spring Harb. Symp. quant. Biol.*, **28**, 43–46. *(200)*

CALEF, E. (1957). Effect on linkage maps of selection of crossovers between closely linked markers. *Heredity*, **11**, 265–279. *(268, 285)*

CALLAN, H. G. (1963). The nature of lampbrush chromosomes. *Int. Rev. Cytol.*, **15**, 1–34. *(297–300, 309)*

CALLAN, H. G. and LLOYD, L. (1956). Visual demonstration of allelic differences within cell nuclei. *Nature, Lond.*, **178**, 355–357. *(120)*

CALLAN, H. G. and MACGREGOR, H. C. (1958). Action of deoxyribonuclease on lampbrush chromosomes. *Nature, Lond.*, **181**, 1479–1480. *(297–9)*

CARLSON, E. A. (1961). Limitations of geometrical models for complementation mapping of allelic series. *Nature, Lond.*, **191**, 788–790. *(221–2)*

CAROTHERS, E. E. (1913). The Mendelian ratio in relation to certain Orthopteran chromosomes. *J. Morph.*, **24**, 487–511. *(69, 107, 114–5)*

CARTER, T. C. (1955). The estimation of total genetical map lengths from linkage test data. *J. Genet.*, **53**, 21–28. *(113)*

CARTER, T. C. and ROBERTSON, A. (1952). A mathematical treatment of genetical recombination using a four-strand model. *Proc. R. Soc. B.*, **139**, 410–426. *(111)*

CASE, M. E. and GILES, N. H. (1958). Evidence from tetrad analysis for both normal and aberrant recombination between allelic mutants in *Neurospora crassa. Proc. natn. Acad. Sci. U.S.A.*, **44**, 378–390. *(267)*

CASE, M. E. and GILES, N. H. (1960). Comparative complementation and genetic maps of the *pan*-2 locus in *Neurospora crassa. Proc. natn. Acad. Sci. U.S.A.*, **46**, 659–676. *(220–1)*

CASPERSSON, T. and SCHULTZ, J. (1938). Nucleic acid metabolism of the chromosomes in relation to gene reproduction. *Nature, Lond.*, **142**, 294–295. *(305)*

CATCHESIDE, D. G. (1939). A position effect in *Oenothera. J. Genet.*, **38**, 345–352. *(304)*

CATCHESIDE, D. G. (1947). The *P*-locus position effect in *Oenothera. J. Genet.*, **48**, 31–42. *(303–4)*

CATCHESIDE, D. G. (1960). Complementation among histidine mutants of *Neurospora crassa. Proc. R. Soc. B.*, **153**, 179–194. *(217)*

CATCHESIDE, D. G. (1965). Multiple enzymic functions of a gene in *Neurospora crassa. Biochem. biophys. Res. Commun.*, **18**, 648–651. *(294)*

CATCHESIDE, D. G. and OVERTON, A. (1959). Complementation between alleles in heterocaryons. *Cold Spring Harb. Symp. quant. Biol.*, **23**, 137–140.   *(215–7)*

CAVALIERI, L. F. and ROSENBERG, B. H. (1963). Nucleic acids and information transfer. *Prog. Nucleic Acid Res.*, **2**, 1–18.   *(190)*

CHAMBERLIN, M. and BERG, P. (1962). Deoxyribonucleic acid-directed synthesis of ribonucleic acid by an enzyme from *Escherichia coli. Proc. natn. Acad. Sci. U.S.A.*, **48**, 81–94.   *(241)*

CHAMPE, S. P. and BENZER, S. (1962). Reversal of mutant phenotypes by 5-fluorouracil: an approach to nucleotide sequences in messenger-RNA. *Proc. natn. Acad. Sci. U.S.A.*, **48**, 532–546.   *(242)*

CHAPEVILLE, F., LIPMANN, F., VON EHRENSTEIN, G., WEISBLUM, B., RAY, W. J. and BENZER, S. (1962). On the role of soluble ribonucleic acid in coding for amino acids. *Proc. natn. Acad. Sci. U.S.A.* **48**, 1086–1092.   *(248)*

CHARGAFF, E. (1950). Chemical specificity of nucleic acids and mechanism of their enzymatic degradation. *Experientia*, **6**, 201–209.   *(173)*

CHARGAFF, E., BUCHOWICZ, J., TÜRLER, H. and SHAPIRO, H. S. (1965). A direct test of antiparallelism in complementary sequences of calf thymus deoxyribonucleic acid. *Nature, Lond.*, **206**, 145–147.   *(196)*

CHARGAFF, E., VISCHER, E., DONIGER, R, GREEN, C. and MISANI, F. (1949). The composition of the desoxypentose nucleic acids of thymus and spleen. *J. biol. Chem.*, **177**, 405–416.   *(173)*

CHASE, M. and DOERMANN, A. H. (1958). High negative interference over short segments of the genetic structure of bacteriophage T4. *Genetics, Princeton*, **43**, 332–353.   *(272)*

CHUN, E. H. L., VAUGHAN, M. H. and RICH, A. (1963). The isolation and characterization of DNA associated with chloroplast preparations. *J. molec. Biol.*, **7**, 130–141.   *(313)*

CLEVER, U. (1961). Genaktivitäten in den Riesenchromosomen von *Chironomus tentans* und ihre Beziehungen zur Entwicklung. 1. Genaktivierung durch Ecdyson. *Chromosoma*, **12**, 607–675.   *(309)*

COLLINS, G. N. (1912). Gametic coupling as a cause of correlations. *Am. Nat.*, **46**, 569–590.   *(84)*

COOPER, K. W. (1949). The cytogenetics of meiosis in *Drosophila*. Mitotic and meiotic autosomal chiasmata without crossing over in the male. *J. Morph.*, **84**, 81–122.   *(130)*

CORRENS, C. (1900). G. Mendels Regel über das Verhalten der Nachkommenschaft der Rassenbartarde. *Ber. dt. bot. Ges.*, **18**, 158–168. (English translation entitled 'G. Mendel's law concerning the behavior of progeny of varietal hybrids' in *Genetics, Princeton* (1950), **35**, suppl. pp. 33–41.)   *(9)*

CORRENS, C. (1909). Vererbungsversuche mit blass(gelb)grünen und buntblättrigen Sippen bei *Mirabilis Jalapa, Urtica pilulifera* und *Lunaria annua. Z. VererbLehre*, **1**, 291–329.   *(14–15, 51, 53)*

CRAWFORD, I. P. and YANOFSKY, C. (1958). On the separation of the tryptophan synthetase of *Escherichia coli* into two protein components. *Proc. natn. Acad. Sci. U.S.A.*, **44**, 1161–1170.   *(220)*

CREIGHTON, H. B. and MC CLINTOCK, B. (1931). A correlation of cytological and genetical crossing-over in *Zea mays. Proc. natn. Acad. Sci. U.S.A.*, **17**, 492–497.   *(86–8)*

CRICK, F. H. C. (1957). The structure of nucleic acids and their role in protein synthesis. *Biochem. Soc. Symp.*, **14**, 25–26. (*244–5, 248*)

CRICK, F. H. C. (1963). The recent excitement in the coding problem. *Prog. Nucleic Acid. Res.*, **1**, 163–217. (*326*)

CRICK, F. H. C., BARNETT, L., BRENNER, S. and WATTS-TOBIN, R. J. (1961). General nature of the genetic code for proteins. *Nature, Lond.*, **192**, 1227–1232. (*232–5*)

CRICK, F. H. C. and ORGEL, L. E. (1964). The theory of inter-allelic complementation. *J. molec. Biol.*, **8**, 161–165. (*222*)

CRICK, F. H. C. and WATSON, J. D. (1954). The complementary structure of deoxyribonucleic acid. *Proc. R. Soc. A.*, **223**, 80–96. (*178*)

CUÉNOT, L. (1902). La loi de Mendel et l'hérédité de la pigmentation chez les souris. *Archs Zool. exp. gén.*, 3ᵉ Serie, **10**, Notes et Revue, pp. 27–30. (*11*)

CUÉNOT, L. (1904). L'Hérédité de la pigmentation chez les souris (3ᵐᵉ Note). *Archs Zool. exp. gén.*, 4ᵉ Serie, **2**, Notes et Revue, pp. 45–56. (*132*)

DARLINGTON, C. D. (1929a). Ring-formation in *Oenothera* and other genera. *J. Genet.*, **20**, 345–363. (*128*)

DARLINGTON, C. D. (1929b). Meiosis in polyploids. Part II. Aneuploid hyacinths. *J. Genet.*, **21**, 17–56. (*64, 120, 128*)

DARLINGTON, C. D. (1930). A cytological demonstration of "genetic" crossing-over. *Proc. R. Soc. B.*, **107**, 50–59. (*120*)

DARLINGTON, C. D. (1931a). Meiosis in diploid and tetraploid *Primula sinensis*. *J. Genet.*, **24**, 65–96. (*127–129*)

DARLINGTON, C. D. (1931b). Cytological theory in relation to heredity. *Nature, Lond.*, **127**, 709–712. (*128, 173*)

DARLINGTON, C. D. (1931c). The cytological theory of inheritance in *Oenothera*. *J. Genet.*, **24**, 405–474. (*125, 128*)

DARLINGTON, C. D. (1932). *Recent Advances in Cytology*, London, J. & A. Churchill, 559 pp. (*115*)

DARLINGTON, C. D. (1934a). Anomalous chromosome pairing in the male *Drosophila pseudo-obscura*. *Genetics, Princeton*, **19**, 95–118. (*130*)

DARLINGTON, C. D. (1934b). The origin and behaviour of chiasmata. VII. *Zea mays*. *Z. VererbLehre*, **67**, 96–114. (*112–3*)

DARLINGTON, C. D. (1935). The time, place and action of crossing-over. *J. Genet.*, **31**, 185–212. (*126*)

DARLINGTON, C. D. (1936a). The external mechanics of the chromosomes. *Proc. R. Soc. B.*, **121**, 264–319. (*324*)

DARLINGTON, C. D. (1936b). Crossing-over and its mechanical relationships in *Chorthippus* and *Stauroderus*. *J. Genet.*, **33**, 465–500. (*124*)

DARWIN, C. (1868). *The variation of animals and plants under domestication*. London, John Murray. (*2, 11, 315, 327*)

DARWIN, C. (1875). *The variation of animals and plants under domestication*. 2nd edn. London, John Murray. (*2*)

DAVIES, J., GILBERT, W. and GORINI, L. (1964). Streptomycin, suppression, and the code. *Proc. natn. Acad. Sci. U.S.A.*, **51**, 883–890. (*256*)

DAWSON, G. W. P. and SMITH-KEARY, P. F. (1963). Episomic control of mutation in *Salmonella typhimurium*. *Heredity*, **18**, 1–20. (*306, 308*)

DELBRÜCK, M. and BAILEY, W. T. (1947). Induced mutations in bacterial viruses. *Cold Spring Harb. Symp. quant. Biol.*, **11**, 33–37. (*206, 271*)

DELBRÜCK, M. and STENT, G. S. (1957). On the mechanism of DNA replication. In *The Chemical Basis of Heredity* edited by W. D. MC ELROY and B. GLASS, Baltimore, Johns Hopkins Press, pp. 699–736. (*181, 331*)

DEMEREC, M. (1924). A case of pollen dimorphism in maize. *Am. J. Bot.*, **11**, 461–464. (*46*)

DEMEREC, M. (1962). "Selfers"—attributed to unequal crossovers in *Salmonella*. *Proc. natn. Acad. Sci. U.S.A.*, **48**, 1696–1704. (*283*)

DEMEREC, M., BLOMSTRAND, I. and DEMEREC, Z. E. (1955). Evidence of complex loci in *Salmonella*. *Proc. natn. Acad. Sci. U.S.A.*, **41**, 359–364. (*287*)

DEMEREC, M. and DEMEREC, Z. E. (1956). Analysis of linkage relationships in *Salmonella* by transduction techniques. *Brookhaven Symp. Biol.*, **8**, 75–87. (*287*)

DE SERRES, F. J. (1964). Genetic analysis of the structure of the *ad*-3 region of *Neurospora crassa* by means of irreparable recessive lethal mutations. *Genetics, Princeton*, **50**, 21–30. (*294*)

DE VRIES, H. (1900). Das Spaltungsgesetz der Bastarde. *Ber. dt. bot. Gesell.*, **18**, 83–90. (English translation entitled 'The law of separation of characters in crosses' in *Jl R. hort. Soc.*, 1901, **25**, 243–248.) (*9, 10, 18*)

DE VRIES, H. (1901). *Die Mutationstheorie*. (English translation entitled *The Mutation Theory*; 2 vols. London, Kegan Paul, Trench, Trübner & Co., 1910, 1911, 582 and 683 pp.) (*135*)

DE VRIES, H. (1903). *Befruchtung und Bastardierung*, 62 pp., Leipzig. (English translation by C. S. GAGER entitled *Fertilization and Hybridization* as pp. 217–263 of *Intracellular pangenesis including a paper on fertilization and hybridization*, Chicago-Open Court Publ. Co., 1910.) (*77, 95*)

DINTZIS, H. M. (1961). Assembly of the peptide chains of hemoglobin. *Proc. natn. Acad. Sci. U.S.A.*, **47**, 247–261. (*248*)

DJORDJEVIC, B. and SZYBALSKI, W. (1960). Genetics of human cell lines. III. Incorporation of 5-bromo- and 5-iododeoxyuridine into the deoxyribonucleic acid of human cells and its effect on radiation sensitivity. *J. exp. Med.*, **112**, 509–531. (*189*)

DOBZHANSKY, T. (1929). Genetical and cytological proof of translocations involving the third and fourth chromosome of *Drosophila melanogaster*. *Biol. Zbl.*, **49**, 408–419. (*142*)

DODGE, B. O. (1929). The nature of giant spores and segregation of sex factors in *Neurospora*. *Mycologia*, **21**, 222–231. (*101*)

DONCASTER, L. (1908). On sex-inheritance in the moth *Abraxas grossulariata* and its var. *lacticolor*. *Rep. Evol. Comm. R. Soc.*, **4**, 53–57. (*21, 22*)

DONCASTER, L. and RAYNOR, G. H. (1906). On breeding experiments with Lepidoptera. *Proc. zool. Soc. Lond.*, **1**, 125–133. (*20–22*)

DOUNCE, A. L. (1952). Duplicating mechanism for peptide chain and nucleic acid synthesis. *Enzymologia*, **15**, 251–258. (*203, 211, 221, 226, 227*)

DUNN, D. B. and SMITH, J. D. (1954). Incorporation of halogenated pyrimidines into the deoxyribonucleic acids of *Bacterium coli* and its bacteriophages. *Nature, Lond.*, **174**, 305–306. (*192, 228*)

DURRANT, A. (1962). The environmental induction of heritable change in *Linum*. *Heredity*, **17**, 27–61. (*2*)

DUTT, M. K. and KAUFMANN, B. P. (1959). Degradational action of deoxyribonuclease on unfixed chromosomes of *Drosophila* and grasshoppers. *Nucleus, Calcutta*, **2**, 85–98. *(299)*

EAST, E. M. (1910). A Mendelian interpretation of variation that is apparently continuous. *Am. Nat.*, **44**, 65–82. *(33–5, 37)*

EBERSOLD, W. T. and LEVINE, R. P. (1959). A genetic analysis of linkage group I of *Chlamydomonas reinhardi*. *Z. VererbLehre*, **90**, 74–82. *(111)*

ECHLIN, P. and MORRIS, I. (1965). The relationships between blue-green algae and bacteria. *Biol. Rev.*, **40**, 143–187. *(317)*

EDSTRÖM, J.-E. and BEERMANN, W. (1962). The base composition of nucleic acids in chromosomes, puffs, nucleoli, and cytoplasm of *Chironomus* salivary gland cells. *J. Cell Biol.*, **14**, 371–380. *(309)*

EHRENSTEIN, G. VON, and DAIS, D. (1963). A leucine acceptor sRNA with ambiguous coding properties in polynucleotide-stimulated polypeptide synthesis. *Proc. natn. Acad. Sci. U.S.A.*, **50**, 81–86. *(256, 258)*

EHRENSTEIN, G. VON, and LIPMANN, F. (1961). Experiments on hemoglobin biosynthesis. *Proc. natn. Acad. Sci. U.S.A.*, **47**, 941–950. *(253, 256)*

EHRENSTEIN, G. VON, WEISBLUM, B. and BENZER, S. (1963). The function of sRNA as amino acid adaptor in the synthesis of hemoglobin. *Proc. natn. Acad. Sci. U.S.A.*, **49**, 669–675. *(248)*

ELSDALE, T. R., FISCHBERG, M. and SMITH, S. (1958). A mutation that reduces nucleolar number in *Xenopus laevis*. *Expl Cell Res.*, **14**, 642–643. *(310)*

EMERSON, R. A. (1911). Genetic correlation and spurious allelomorphism in maize. *Rep. Neb. agric. Exp. Stn*, **24**, 58–90. *(132)*

EMERSON, R. A. (1914). The inheritance of a recurring somatic variation in variegated ears of maize. *Am. Nat.*, **48**, 87–115. *(302)*

EMERSON, R. A. and EAST, E. M. (1913). The inheritance of quantitative characters in maize. *Res. Bull. Neb. agric. Exp. Stn*, **2**, 1–120. *(35, 37)*

EMERSON, S. and BEADLE, G. W. (1933). Crossing-over near the spindle fiber in attached-X chromosomes of *Drosophila melanogaster*. *Z. VererbLehre*, **45**, 129–140. *(109)*

EPHRUSSI, B. (1953). *Nucleo-cytoplasmic Relations in Micro-organisms*. Oxford, Clarendon Press, 127 pp. *(56)*

EPSTEIN, R. H., BOLLE, A., STEINBERG, C. M., KELLENBERGER, E., BOY DE LA TOUR, E., CHEVALLEY, R., EDGAR, R. S., SUSMAN, M., DENHARDT, G. H. and LIELAUSIS, A. (1964). Physiological studies of conditional lethal mutants of bacteriophage T4D. *Cold Spring Harb. Symp. quant. Biol.*, **28**, 375–394. *(271, 292, 293, 313)*

FARGIE, B. and HOLLOWAY, B. W. (1965). *Genet. Res.*, **6**, 284–299. *(287)*

FARMER, J. B. and MOORE, J. E. S. (1905). On the maiotic phase (reduction divisions) in animals and plants. *Q. Jl microsc. Sci.*, **48**, 489–557. *(62, 329)*

FEUGHELMAN, M., LANGRIDGE, R., SEEDS, W. E., STOKES, A. R., WILSON, H. R., HOOPER, C. W., WILKINS, M. H. F., BARCLAY, R. K. and HAMILTON, L. D. (1955). Molecular structure of deoxyribose nucleic acid and nucleoprotein. *Nature, Lond.*, **175**, 834–838. *(180, 300)*

FINCHAM, J. R. S. (1959a). On the nature of the glutamic dehydrogenase produced by inter-allele complementation at the *am* locus of *Neurospora crassa*. *J. gen. Microbiol.*, **21**, 600–611. *(215, 217, 326)*

FINCHAM, J. R. S. (1959b). The biochemistry of genetic factors. *A. Rev. Biochem.*, **28**, 343–364. *(163)*

FINCHAM, J. R. S. and CODDINGTON, A. (1963). Complementation at the *am* locus of *Neurospora crassa*: a reaction between different mutant forms of glutamate dehydrogenase. *J. molec. Biol.*, **6**, 361–373.   *(217)*

FINCHAM, J. R. S. and DAY, P. R. (1965). *Fungal Genetics*. 2nd edn. Oxford, Blackwell, 326 pp.   *(57, 163)*

FINCHAM, J. R. S. and PATEMAN, J. A. (1957). Formation of an enzyme through complementary action of mutant 'alleles' in separate nuclei in a heterocaryon. *Nature, Lond.*, **179**, 741-742.   *(211, 215, 217)*

FISHER, R. A. (1918). The correlation between relatives on the supposition of Mendelian inheritance. *Trans. R. Soc. Edinb.*, **52**, 399–433.   *(31, 36–37)*

FISHER, R. A. (1936). Has Mendel's work been rediscovered? *Ann. Sci.*, **1**, 115–137.   *(28–9)*

FISHER, R. A. (1963). *Statistical Methods for Research Workers*. 13th edn. Edinburgh, Oliver and Boyd.   *(23, 27)*

FLEMMING, W. (1879), Beiträge zur Kenntniss der Zelle und ihre Lebenserscheinungen. *Arch. mikrosk. Anat.*, **16**, 302–436.   *(58)*

FLEMMING, W. (1882). *Zellsubstanz, Kern- und Zelltheilung*. Leipzig. 424 pp. *(58, 329)*

FLEMMING, W. (1887). Neue Beiträge zur Kenntniss der Zelle. *Arch. mikrosk. Anat.*, **29**, 389–463.   *(62)*

FORD, C. E. and HAMERTON, J. L. (1956). The chromosomes of man. *Nature, Lond.*, **178**, 1020–1023.   *(68)*

FOX, E. and MESELSON, M. (1963). Unequal photosensitivity of the two strands of DNA in bacteriophage λ. *J. molec. Biol.*, **7**, 583–589.   *(243)*

FRAENKEL-CONRAT, H. (1956). The role of the nucleic acid in the reconstitution of active tobacco mosaic virus. *J. Am. chem. Soc.*, **78**, 882–883.   *(236)*

FRAENKEL-CONRAT, H. and SINGER, B. (1957). Virus reconstitution. II. Combination of protein and nucleic acid from different strains. *Biochim. biophys. Acta.*, **24**, 540–548.   *(236-7)*

FRANKLIN, R. E. and GOSLING, R. G. (1953). Molecular configuration in sodium thymonucleate. *Nature, Lond.*, **171**, 740–741.   *(178, 179)*

FREESE, E. (1957). The correlation effect for a histidine locus of *Neurospora crassa*. *Genetics, Princeton*, **42**, 671–684.   *(273)*

FREESE, E. (1959). The difference between spontaneous and base-analogue induced mutations of phage T4. *Proc. natn. Acad. Sci. U.S.A.*, **45**, 622-633.
                                                                       (229, 232, 332)

FREESE, E., BAUTZ, E. and BAUTZ-FREESE, E. (1961). The chemical and mutagenic specificity of hydroxylamine. *Proc. natn. Acad. Sci. U.S.A.*, **47**, 845–855.   *(231)*

FRIEDMAN, S. M. and WEINSTEIN, I. B. (1964). Lack of fidelity in the translation of synthetic polyribonucleotides. *Proc. natn. Acad. Sci. U.S.A.*, **52**, 988–996. *(256)*

GALL, J. G. (1956). On the submicroscopic structure of chromosomes. *Brookhaven Symp. Biol.*, **8**, 17–32.   *(297–8, 300)*

GALL, J. G. (1963). Kinetics of deoxyribonuclease action on chromosomes. *Nature, Lond.*, **198**, 36–38.   *(299, 300)*

GALL, J. G. and CALLAN, H. G. (1962). H³ uridine incorporation in lampbrush chromosomes. *Proc. natn. Acad. Sci. U.S.A.*, **48**, 562–570.   *(309)*

GALTON, F. (1889). *Natural Inheritance*. London, Macmillan, 259 pp.   *(30–31)*

GAMOW, G. (1954). Possible relation between deoxyribonucleic acid and protein structures. *Nature, Lond.*, **173**, 318.   *(203, 211, 221, 226, 227)*

GAMOW, G. and YCAS, M. (1955). Statistical correlation of protein and ribonucleic acid composition. *Proc. natn Acad. Sci. U.S.A.* **41**, 1011–1019. *(227)*

GARDNER, R. S., WAHBA, A. J., BASILIO, C., MILLER, R. S., LENGYEL, P. and SPEYER, J. F· (1962). Synthetic polynucleotides and the amino acid code. VII. *Proc. natn· Acad. Sci. U.S.A.*, **48**, 2087–2094. *(255)*

GARROD, A. E. (1909). *Inborn Errors of Metabolism.* London, Oxford Univ. Press, *(159)*

GIACOMONI, D. and SPIEGELMAN, S. (1962). Origin and biologic individuality of the genetic dictionary. *Science, N.Y.*, **138**, 1328–1331. *(294)*

GIBOR, A. and IZAWA, M. (1963). The DNA content of the chloroplasts of *Acetabularia. Proc. natn. Acad. Sci. U.S.A.*, **50**, 1164–1169. *(313)*

GIERER, A. (1963). Function of aggregated reticulocyte ribosomes in protein synthesis. *J. molec. Biol.* **6**, 148–157. *(253)*

GIERER, A. and SCHRAMM G. (1956). Infectivity of ribonucleic acid from tobacco mosaic virus. *Nature, Lond.*, **177**, 702–703. *(236)*

GILBERT, W. (1963). Polypeptide synthesis in *Escherichia coli.* II. The polypeptide chain and S-RNA. *J. molec. Biol.*, **6**, 389–403. *(253)*

GILES, N. H. (1952). Studies on the mechanism of reversion in biochemical mutants of *Neurospora crassa. Cold Spring Harb. Symp. quant. Biol.*, **16**, 283–313. *(267, 272)*

GILES, N. H. (1965). Genetic fine structure in relation to function in *Neurospora. Proc.* 11*th int. Congr. Genet.* 1963, **2**, 17–30. Oxford, Pergamon Press. *(294)*

GILES, N. H., PARTRIDGE, C. W. H. and NELSON, N. J. (1957). The genetic control of adenylosuccinase in *Neurospora crassa. Proc. natn. Acad. Sci. U.S.A.*, **43**, 305–317. *(211, 215, 217)*

GOLDSCHMIDT, R. B. (1938). *Physiological Genetics.* New York, McGraw-Hill, 375 pp. *(152–153)*

GOODMAN, H. M. and RICH, A. (1962). Formation of a DNA-soluble RNA hybrid and its relation to the origin, evolution, and degeneracy of soluble RNA. *Proc. natn. Acad. Sci. U.S.A.*, **48**, 2101–2109. *(294)*

GOSS, J. (1824). On the variation in the colour of peas, occasioned by cross impregnation. *Trans. hort. Soc. Lond.*, **5**, 234–236. *(3, 6)*

GOSSOP, G. H., YUILL, E. and YUILL, J. L. (1940). Heterogeneous fructifications in species of *Aspergillus. Trans. Br. mycol. Soc.*, **24**, 337–344. *(46)*

GRAY, C. H. and TATUM, E. L. (1944). X-ray induced growth factor requirements in bacteria. *Proc. natn. Acad. Sci. U.S.A.*, **30**, 404–410. *(163)*

GREEN, M. M. and GREEN, K. C. (1949). Crossing-over between alleles at the lozenge locus in *Drosophila melanogaster. Proc. natn. Acad. Sci. U.S.A.*, **35**, 586–591. *(206)*

GRÉGOIRE, V. (1904). La réduction numérique des chromosomes et les cinèses de maturation. *Cellule*, **21**, 297–314. *(62, 329)*

GRÉGOIRE, V. (1907). La formation des gemini hétérotypiques dans les végétaux. *Cellule*, **24**, 369–420. *(62, 332)*

GRIFFITH, F. (1928). Significance of pneumococcal types. *J. Hyg., Camb.*, **27**, 113–159. *(168, 270, 332)*

GROSS, S. R. (1962). On the mechanism of complementation at the *leu*-2 locus of *Neurospora. Proc. natn. Acad. Sci. U.S.A.*, **48**, 922–930. *(219, 221)·*

GRUNBERG-MANAGO, M. and OCHOA, S. (1955). Enzymatic synthesis and breakdown of polynucleotides; polynucleotide phosphorylase. *J. Am. chem. Soc.*, **77**, 3165–3166. *(238, 255)*

GUILD, W. R. and ROBISON, M. (1963). Evidence for message reading from a unique strand of pneumococcal DNA. *Proc. natn. Acad. Sci. U.S.A.*, **50**, 106–112. *(243)*

HÄCKER, V. (1897). Ueber weitere Uebereinstimmungen zwischen den Fortpflanzungs-vorgängen der Tiere und Pflanzen. *Biol. Zbl.*, **17**, 689–705 and 721–745.
(*65, 326*)

HAGA, T. (1944). Meiosis in *Paris*. I. Mechanism of chiasma formation. *J. Fac. Sci. Hokkaido Univ.*, Ser. V. (Botany), **5**, 121–198.   (*117–118*)

HALDANE, J. B. S. (1919). The probable errors of calculated linkage values, and the most accurate method of determining gametic from certain zygotic series. *J. Genet.*, **8**, 291–297.   (*20*)

HALDANE, J. B. S. (1931). The cytological basis of genetical interference. *Cytologia*, **3** 54–65.   (*109, 111–2*)

HALDANE, J. B. S. (1941). *New Paths in Genetics*. London, Allen and Unwin, 206 pp.
(*206, 325, 331*)

HALL, B. D. and SPIEGELMAN, S. (1961). Sequence complementarity of T2-DNA and T2-specific RNA. *Proc. natn. Acad. Sci. U.S.A.*, **47**, 137–146.   (*239–240, 290*)

HÄMMERLING, J. (1963). Nucleo-cytoplasmic relationships in the development of *Acetabularia*. *Int. Rev. Cytol.*, **2**, 475–498.   (*42*)

HÄMMERLING, J. (1963). Nucleo-cytoplasmic interactions in *Acetabularia* and other cells. *A. Rev. Pl. Physiol.*, **14**, 65–92.   (*42*)

HARDY, G. H. (1908). Mendelian proportions in a mixed population. *Science, N.Y.*, **28**, 49–50.   (*13*)

HARRIS, H. and SABATH, L. D. (1964). Induced enzyme synthesis in the absence of concomitant ribonucleic acid synthesis. *Nature, Lond.*, **202**, 1078–1080. (*291, 307*)

HARRISON, B. J. and FINCHAM, J. R. S. (1964). Instability at the *pal* locus in *Antirrhinum majus*. 1. Effects of environment on frequencies of somatic and germinal muta-tion. *Heredity*, **19**, 237–258.   (*315*)

HARTMAN, P. E. (1956). Linked loci in the control of consecutive steps in the primary pathway of histidine synthesis in *Salmonella typhimurium*. *Publs Carnegie Instn*, **612**, 35–61.   (*287*)

HARTMAN, P. E., LOPER, J. C. and SERMAN, D. (1960). Fine structure mapping by complete transduction between histidine-requiring *Salmonella* mutants. *J. gen. Microbiol.*, **22**, 323–353.   (*289*)

HASTINGS, P. J. and WHITEHOUSE, H. L. K. (1964). A polaron model of genetic recombi-nation by the formation of hybrid deoxyribonucleic acid. *Nature, Lond.*, **201**, 1052–1054.   (*275, 286*)

HAYASHI, M., HAYASHI, M. N. and SPIEGELMAN, S. (1964). DNA circularity and the mechanism of strand selection in the generation of genetic messages. *Proc. natn. Acad. Sci. U.S.A.*, **51**, 351–359.   (*200, 244*)

HAYASHI, M., SPIEGELMAN, S., FRANKLIN, N. C. and LURIA, S. E. (1963). Separation of the RNA message transcribed in response to a specific inducer. *Proc. natn. Acad. Sci. U.S.A.*, **49**, 729–736.   (*291*)

HAYES, W. (1964). *The Genetics of Bacteria and their Viruses*. Oxford, Blackwell, 740 pp.
(*269, 270*)

HEIDENHAIN, M. (1894). Neue Untersuchungen über die Centralkörper und ihre Beziehungen zum Kern- und Zellenprotoplasma. *Arch. mikrosk. Anat.*, **43**, 423–758.   (*59, 331*)

HEITZ, E. (1928). Das Heterochromatin der Moose. I. *Jb. wiss. Bot.*, **69**, 762–818.
(*295, 328*)

HENDERSON, S. A. (1964). RNA synthesis during male meiosis and spermiogenesis. *Chromosoma*, **15**, 345–366.   (*311*)

HENKING, H. VON. (1891). Untersuchungen über die ersten Entwicklungsvorgänge in den Eiern der Insekten. II. Über Spermatogenese und deren Beziehung zur Eientwicklung bei *Pyrrhocoris apterus L. Z. wiss Zool.*, **51**, 685–736.   *(69, 70)*

HENNING, U. and YANOFSKY, C. (1962). Amino acid replacements associated with reversion and recombination within the A gene. *Proc. natn. Acad. Sci. U.S.A.*, **48**, 1497–1504.   *(260, 261, 271)*

HERSHEY, A. D. (1947). Spontaneous mutations in bacterial viruses. *Cold Spring Harb. Symp. quant. Biol.*, **11**, 67–77.   *(206, 271)*

HERSHEY, A. D. and CHASE, M. (1952a). Genetic recombination and heterozygosis in bacteriophage. *Cold Spring Harb. Symp. quant. Biol.*, **16**, 471–479.   *(271)*

HERSHEY, A. D. and CHASE, M. (1952b). Independent functions of viral protein and nucleic acid in growth of bacteriophage. *J. gen. Physiol.*, **36**, 39–56.   *(171, 180)*

HERSHEY, A. D. and ROTMAN, R. (1948). Linkage among genes controlling inhibition of lysis in a bacterial virus. *Proc. natn. Acad. Sci. U.S.A.*, **34**, 89–96.   *(206–7)*

HERSHEY, A. D. and ROTMAN, R. (1949). Genetic recombination between host-range and plaque-type mutants of bacteriophage in single bacterial cells. *Genetics, Princeton*, **34**, 44–71.   *(271)*

HERTWIG, O. (1875). Beiträge zur Kenntniss der Bildung, Befruchtung und Theilung des thierischen Eies. *Morph. Jb.*, **1**, 347–434.   *(40)*

HIPPOCRATES (ca. 400 B.C.). *On airs, waters and places*, chap. 14. (English translation by F. ADAMS, London, Baillière, Tindall and Cox, 1939.)   *(1)*

HOAGLAND, M. B., ZAMECNIK, P. C. and STEPHENSON, M. L. (1957). Intermediate reactions in protein biosynthesis. *Biochim. biophys. Acta*, **24**, 215–216. *(245, 248)*

HOLLEY, R. W., APGAR, J., EVERETT, G. A., MADISON, J. T., MARQUISEE, M., MERRILL. S. H., PENSWICK, J. R. and ZAMIR, A. (1965). Structure of a ribonucleic acid. *Science, N.Y.*, **147**, 1462–1465.   *(252)*

HOLLIDAY, R. (1962). Mutation and replication in *Ustilago maydis*. *Genet. Res.*, **3**, 472–486.   *(278)*

HOLLIDAY, R. (1964). A mechanism for gene conversion in fungi. *Genet. Res.*, **5**, 282–304.   *(274, 281–2)*

HOPWOOD, D. A. (1965). *J. molec. Biol.* **12**, 514–516.   *(269)*

HOPWOOD, D. A. and SERMONTI, G. (1962). The genetics of *Streptomyces coelicolor*. *Adv. Genet.* **11**, 273–342.   *(287)*

HOROWITZ, N. H., FLING, M., MACLEOD, H. and SUEOKA, N. (1961). A genetic study of two new structural forms of tyrosinase in *Neurospora*. *Genetics, Princeton*, **46**, 1015–1024.   *(163)*

HOTTA, Y. and STERN, H. (1961). Transient phosphorylation of deoxyribosides and regulation of deoxyribonucleic acid synthesis. *J. biophys. biochem. Cytol.*, **11**, 311–319.   *(275)*

HOWARD, A. and PELC, S. R. (1951a). Nuclear incorporation of P^{32} as demonstrated by autoradiographs. *Expl Cell Res.*, **2**, 178–187.   *(172, 181)*

HOWARD, A. and PELC, S. R. (1951b). Synthesis of nucleoprotein in bean root cells, *Nature, Lond.*, **167**, 599–601.   *(173)*

HOWARD-FLANDERS, P. and BOYCE, R. P. (1964). A biochemical pathway in the repair of DNA after UV-irradiation that may have steps in common with those of genetic recombination by breakage-reunion. *Genetics, Princeton*, **50**, 256–257 (Abstr.).   *(282)*

HOWARD-FLANDERS, P., CLARK, A. J., SIMSON, E., THERIOT, L. and BOYCE, R. P. (1965). The role of DNA repair in genetic recombination. *Biophys. Soc. 9th A. Meet. Abstr.* p. 163.   *(283)*

HUNT, J. A. and INGRAM, V. M. (1958). Allelomorphism and the chemical differences of the human haemoglobins A, S and C. *Nature, Lond.*, **181,** 1062–1063.   (*219*)

HURWITZ, J., FURTH, J. J., ANDERS, M., ORITZ, P. J. and AUGUST, J. T. (1962). The enzymatic incorporation of ribonucleotides into RNA and the role of DNA. *Cold Spring Harb. Symp. quant. Biol.*, **26,** 91–100.   (*240*)

INGRAM, V. M. (1956). A specific chemical difference between the globins of normal human and sickle-cell anaemia haemoglobin. *Nature, Lond.*, **178,** 792–794.
(*212, 214*)

INGRAM, V. M. (1957). Gene mutations in human haemoglobin: the chemical difference between normal and sickle cell haemoglobin. *Nature, Lond.*, **180,** 326–328.
(*214*)

ITANO, H. A. and NEEL, J. V. (1950). A new inherited abnormality of human hemoglobin. *Proc. natn. Acad. Sci. U.S.A.*, **36,** 613–617.   (*218*)

ITANO, H. A. and ROBINSON, E. (1959). Formation of normal and doubly abnormal haemoglobins by recombination of haemoglobin I with S and C. *Nature, Lond.*, **183,** 1799–1800.   (*219*)

ITANO, H. A. and ROBINSON, E. A. (1960). Genetic control of the α- and β-chains of hemoglobin. *Proc. natn. Acad. Sci. U.S.A.*, **46,** 1492–1501.   (*219*)

IZAWA, M., ALLFREY, B. G. and MIRSKY, A. E. (1963). The relationship between RNA synthesis and loop structure in lampbrush chromosomes. *Proc. natn. Acad. Sci. U.S.A.*, **49,** 544–551.   (*311*)

JACKSON, R. C. (1957). New low chromosome number for plants. *Science, N.Y.*, **126,** 1115–1116.   (*68*)

JACOB, F. and BRENNER, S. (1963). Sur la régulation de la synthèse du DNA chez les bactéries: l'hypothèse du réplicon. *C.r. hebd. Séanc. Acad. Sci., Paris*, **256,** 298–300.
(*201, 292, 331*)

JACOB F., BRENNER S. and CUZIN F. (1964) On the regulation of DNA replication in bacteria. *Cold Spring Harb. Symp. quant. Biol.* **28,** 329–348.   (*292*)

JACOB, F. and MONOD, J. (1961). Genetic regulatory mechanisms in the synthesis of proteins. *J. molec. Biol.*, **3,** 318–356.   (*288–291, 294–5*)

JACOB, F. and MONOD, J. (1962). On the regulation of gene activity. *Cold Spring Harb. Symp. quant. Biol.*, **26,** 193–211.   (*288–9, 294–5*)

JACOB, F., PERRIN, D., SANCHEZ, C., and MONOD, J. (1960). L'opéron: groupe de gènes à expression coordonée pare un opérateur. *C.r. hebd. Séanc. Acad. Sci., Paris*, **250,** 1727–1729.   (*288, 330*)

JACOB, F. and WOLLMAN, E. L. (1958a). Genetic and physical determinations of chromosomal segments in *E. coli*. *Symp. Soc. exp. Biol.*, **12,** 75–92.   (*269, 271*)

JACOB, F. and WOLLMAN, E. L. (1958b). Les épisomes, éléments génétique ajoutés. *C.r. hebd. Séanc. Acad. Sci., Paris*, **247,** 154–156.   (*270, 306, 327*)

JACOBS, P. A. and STRONG, J. A. (1959). A case of human intersexuality having a possible XXY sex-determining mechanism. *Nature, Lond.*, **183,** 302–303.   (*76*)

JANSSENS, F. A. (1909). Spermatogénèse dans les Batraciens. V. La théorie de la chiasmatypie. Nouvelles interprétation des cinèses de maturation. *Cellule*, **25,** 387–411.   (*91–96, 107, 114, 127, 131, 324*)

JENKINS, M. T. (1924). Heritable characters of maize. XX. Iojap-striping, a chlorophyll defect. *J. Hered.*, **15,** 467–472.   (*50*)

JESSOP, A. P. and CATCHESIDE, D. G. (1965). Interallelic recombination at the *his*-1 locus in *Neurospora crassa* and its genetic control. *Heredity*, **20,** 237–256.   (*285*)

JINKS, J. L. (1954). Somatic selection in fungi. *Nature, Lond.*, **174**, 409–410.   *(55)*

JINKS, J. L. (1964). *Extrachromosomal inheritance.* New Jersey, Prentice-Hall, 177 pp.
                                                                     (55, 57)

JOHANNSEN, W. (1903). *Über Erblichkeit in Populationen und in reinen Linien.* Jena, Gustav Fischer.   *(32)*

JOHANNSEN, W. (1909). *Elemente der exakten Erblichkeitslehre.* Jena, Gustav Fischer.
                                                        (23, 31, 327, 328, 330)

JOSSE, J., KAISER, A. D. and KORNBERG, A. (1961). Enzymatic synthesis of deoxy-ribonucleic acid. VIII. Frequencies of nearest neighbor base sequences in deoxy-ribonucleic acid. *J. biol. Chem.*, **236**, 864–875.   *(194–196)*

KAISER, D., TABOR, H. and TABOR, C. W. (1963). Spermine protection of coliphage λ DNA against breakage by hydrodynamic shear. *J. molec. Biol.*, **6**, 141–147. *(301)*

KAPULER, A. M. and BERNSTEIN, H, (1963). A molecular model for an enzyme based on a correlation between the genetic and complementation maps of the locus specifying the enzyme. *J. molec. Biol.*, **6**, 443–451.   *(221)*

KAUFMANN, B. P. and MCDONALD, M. R. (1957). Organization of the chromosome. *Cold Spring Harb. Symp. quant. Biol.*, **21**, 233–246.   *(297)*

KAYANO, H. (1960a). Chiasma studies in structural hybrids. III. Reductional and equational separation in *Disporum sessile. Cytologia*, **25**, 461–467.   *(117, 119)*

KAYANO, H. (1960b). Chiasma studies in structural hybrids. IV. Crossing-over in *Disporum sessile. Cytologia*, **25**, 468–475.   *(126)*

KAYANO, H. and NAKAMURA, K. (1960). Chiasma studies in structural hybrids. V. Heterozygotes for a centric fusion and for a translocation in *Acrida lata. Cytologia*, **25**, 476–480.   *(119)*

KELLENBERGER, E. (1961). Vegetative bacteriophage and the maturation of the virus particles. *Adv. Virus Res.*, **8**, 1–61.   *(301)*

KELLENBERGER, G., ZICHICHI, M. L. and WEIGLE, J. (1961). Exchange of DNA in the recombination of bacteriophage λ. *Proc. natn. Acad. Sci. U.S.A.*, **47**, 869–878.
                                                                     (272)

KELNER, A. (1949). Effect of visible light on the recovery of *Streptomyces griseus* conidia from ultraviolet irradiation injury. *Proc. natn. Acad. Sci. U.S.A.*, **35**, 73–79.   *(277)*

KIHLMAN, B. A. (1961). Biochemical aspects of chromosome breakage. *Adv. Genet.*, **10**, 1–59.   *(144–145)*

KING, T. J. and BRIGGS, R. (1955). Changes in the nuclei of differentiating gastrula cells, as demonstrated by nuclear transplantation. *Proc. natn. Acad. Sci. U.S.A.*, **41**, 321–325.   *(309)*

KITANI, Y., OLIVE, L. S. and EL-ANI, A. S. (1962). Genetics of *Sordaria fimicola*. V. Aberrant segregation at the *g* locus. *Am. J. Bot.*, **49**, 697–706.   *(264–5, 273–4, 278–281)*

KLEINSCHMIDT, A. K., LANG, D., JACHERTS, D. and ZAHN, R. K. (1962). Darstellung und Langenmessungen des gesamten Desoxyribonucleinsäure-inhaltes von T2-Bakteriophagen. *Biochim. biophys. Acta*, **61**, 857–864.   *(170, 200)*

KNAPP, E. and MÖLLER, E. (1955). Tetradenanalytische Auswertung eines 3-Punktver-suchs bei *Sphaerocarpus donnellü* Aust. *Z. VererbLehre*, **87**, 298–310.   *(111)*

KNIGHT, T. A. (1799). An account of some experiments on the fecundation of vege-tables. *Phil. Trans. R. Soc.*, **1**, 195–204.   *(3, 6)*

KOLLER, P. C. (1935). The internal mechanics of the chromosomes, IV. Pairing and coiling in salivary gland nuclei of *Drosophila. Proc. R. Soc. B.*, **118**, 371–397. *(330)*

KOLLER, P. C. (1938). The genetical and mechanical properties of the sex-chromosomes. IV. The golden hamster. *J. Genet.*, **36**, 177–195.   (*118*)

KÖLREUTER, J. G. (1763). Vorläufige Nachricht von einigen das Geschlecht der Pflanzen betreffenden Versuchen und Beobachten, Forsetzungen 1. (Ostwald's Klassiker der exacten Wissenschaften. 41. Leipzig, 1893.)   (*3, 6, 35*)

KÜHN, A. (1937). Entwicklungsphysiologisch-genetische Ergebnisse an *Ephestia kuhniella*. *Z. VererbLehre*, **73**, 419–455.   (*48*)

KUHN, W. (1957). Zeitbedarf der Längsteilung von miteinander verzwirnten Fadenmolekülen. *Experientia*, **13**, 301–307.   (*200*)

LA COUR, L. F. and PELC, S. R. (1959). Effect of colchicine on the utilization of thymidine labelled with tritium during chromosomal reproduction. *Nature, Lond.*, **183**, 1455–1456.   (*188*)

LAMARCK, J. B. (1809). *Philosophie Zoologique*. Paris. (Translation, entitled 'Zoological Philosophy,' by H. ELLIOT, London, Macmillan, 1914, 410 pp.)   (*40*)

LANDSTEINER, K. and WIENER, A. S. (1941). Studies on an agglutinogen (Rh) in human blood reacting with anti-rhesus sera and with human isoantibodies. *J. exp. Med.*, **74**, 309–320.   (*157*)

LAWRENCE, W. J. C. (1950). Genetic control of biochemical synthesis as exemplified by plant genetics—flower colours. *Biochem. Soc. Symp.*, **4**, 3–9.   (*160*)

LEDERBERG, J. (1955). Recombination mechanisms in bacteria. *J. cell. comp. Physiol.*, **45**, suppl. 2, 75–107.   (*273*)

LEDERBERG, J., LEDERBERG, E. M., ZINDER, N. D. and LIVELY, E. R. (1952). Recombination analysis of bacterial heredity. *Cold Spring Harb. Symp. quant. Biol.*, **16**, 413–443.   (*270, 332*)

LEDERBERG, J. and TATUM, E. L. (1946). Gene recombination in *Escherichia coli*. *Nature, Lond.*, **158**, 558.   (*163, 268*)

LEHMAN, I. R., BESSMAN, M. J., SIMMS, E. S. and KORNBERG, A. (1958). Enzymatic synthesis of deoxyribonucleic acid. I. Preparation of substrates and partial purification of an enzyme from *Escherichia coli*. *J. biol. Chem.*, **233**, 163–170.   (*190*)

LEHMAN, I. R., ZIMMERMAN, S. B., ADLER, J., BESSMAN, M. J., SIMMS, E. S. and KORNBERG, A. (1958). Enzymatic synthesis of deoxyribonucleic acid. V. Chemical composition of enzymatically synthesized deoxyribonucleic acid. *Proc. natn. Acad. Sci. U.S.A.*, **44**, 1191–1196.   (*190*)

LEJEUNE, J., GAUTIER, M. and TURPIN, R. (1959). Étude des chromosomes somatiques de neuf enfants mongoliens. *C.r. hebd. Séanc. Acad. Sci., Paris*, **248**, 1721–1722.   (*68*)

LENGYEL, P., SPEYER, J. F. and OCHOA, S. (1961). Synthetic polynucleotides and the amino acid code. *Proc. natn. Acad. Sci. U.S.A.*, **47**, 1936–1942.   (*255*)

LEVINTHAL, C. (1954). Recombination in phage T2: its relationship to heterozygosis and growth. *Genetics, Princeton*, **39**, 169–184.   (*272*)

LEVINTHAL, C. and CRANE, H. R. (1956). On the unwinding of DNA. *Proc. natn. Acad. Sci. U.S.A.*, **42**, 436–438.   (*199*, 201)

LEWIS, E. B. (1941). Another case of unequal crossing-over in *Drosophila melanogaster*. *Proc. natn. Acad. Sci. U.S.A.*, **27**, 31–35.   (*156*)

LEWIS, E. B. (1945). The relation of repeats to position effect in *Drosophila melanogaster*. *Genetics, Princeton*, **30**, 137–166.   (*156, 206*)

LEWIS, E. B. (1952). The pseudoallelism of white and apricot in *Drosophila melanogaster*. *Proc. natn. Acad. Sci. U.S.A.*, **38**, 953–961.   (*206*)

LINDEGREN, C. C. (1932). The genetics of *Neurospora*—II. Segregation of the sex factors in asci of *N. crassa, N. sitophila,* and *N. tetrasperma. Bull. Torrey bot. Club,* **59,** 119–138. *(101–2)*

LINDEGREN, C. C. (1933). The genetics of *Neurospora*—III. Pure bred stocks and crossing-over in *N. crassa. Bull. Torrey bot. Club,* **60,** 133–154. *(100, 102–5, 263)*

LINDEGREN, C. C. (1953). Gene conversion in *Saccharomyces. J. Genet.,* **51,** 625–637. *(264, 326)*

LISSOUBA, P., MOUSSEAU, J., RIZET, G. and ROSSIGNOL, J. L. (1962). Fine structure of genes in the ascomycete *Ascobolus immersus. Adv. Genet.,* **11,** 343–380. *(267, 284)*

LISSOUBA, P. and RIZET, G. (1960). Sur l'existence d'une génétique polarisée ne subissant que des échanges non réciproques. *C.r. hebd. Séanc. Acad. Sci., Paris,* **250,** 3408–3410. *(266–7, 275, 279, 282, 284, 330)*

LITMAN, R. M. and PARDEE, A. B. (1956). Production of bacteriophage mutants by a disturbance of deoxyribonucleic acid metabolism. *Nature, Lond.,* **178,** 529–531. *(228)*

LONGLEY, A. E. (1945). Abnormal segregation during megasporogenesis in maize. *Genetics, Princeton,* **30,** 100–113. *(296)*

LONGUET-HIGGINS, H. C. and ZIMM, B. H. (1960). Calculation of the rate of uncoiling of the DNA molecule. *J. molec. Biol.,* **2,** 1–4. *(200)*

LOPER, J. C. (1961). Enzyme complementation in mixed extracts of mutants from the *Salmonella* histidine B locus. *Proc. natn. Acad. Sci. U.S.A.,* **47,** 1440–1450. *(220)*

LYON, M. F. (1961). Gene action in the X-chromosome of the mouse (*Mus musculus* L.) *Nature, Lond.,* **190,** 372–373. *(310–1)*

LYON, M. F. (1962). Sex chromatin and gene action in the mammalian X-chromosome. *Am. J. hum. Genet.,* **14,** 135–148. *(310–1)*

McCLINTOCK, B. (1931). Cytological observations of deficiencies involving known genes, translocations and an inversion in *Zea mays. Res. Bull. Mo. agric. Exp. Stn,* **163,** 1–30. *(121)*

McCLINTOCK, B. (1933). The association of non-homologous parts of chromosomes in the mid-prophase of meiosis in *Zea mays. Z. Zellforsch. mikrosk. Anat.,* **19,** 191–237. *(122)*

McCLINTOCK, B. (1944). The relation of homozygous deficiencies to mutations and allelic series in maize. *Genetics, Princeton,* **29,** 478–502. *(156–158)*

McCLINTOCK, B. (1950). The origin and behavior of mutable loci in maize. *Proc. natn. Acad. Sci. U.S.A.,* **36,** 344–355. *(305)*

McCLINTOCK, B. (1952). Chromosome organization and genic expression. *Cold Spring Harb. Symp. quant. Biol.,* **16,** 13–47. *(305)*

McCLINTOCK, B. (1957). Controlling elements and the gene. *Cold Spring Harb. Symp. quant. Biol.,* **21,** 197–216. *(306)*

McCLUNG, C. E. (1900). The spermatocyte divisions of the Acrididae. *Kans. Univ. Q.,* **9,** 73–100. *(325)*

McCLUNG, C. E. (1902). The accessory chromosome—sex determinant? *Biol. Bull. mar. biol. Lab., Woods Hole,* **3,** 43–84. *(69)*

McFALL, E. and MANDELSTAM, J. (1963). Specific metabolic repression of induced enzymes in *Escherichia coli. Nature, Lond.,* **197,** 880–881. *(291)*

MACGREGOR, H. C. and CALLAN, H. G. (1962). The action of enzymes on lampbrush chromosomes. *Q. Jl microsc. Sci.,* **103,** 173–203. *(299)*

MACKENDRICK, M. E. and PONTECORVO, G. (1952). Crossing-over between alleles at the *w* locus in *Drosophila melanogaster*. *Experientia*, **8**, 390–391.   (*206*)

McLEISH, J. (1964). Deoxyribonucleic acid in plant nucleoli. *Nature, Lond.*, **204**, 36–39.   (*310*)

MADISON, J. T. and HOLLEY, R. W. (1965). The presence of 5,6-dihydrouridylic acid in yeast "soluble" ribonucleic acid. *Biochem. biophys. Res. Commun.*, **18**, 153–157.   (*252–3*)

MAEDA, T. (1930). On the configurations of gemini in the pollen mother cells of *Vicia faba* L. *Mem. Coll. Sci. Kyoto Univ. B.*, **5**, 125–137.   (*111*)

MAGNI, G. E. (1963). The origin of spontaneous mutations during meiosis. *Proc. natn. Acad. Sci. U.S.A.*, **50**, 975–980.   (*283*)

MAGNI, G. E. (1964). Origin and nature of spontaneous mutations in meiotic organisms *J. cell. comp. Physiol.*, **64**, suppl. 1, 165–172.   (*283*)

MAGNI, G. E. and VON BORSTEL, R. C. (1962). Different rates of spontaneous mutation during mitosis and meiosis in yeast. *Genetics, Princeton*, **47**, 1097–1108.   (*283*)

MANTON, I. and SLEDGE, W. A. (1955). Observations on the cytology and taxonomy of the pteridophyte flora of Ceylon. *Phil. Trans. R. Soc. B.*, **238**, 127–185.   (*68*)

MARIMUTHU, K. M. and THRELKELD, S. F. H (1964). Tetrad analysis by autoradiography. *Nature, Lond.*, **203**, 101–102.   (*188*)

MARMUR, J. and LANE, D. (1960). Strand separation and specific recombination in deoxyribonucleic acids: biological studies. *Proc. natn. Acad. Sci. U.S.A.*, **46**, 453–461.   (*240, 274*)

MARTIN, R. G. (1964). The one operon—one messenger theory of transcription. *Col Spring Harb. Symp. quant. Biol.*, **28**, 357–361.   (*290*

MATHER, K. (1933a). The relation between chiasmata and crossing-over in diploid and triploid *Drosophila melanogaster*. *J. Genet.*, **27**, 243–259.   (*109–112, 328*)

MATHER, K. (1933b). Interlocking as a demonstration of the occurrence of genetical crossing-over during chiasma formation. *Am. Nat.*, **67**, 476–479.   (*126*)

MATHER, K. (1935). Meiosis in *Lilium*. *Cytologia*, **6**, 354–380.   (*126*)

MATHER, K. (1944). The genetical activity of heterochromatin. *Proc. R. Soc. B.*, **132**, 308–332.   (*296*)

MATHER, K. (1949a). *Biometrical Genetics*. London, Methuen, 162 pp.   (*37*)

MATHER, K. (1949b). Chapter 4 in DARLINGTON, C. D. and MATHER, K. *The Elements of Genetics*, London, Allen and Unwin.   (*39*)

MAZIA, D. (1955). The organization of the mitotic apparatus. *Symp. Soc. exp. Biol.*, **9**, 335–357.   (*61*)

MENDEL, G. (1866). Versuche über Pflanzenhybriden. *Verh. naturf. Ver. Brünn*, **4**, 3–44. (Reprinted in *Flora, Jena*, 1901, **89**, 364–403. English translations entitled 'Experiments in plant-hybridisation' in *Jl R. hort. Soc.*, 1901, **26**, 1–32 and in Bateson (1909), pp. 317–361).   (*2, 4, 6–23, 81, 327, 330*)

MESELSON, M. (1964). On the mechanism of genetic recombination between DNA molecules. *J. molec. Biol.*, **9**, 734–745.   (*272, 277*)

MESELSON, M. (1965). The duplication and recombination of genes. *Proc. 16th int. Congr. Zool.* 1963, New York (in press).   (*274*)

MESELSON, M. and STAHL, F. W. (1958). The replication of DNA in *Escherichia coli*. *Proc. natn. Acad. Sci. U.S.A.*, **44**, 671–682.   (*188–9*)

MESELSON, M. and WEIGLE, J. J. (1961). Chromosome breakage accompanying genetic recombination in bacteriophage. *Proc. natn. Acad. Sci. U.S.A.*, **47**, 857–868. (*272*)

MEYER, G. F. (1961). Fine structure of spermatocyte nuclei of *Drosophila melanogaster*. *Proc. 2nd Eur. Reg. Conf. Electron Microsc.*, pp. 951–954. Delft. *(131)*

MEYER, G. F. (1964). A possible correlation between the submicroscopic structure of meiotic chromosomes and crossing over. *Proc. 3rd Eur. Reg. Conf. Electron Microsc.*, pp. 461–462. Prague. *(131)*

MICHAELIS, P. (1954). Cytoplasmic inheritance in *Epilobium* and its theoretical significance. *Adv. Genet.*, **6,** 287–401. *(54)*

MICHIE, D. and WALLACE, M. E. (1953). Affinity: a new genetic phenomenon in the house mouse. *Nature, Lond.*, **171,** 26–28. *(296)*

MIESCHER, F. (1871). Ueber die chemische Zusammensetzung der Eiterzellen. In HOPPE-SEYLER, F., *Medicinisch-chemische Untersuchungen*, pp. 441–460, Berlin, August Hirschwald. *(167)*

MIESCHER, F. (1897). In VOGEL F. C. W., *Die histochemischen und physiologischen Arbeiten von Friedrich Miescher*. Leipzig. *(167)*

MIRSKY, A. E. and RIS, H. (1949). Variable and constant components of chromosomes. *Nature, Lond.*, **163,** 666–667. *(172)*

MITCHELL, H. K. and LEIN, J. (1948). A *Neurospora* mutant deficient in the enzymatic synthesis of tryptophan. *J. biol. Chem.*, **175,** 481–482. *(163)*

MITCHELL, M. B. (1955). Aberrant recombination of pyridoxine mutants of *Neurospora*. *Proc. natn. Acad. Sci. U.S.A.*, **41,** 215–220. *(264)*

MITCHELL, M. B. (1956). A consideration of aberrant recombination in *Neurospora*. *C.r. Trav. Lab. Carlsberg, Ser. Physiol.*, **26,** 285–298. *(268)*

MONESI, V. (1962). Autoradiographic study of DNA synthesis and the cell cycle in spermatogonia and spermatocytes of mouse testis using tritiated thymidine. *J. Cell Biol.*, **14,** 1–18. *(173)*

MONOD, J. and JACOB, F. (1962). General conclusions: teleonomic mechanisms in cellular metabolism, growth, and differentiation. *Cold Spring Harb. Symp. quant. Biol.*, **26,** 389–401. *(295, 307–8, 314, 330)*

MONTGOMERY, T. H. (1901). A study of the chromosomes of the germ cells of Metazoa. *Trans. Am. phil. Soc.*, **20,** 154–236. *(66)*

MONTGOMERY, T. H. (1906). The terminology of aberrant chromosomes and their behavior in certain Hemiptera. *Science, N.Y.*, **23,** 36–38. *(324)*

MORGAN, T. H. (1910). Sex limited inheritance in *Drosophila*. *Science, N.Y.*, **32,** 120–122. *(22, 72, 73)*

MORGAN, T. H. (1911a). The application of the conception of pure lines to sex-limited inheritance and to sexual dimorphism. *Am. Nat.*, **45,** 65–78. *(71–73, 78, 95)*

MORGAN, T. H. (1911b). An attempt to analyze the constitution of the chromosomes on the basis of sex-limited inheritance in *Drosophila*. *J. exp. Zool*, **11,** 365–414. *(78, 81–82, 107, 133)*

MORGAN, T. H. (1912). Further experiments with mutations in eye-color of *Drosophila*: the loss of the orange factor. *J. Acad. nat. Sci. Philad.*, **15,** 321–346. *(133)*

MORGAN, T. H. (1919). *The Physical Basis of Heredity*. Philadelphia, J. B. Lippincott, 305 pp. *(22, 81, 82, 108, 112)*

MORGAN, T. H. (1926). *The Theory of the Gene*. New Haven, Yale Univ. Press, 343 pp. *(106)*

MORGAN, T. H. and CATTELL, E. (1912). Data for the study of sex-linked inheritance in *Drosophila*. *J. exp. Zool.*, **13**, 79–101.   *(81, 326)*

MORGAN, T. H., STURTEVANT, A. H., MULLER, H. J. and BRIDGES, C. B. (1915). The *Mechanism of Mendelian Heredity*. New York, Henry Holt, 262 pp. *(112, 130, 134)*

MOSES, M. J. (1956). Chromosomal structures in crayfish spermatocytes. *J. biophys. biochem. Cytol.*, **2**, 215–217.   *(131)*

MOSES, M. J. and COLEMAN, J. R. (1964). Structural patterns and the functional organization of chromosomes. In *The role of chromosomes in development* edited by M. LOCKE, New York, Academic Press, pp. 11–49.   *(131, 301)*

MULLER, H. J. (1916). The mechanism of crossing-over. *Am. Nat.*, **50**, 193–221, 284–305, 350–366, 421–434.   *(85, 95, 107, 127, 268, 328)*

MULLER, H. J. (1927). Artificial transmutation of the gene. *Science, N.Y.*, **66**, 84–87.   *(138, 142)*

MULLER, H. J. (1928a). The measurement of gene mutation rate in *Drosophila*, its high variability, and its dependence upon temperature. *Genetics, Princeton*, **13**, 279–357.   *(136)*

MULLER, H. J. (1928b). The problem of genic modification. *Z. VererbLehre*, Suppl. 1, 234–260.   *(138)*

MULLER, H. J. (1930a). Types of visible variations induced by X-rays in *Drosophila*. *J. Genet.*, **22**, 299–334.   *(303–4)*

MULLER, H. J. (1930b). Radiation and genetics. *Am. Nat.*, **64**, 220–251.   *(140)*

MULLER, H. J. and ALTENBURG, E. (1930). The frequency of translocations produced by X-rays in *Drosophila*. *Genetics, Princeton*, **15**, 283–311.   *(142)*

MULLER, H. J. and PAINTER, T. S. (1929). The cytological expression of changes in gene alignment produced by X-rays in *Drosophila*. *Am. Nat.*, **63**, 193–200. *(142)*

MULLER, H. J., PROKOFYEVA, A. A. and KOSSIKOV, K. V. (1936). Unequal crossing-over in the bar mutant as a result of duplication of a minute chromosome section. *C.r. Acad. Sci. U.R.S.S.*, **2**, 78.   *(154)*

MÜNTZING, A. (1959). A new category of chromosomes, *Proc. 10th int. Congr. Genet.*, **1**, 453–467. Univ. Toronto Press.   *(296)*

MURRAY, N. E. (1963). Polarized recombination and fine structure within the *me-2* gene of *Neurospora crassa*. *Genetics, Princeton*, **48**, 1163–1183.   *(267, 284)*

NASS, M. K. K. and NASS, S. (1963). Intramitochondrial fibers with DNA characteristics. *J. Cell Biol.*, **19**, 593–629.   *(313)*

NEEL, J. V. (1949). Inheritance of sickle cell anemia. *Science, N.Y.*, **110**, 64–66.   *(211, 218)*

NEWTON, W. C. F. and DARLINGTON, C. D. (1929). Meiosis in polyploids. Part I. Triploid and pentaploid tulips. *J. Genet.*, **21**, 1–15.   *(120, 325)*

NILSSON-EHLE, H. (1909). Kreuzungsuntersuchungen an Hafer und Weizen. *Acta Univ. lund.*, ser 2, **5**, no. 2, 1–122.   *(33)*

NIRENBERG, M. W. and LEDER, P. (1964). RNA codewords and protein synthesis. *Science, N.Y.*, **145**, 1399–1407.   *(262)*

NIRENBERG, M. W., LEDER, P., BERNFIELD, M. R., BRIMACOMBE, R. L. C., TRUPIN, J. S., ROTTMAN, F. M., and O'NEAL, C. (1965). RNA codewords and protein synthesis, VII. On the general nature of the RNA code. *Proc. natn. Acad. Sci. U.S.A.*, **53**, 1161–1168.   *(262)*

NIRENBERG, M. W. and MATTHAEI, J. H. (1961). The dependence of cell-free protein synthesis in *E. coli* upon naturally occurring or synthetic polyribonucleotides. *Proc. natn. Acad. Sci. U.S.A.*, **47**, 1588–1602.   *(242, 255, 311)*

NODA, S. (1960). Chiasma studies in structural hybrids. II. Reciprocal translocation in *Lilium maximowiczii. Cytologia*, **25**, 456–460. (*119*)

NODA, S. (1961). Chiasma studies in structural hybrids. VII. Reciprocal translocation in *Scilla scilloides. Cytologia*, **26**, 74–77. (*117, 119*)

NUFFER, M. G. (1955). Dosage effect of multiple *Dt* loci on mutation of *a* in the maize endosperm. *Science, N.Y.*, **121**, 399–400. (*305*)

NUR, U. (1961). Meiotic behavior of an unequal bivalent in the grasshopper *Calliptamus palaestinensis* Bdhr. *Chromosoma*, **12**, 272–279. (*115–7*)

OEHLKERS, F. (1943). Die Auslösung von Chromosomenmutationen in der Meiosis durch Einwirkung von Chemikalien. *Z. VererbLehre*, **81**, 313–341. (*144*)

OLIVE, L. S. (1959). Aberrant tetrads in *Sordaria fimicola. Proc. natn. Acad. Sci. U.S.A.*, **45**, 727–732. (*264*)

OLIVER, C. P. (1940). A reversion to wild-type associated with crossing-over in *Drosophila melanogaster. Proc. natn. Acad. Sci. U.S.A.*, **26**, 452–454. (*155, 158*)

PAINTER, T. S. (1934). A new method for the study of chromosome aberrations and the plotting of chromosome maps in *Drosophila melanogaster. Genetics, Princeton*, **19**, 175–188. (*142–3*)

PALADE, G. E. (1955). A small particulate component of the cytoplasm. *J. biophys. biochem. Cytol.*, **1**, 59–68. (*238*)

PARDEE, A. B., JACOB, F. and MONOD, J. (1959). The genetic control and cytoplasmic expression of inducibility in the synthesis of β-galactosidase by *E. coli. J. molec. Biol.*, **1**, 165–178. (*289*)

PARNELL, F. R. (1921). Note on the detection of segregation by examination of the pollen of rice. *J. Genet.*, **11**, 209–212. (*45, 46*)

PASCHER, A. (1918). Ueber die Beziehung der Reduktionsteilung zur Mendelschen Spaltung. *Ber. dt. bot. Ges.*, **36**, 163–168. (*100*)

PASZEWSKI, A. and SURZYCKI, S. (1964). 'Selfers' and high mutation rate during meiosis in *Ascobolus immersus. Nature, Lond.*, **204**, 809. (*283*)

PATEMAN, J. A., COVE, D. J., REVER, B. M. and ROBERTS, D. B. (1964). A common co-factor for nitrate reductase and xanthine dehydrogenase which also regulates the synthesis of nitrate reductase. *Nature, Lond.*, **201**, 58–60. (*294, 308*)

PATEMAN, J. A. and FINCHAM, J. R. S. (1958). Gene-enzyme relationships at the *am* locus in *Neurospora crassa. Heredity*, **12**, 317–332. (*215, 216*)

PAULING, L., ITANO, H. A., SINGER, S. J. and WELLS, I. C. (1949). Sickle cell anemia, a molecular disease. *Science, N.Y.*, **110**, 543–548. (*212*)

PEACOCK, W. J. (1963). Chromosome duplication and structure as determined by autoradiography. *Proc. natn. Acad. Sci. U.S.A.*, **49**, 793–801. (*188*)

PEARSON, K. (1897). Mathematical contributions to the theory of evolution. III. Regression, heredity and panmixia. *Phil. Trans. R. Soc. A.*, **187**, 253–318. (*31*)

PEARSON, K. (1900). On the criterion that a given system of deviations from the probable in the case of a correlated system of variables is such that it can be reasonably supposed to have arisen from random sampling. *Phil. Mag.*, Ser. V, **50**, 157–175. (*26*)

PEARSON, K. (1904). Mathematical contributions to the theory of evolution. XII. On a generalised theory of alternative inheritance, with special reference to Mendel's laws. *Phil. Trans. R. Soc. A.*, **203**, 53–86. (*31*)

PEARSON, K. and LEE A. (1903) On the laws of inheritance in man. I. Inheritance of physical characters. *Biometrika*, **2**, 357–462.   *(31, 36)*

PENROSE, L. S. (1963). *The Biology of Mental Defect*, 3rd edn. London, Sidgwick and Jackson.   *(31)*

PONTECORVO, G. (1947). Genetic systems based on heterocaryosis. *Cold Spring Harb. Symp. quant. Biol.*, **11**, 193–201.   *(46)*

PONTECORVO, G. (1950). New fields in the biochemical genetics of microorganisms. *Biochem. Soc. Symp.*, **4**, 40–50.   *(206, 325, 331)*

PONTECORVO, G. (1952a). Genetical analysis of cell organization. *Symp. Soc. exp. Biol.*, **6**, 218–229.   *(166)*

PONTECORVO, G. (1952b). The genetic formulation of gene structure and action. *Adv. Enzymol.*, **13**, 121–149.   *(204)*

PONTECORVO, G. (1958). *Trends in Genetic Analysis*. New York, Columbia Univ. Press.   *(280)*

PONTECORVO, G. and GEMMELL, A. R. (1944). Genetic proof of heterokaryosis in *Penicillium notatum*. *Nature, Lond.*, **154**, 514–515.   *(47)*

PRESCOTT, D. M. and BENDER, M. A. (1963). Autoradiographic study of chromatid distribution of labeled DNA in two types of mammalian cells *in vitro*. *Expl Cell Res.*, **29**, 430–442.   *(188)*

PRINGSHEIM, E. G. and PRINGSHEIM, O. (1952). Experimental elimination of chromatophores and eye-spot in *Euglena gracilis*. *New Phytol.*, **51**, 65–76.   *(56*

PRITCHARD, R. H. (1955). The linear arrangement of a series of alleles of *Aspergillus nidulans*. *Heredity*, **9**, 343–371.   *(204, 263, 267–8, 272–3)*

PROVASOLI, L., HUTNER, S. H. and SCHATZ, A. (1948). Streptomycin-induced chlorophyll-less races of *Euglena*. *Proc. Soc. exp. Biol. Med.*, **69**, 279–282.   *(56)*

PUNNETT, R. C. (1917). Reduplication series in sweet peas. II. *J. Genet.*, **6**, 185–193.   *(19)*

PUNNETT, R. C. and BATESON, W. (1908). The heredity of sex. *Science, N.Y.*, **27**, 785–787.   *(20–2, 71, 331)*

RACE, R. R. (1944). An 'incomplete' antibody in human serum. *Nature, Lond.*, **153**, 771–772.   *(157)*

RACE, R. R. and SANGER, R. (1962). *Blood Groups in Man*, 4th edn. Oxford, Blackwell.   *(135, 157)*

RAFFEL, D. and MULLER, H. J. (1940). Position effect and gene divisibility considered in connection with three strikingly similar scute mutations. *Genetics, Princeton*, **25**, 541–583.   *(152, 155)*

RANDOLPH, L. F. (1928). Types of supernumerary chromosomes in maize. *Anat. Rec.*, **41**, 102.   *(325)*

RAPOPORT, J. A. (1946). Carbonyl compounds and the chemical mechanism of mutation. *C.r. Acad. Sci. U.R.S.S.*, **54**, 65.   *(141)*

RASMUSSEN, R. E. and PAINTER, R. B. (1964). Evidence for repair of ultra-violet damaged deoxyribonucleic acid in cultured mammalian cells. *Nature, Lond.*, **203**, 1360–1362.   *(278)*

REICH, E., FRANKLIN, R. M., SHATKIN, A. J. and TATUM, E. L. (1962). Action of actinomycin D on animal cells and viruses. *Proc. natn. Acad. Sci. U.S.A.*, **48**, 1238–1245.   *(312)*

RENNER, O. (1924). Die Scheckung der Oenotherenbastarde. *Biol. Zbl.*, **44**, 309–336.   *(52, 54)*

REVELL, S. H. (1955). A new hypothesis for 'chromatid' changes. In *Radiobiology Symposium* 1954 (eds. BACQ, Z. M. and ALEXANDER, P.) pp. 243–253. London, Butterworth. *(146–151)*

REVELL, S. H. (1959). The accurate estimation of chromatid breakage, and its relevance to a new interpretation of chromatid aberrations induced by ionizing radiations. *Proc. R. Soc. B.*, **150**, 563–589. *(149–151)*

RHOADES, M. M. (1936). The effect of varying gene dosage on aleurone colour in maize. *J. Genet.*, **33**, 347–354. *(302,309)*

RHOADES, M. M. (1938). Effect of the *Dt* gene on the mutability of the a_1 allele in maize. *Genetics, Princeton*, **23**, 377–397. *(302)*

RHOADES, M. M. (1942). Preferential segregation in maize. *Genetics, Princeton*, **27**, 395–407. *(296)*

RHOADES, M. M. (1943). Genic induction of an inherited cytoplasmic difference. *Proc. natn. Acad. Sci. U.S.A.*, **29**, 327–329. *(50–1)*

RHOADES, M. M. (1945). On the genetic control of mutability in maize. *Proc. natn. Acad. Sci. U.S.A.*, **31**, 91–95. *(303)*

RHOADES, M. M. (1947). Plastid mutations. *Cold Spring Harb. Symp. quant. Biol.*, **11**, 202–207. *(53)*

RHOADES, M. M. (1950). Meiosis in maize. *J. Hered.*, **41**, 58–67. *(112–3)*

RICHARDSON, C. C., INMAN, R. B. and KORNBERG, A. (1964). Enzymic synthesis of deoxyribonucleic acid. XVIII. The repair of partially single-stranded DNA templates by DNA polymerase. *J. molec. Biol.*, **9**, 46–69. *(278)*

RICHARDSON, C. C., SCHILDKRAUT, C. L. and KORNBERG, A. (1964). Studies on the replication of DNA by DNA polymerases. *Cold Spring Harb. Symp. quant. Biol.*, **28**, 9–19. *(192, 194, 278)*

RILEY, R. and CHAPMAN, V. (1958). Genetic control of the cytologically diploid behaviour of hexaploid wheat. *Nature, Lond.*, **182**, 713–715. *(64)*

RIS, H. (1949). The anaphase movement of chromosomes in the spermatocytes of the grasshopper. *Biol. Bull. mar. biol. Lab.*, *Woods Hole*, **96**, 90–106. *(61)*

RIS, H. (1957). Chromosome structure. In *The Chemical Basis of Heredity* edited by W. D. McELROY and B. GLASS, Baltimore, Johns Hopkins Press, pp. 23–69. *(296–7)*

RIS, H. and MIRSKY, A. E. (1949). Quantitative cytochemical determination of desoxyribonucleic acid with the Feulgen nucleal reaction. *J. gen. Physiol.*, **33**, 125–146. *(172)*

RITOSSA, F. M. and SPIEGELMAN, S. (1965). Localization of DNA complementary to ribosomal RNA in the nucleolus organizer region of *Drosophila melanogaster*. *Proc. natn. Acad. Sci. U.S.A.*, **53**, 737–745. *(310)*

ROBERTS, R. B. (1958). In introduction to *Microsomal Particles and Protein Synthesis*, edited by R. B. ROBERTS, Washington, Pergamon Press, 168 pp. *(238, 331)*

ROPER, J. A. (1950). Search for linkage between genes determining a vitamin requirement. *Nature, Lond.*, **166**, 956. *(204, 207)*

ROPER, J. A. (1953). Pseudo-allelism. In PONTECORVO G., The genetics of *Aspergillus nidulans*. *Adv. Genet.*, **5**, 208–218. *(204)*

ROPER, J. A. and PRITCHARD, R. H. (1955). Recovery of the complementary products of mitotic crossing-over. *Nature, Lond.*, **175**, 639. *(205)*

RUPERT, C. S. (1960). Photoreactivation of transforming DNA by an enzyme from bakers' yeast. *J. gen. Physiol.*, **43**, 573–595. *(277)*

RUPERT, C. S., GOODGAL, S. H. and HERRIOTT, R. M. (1958). Photoreactivation in vitro of ultraviolet inactivated *Hemophilus influenzae* transforming factor. *J. gen. Physiol.*, **41**, 451–471.   (*277*)

RUSSELL, L. B. and CHU, E. H. Y. (1961). An XXY male in the mouse. *Proc. natn. Acad. Sci. U.S.A.*, **47**, 571–575.   (*76*)

SAGER, R. (1962). Streptomycin as a mutagen for nonchromosomal genes. *Proc. natn. Acad. Sci. U.S.A.*, **48**, 2018–2026.   (*56*)

SAGER, R. and ISHIDA, M. R. (1963). Chloroplast DNA in *Chlamydomonas*. *Proc. natn. Acad. Sci. U.S.A.*, **50**, 725–730.   (*313*)

SAGER, R. and RAMANIS, Z. (1963). The particulate nature of nonchromosomal genes in *Chlamydomonas*. *Proc. natn. Acad. Sci. U.S.A.*, **50**, 260–268.   (*56*)

ST. LAWRENCE, P. (1956). The *q* locus of *Neurospora crassa*. *Proc. natn. Acad. Sci. U.S.A.*, **42**, 189–194.   (*268*)

SARABHAI, A. S., STRETTON, A. O. W., BRENNER, S. and BOLLE, A. (1964). Co-linearity of the gene with the polypeptide chain. *Nature, Lond.*, **201**, 13–17.   (*222–4*)

SAX, K. (1930). Chromosome structure and the mechanism of crossing-over. *J. Arnold Arbor.*, **11**, 193–220.   (*130*)

SAX, K. (1936). Chromosome coiling in relation to meiosis and crossing-over. *Genetics, Princeton*, **21**, 324–338.   (*130*)

SCHLESINGER, M. J. and LEVINTHAL, C. (1963). Hybrid protein formation of *E. coli* alkaline phosphatase leading to *in vitro* complementation. *J. molec. Biol.*, **7**, 1–12.   (*217*)

SCHMID, W. (1963). DNA replication patterns of human chromosomes. *Cytogenetics*, **2**, 175–193.   (*201, 296*)

SCHRADER, F. and HUGHES-SCHRADER, S. (1956). Polyploidy and fragmentation in the chromosomal evolution of various species of *Thyanta* (Hemiptera). *Chromosoma*, **7**, 469–496.   (*297*)

SCHULTZ, J. (1936). Variegation in *Drosophila* and the inert chromosome regions. *Proc. natn. Acad. Sci. U.S.A.*, **22**, 27–33.   (*305*)

SCHULTZ, J. (1948). The nature of heterochromatin. *Cold Spring Harb. Symp. quant. Biol.*, **12**, 179–191.   (*305, 308*)

SCOTT-MONCRIEFF, R. (1936). A biochemical survey of some mendelian factors for flower colour. *J. Genet.*, **32**, 117–170.   (*160*)

SEARS, E. R. and OKAMOTO, M. (1958). Intergenomic chromosome relationships in hexaploid wheat. *Proc. 10th int. Congr. Genet.*, **2**, 258–259. Univ. Toronto Press.   (*64*)

SETLOW, R. B. and CARRIER, W. L. (1964). The disappearance of thymine dimers from DNA: an error-correcting mechanism. *Proc. natn. Acad. Sci. U.S.A.*, **51**, 226–231.   (*277, 282*)

SHULT, E. E. and LINDEGREN, C. C. (1958). Orthoorientation: a new tool for genetical analysis. *Genetica*, **29**, 58–82.   (*296*)

SIDDIQI, O. H. (1962). The fine genetic structure of the *paba*-1 region of *Aspergillus nidulans*. *Genet. Res.*, **3**, 69–89.   (*267*)

SINSHEIMER, R. L. (1959). A single-stranded deoxyribonucleic acid from bacteriophage ϕX174. *J. molec. Biol.*, **1**, 43–53.   (*241*)

SLAYTER, H. S., WARNER, J. R., RICH, A. and HALL, C. E. (1963). The visualization of polyribosomal structure. *J. molec. Biol.*, **7**, 652–657.   (*253–4*)

SLIZYNSKA, H. and SLIZYNSKI, B. M. (1947). Genetical and cytological studies of lethals induced by chemical treatment in *Drosophila melanogaster*. *Proc. R. Soc. Edinb. B*, **62**, 234–242. *(144)*

SLIZYNSKI, B. M. (1964). Chiasmata in spermatocytes of *Drosophila melanogaster*. *Genet. Res.*, **5**, 80–84. *(130)*

SMITH, D. W. E. and AMES, B. N. (1964). Intermediates in the early steps of histidine biosynthesis. *J. biol. Chem.*, **239**, 1848–1855. *(289)*

SMITH, S. G. (1935). Chromosome fragmentation produced by crossing-over in *Trillium erectum* L. *J. Genet.*, **30**, 227–232. *(122)*

SNEDECOR, G. W. (1956). *Statistical Methods*, 5th edn. Ames, Iowa State Univ. Press. *(23)*

SNYDER, L. H. (1931). Inherited taste deficiency. *Science, N.Y.*, **74**, 151–152. *(13)*

SOKOLOFF, L., FRANCIS, C. M. and CAMPBELL, P. L. (1964). Thyroxine stimulation of amino acid incorporation into protein independent of any action on messenger RNA synthesis. *Proc. natn. Acad. Sci. U.S.A.*, **52**, 728–736. *(312)*

SPENCER, M., FULLER, W., WILKINS, M. H. F. and BROWN, G. L. (1962). Determination of the helical configuration of ribonucleic acid molecules by X-ray diffraction study of crystalline amino-acid—transfer ribonucleic acid. *Nature, Lond.*, **194**, 1014–1020. *(249–252)*

SPENCER, T. and HARRIS, H. (1964). Regulation of enzyme synthesis in an enucleate cell. *Biochem. J.*, **91**, 282–286. *(312, 313)*

SPURWAY, H. (1948). Genetics and cytology of *Drosophila subobscura*. IV. An extreme example of delay in gene action, causing sterility. *J. Genet.*, **49**, 126–140. *(49)*

SRB, A. M. and HOROWITZ, N. H. (1944). The ornithine cycle in *Neurospora* and its genetic control. *J. biol. Chem.*, **154**, 129–139. *(161–162)*

STADLER, D. R. (1956). A map of linkage group VI of *Neurospora crassa*. *Genetics, Princeton*, **41**, 528–543. *(294)*

STADLER, D. R. and TOWE, A. M. (1963). Recombination of allelic cysteine mutants in *Neurospora*. *Genetics, Princeton*, **48**, 1323–1344. *(266, 267, 274)*

STADLER, L. J. (1926). The variability of crossing-over in maize. *Genetics, Princeton*, **11**, 1–37. *(85–86, 108)*

STADLER, L. J. (1928). Mutations in barley induced by X-rays and radium. *Science, N.Y.*, **68**, 186–187. *(140)*

STADLER, L. J. (1930). Some genetic effects of X-rays in plants. *J. Hered.*, **21**, 3–19. *(140)*

STAEHELIN, T., WETTSTEIN, F. O., OURA, H. and NOLL, H. (1964). Determination of the coding ratio based on molecular weight of messenger ribonucleic acid associated with ergosomes of different aggregate size. *Nature, Lond.*, **201**, 264–270. *(253)*

STANIER, R. Y. (1964). Towards a definition of the bacteria. In *The Bacteria*, edited by I. C. GUNSALUS and R. Y. STANIER. New York, Academic Press, vol. 5, pp. 445–464. *(317)*

STERN, C. (1931). Zytologisch-genetische Untersuchungen als Beweise für die Morgansche Theorie des Faktorenaustauschs. *Biol. Zbl.*, **51**, 547–587. *(88–90)*

STERN, C. (1936). Somatic crossing over and segregation in *Drosophila melanogaster*. *Genetics, Princeton*, **21**, 625–730. *(205)*

24

STEVENS, N. M. (1905). Studies in spermatogenesis with especial reference to the 'accessory chromosome.' *Publs Carnegie Instn*, **36**, 1–32.   (*71*)

STEVENS, N. M. (1908). A study of the germ-cells of certain Diptera, with reference to the heterochromosomes and the phenomena of synapsis. *J. exp. Zool.*, **5**, 359–374.   (*71*)

STEVENS, W. L. (1936). The analysis of interference. *J. Genet.*, **32**, 51–64.   (*108–9*)

STRASBURGER, E. (1879). *Die Angiopermen und die Gymnospermen*. Jena, Gustav Fischer, 173 pp.   (*40*)

STRASBURGER. E. (1882). Ueber den Theilungsvorgang der Zellkerne und das Verhältniss der Kerntheilung zur Zelltheilung. *Arch. mikrosk. Anat.*, **21**, 476–590.   (*58*)

STRASBURGER, E. (1884). Die Controversen der indirecten Kerntheilung. *Arch. mikrosk. Anat.*, **23**, 246–304.   (*58, 324, 329, 330*)

STRASBURGER, E. (1888). *Ueber Kern- und Zelltheilung im Pfanzenreiche, nebst einem Anhang über Befruchtung*. Histologische Beiträge, Heft I, Jena, Gustav Fischer, 258 pp.   (*62*)

STRASBURGER, E. (1905). Typische und allotypische Kernteilung. Ergebnisse und Erörterungen. *Jb. wiss. Bot.*, **42**, 1–71.   (*327, 328*)

STRICKLAND, W. N. (1958). An analysis of interference in *Aspergillus nidulans*. *Proc. R. Soc. B.*, **149**, 82–101.   (*111*)

STURTEVANT, A. H. (1913). The linear arrangement of six sex-linked factors in *Drosophila*, as shown by their mode of association. *J. exp. Zool.*, **14**, 43–59.   (*81, 104, 203*)

STURTEVANT, A. H. (1923). Inheritance of direction of coiling in *Limnaea*. *Science, N.Y.*, **58**, 269–270.   (*48*)

STURTEVANT, A. H. (1925). The effects of unequal crossing over at the Bar locus in *Drosophila*. *Genetics, Princeton*, **10**, 117–147.   (*153–5*)

STURTEVANT, A. H. (1926). A cross-over reducer in *Drosophila melanogaster* due to inversion of a section of the third chromosome. *Biol. Zbl.*, **46**, 697–702.   (*328*)

STURTEVANT, A. H. and MORGAN, T. H. (1923). Reverse mutation of the bar gene correlated with crossing over. *Science, N.Y.*, **57**, 746–747.   (*153*)

SUEOKA, N. (1960). Mitotic replication of deoxyribonucleic acid in *Chlamydomonas reinhardi*. *Proc. natn. Acad. Sci. U.S.A.*, **46**, 83–91.   (*189*)

SUEOKA, N. (1961a). Variation and heterogeneity of base composition of deoxyribonucleic acids: a compilation of old and new data. *J. molec. Biol.*, **3**, 31–40.   (*258–259*)

SUEOKA, N. (1961b). Correlation between base composition of deoxyribonucleic acid and amino acid composition of protein. *Proc. natn. Acad. Sci. U.S.A.*, **47**, 1141–1149.   (*258*)

SUTTON, W. S. (1902). On the morphology of the chromosome group in *Brachystola magna*. *Biol. Bull. mar. biol. Lab., Woods Hole*, **4**, 24–39.   (*66*)

SUTTON, W. S. (1903). The chromosomes in heredity. *Biol. Bull. mar. biol. Lab., Woods Hole*, **4**, 231–248.   (*68,77*)

SWARTZ, M. N., TRAUTNER, T. A. and KORNBERG, A. (1962). Enzymatic synthesis of deoxyribonucleic acid. XI. Further studies on nearest neighbor base sequences in deoxyribonucleic acids. *J. biol. Chem.*, **237**, 1961–1967.   (*195–6*)

SWIFT, H. H. (1950). The desoxyribose nucleic acid content of animal nuclei. *Physiol. Zoöl.*, **23**, 169–198.   (*172*)

TATUM, E. L. (1964). Genetic determinants. *Proc. natn. Acad. Sci. U.S.A.*, **51**, 908–915. (*257*)

TATUM, E. L., BONNER, D. and BEADLE, G. W. (1944). Anthrilic acid and the biosynthesis of indole and tryptophan by *Neurodpora. Archs Biochem.*, **3**, 477–478. (*163*)

TAYLOR, J. H. (1953). Autoradiographic detection of incorporation of P³² into chromosomes during meiosis and mitosis. *Expl Cell Res.*, **4**, 164–173. (*172*)

TAYLOR, J. H. (1958). Sister chromatid exchanges in tritium-labeled chromosomes. *Genetics, Princeton*, **43**, 515–529. (*185*)

TAYLOR, J. H. (1959a). The organization and duplication of genetic material. *Proc. 10th int. Congr. Genet.* **1**, 63–78. Univ. Toronto Press. (*185, 299, 300*)

TAYLOR, J. H. (1959b). Autoradiographic studies of nucleic acids and proteins during meiosis in *Lilium longiflorum. Am. J. Bot.*, **46**, 477–484. (*173*)

TAYLOR, J. H. (1965). Distribution of tritium-labeled DNA among chromosomes during meiosis. I. Spermatogenesis in the grasshopper. *J. Cell Biol.* **25**, (2), 57–67. (*188*)

TAYLOR, J. H. and TAYLOR, S. H. (1953). The autoradiograph—a tool for cytogeneticists. *J. Hered.*, **44**, 128–132. (*173*)

TAYLOR, J. H. WOODS, P. S. and HUGHES, W. L. (1957). The organization and duplication of chromosomes as revealed by autoradiographic studies using tritium-labeled thymidine. *Proc. natn. Acad. Sci. U.S.A.*, **43**, 122–128. (*181–4, 202*)

TEAS, H. J., HOROWITZ, N. H. and FLING, M. (1948). Homoserine as a precursor of threonine and methionine in *Neurospora. J. biol. Chem.*, **172**, 651–658. (*164*)

THODAY, J. M. and READ, J. (1947). Effect of oxygen on the frequency of chromosome aberrations produced by X-rays. *Nature, Lond.*, **160**, 608. (*144*)

THOMAS, C. A. (1956). The enzymatic degradation of desoxyribose nucleic acid. *J. Am. chem. Soc.*, **78**, 1861–1868. (*299*)

THOMAS, C. A. and MAC HATTIE, L. A. (1964). Circular T2 DNA molecules. *Proc. natn. Acad. Sci. U.S.A.*, **52**, 1297–1301. (*200*)

TIMOFÉÉFF-RESSOVSKY, N. W. (1934). The experimental production of mutations. *Biol. Rev.*, **9**, 411–457. (*139*)

TJIO, J. H. and LEVAN, A. (1956). The chromosome number of man. *Hereditas*, **42**, 1–6. (*68*)

TSCHERMAK, E. VON. (1900). Über künstliche Kreuzung bei *Pisum sativum. Ber. dt. bot. Ges.*, **18**, 232–239. (English translation, entitled 'Concerning artificial crossing in *Pisum sativum*' in *Genetics, Princeton*, 1950, **35**, suppl. pp. 42–47.) (*9*)

TSUGITA, A. (1962). The proteins of mutants of TMV: classification of spontaneous and chemically evoked strains. *J. molec. Biol.*, **5**, 293–300. (*236*)

TSUGITA, A. and FRAENKEL-CONRAT, H. (1962). The composition of proteins of chemically evoked mutants of TMV RNA. *J. molec. Biol.*, **4**, 73–82. (*259*)

UMBARGER, H. E. (1962). Feedback control by endproduct inhibition. *Cold Spring Harb. Symp. quant. Biol.*, **26**, 301–312. (*307*)

VENDRELY, R. and VENDRELY, C. (1948). La teneur du noyau cellulaire en acide désoxyribonucleique à travers les organes, les individus et les espèces animales. *Experientia*, **4**, 434–436. (*171*)

VISCHER, E., ZAMENHOF, F. and CHARGAFF, E. (1949). Microbial nucleic acids: the desoxypentose nucleic acids of avian tubercle bacilli and yeast. *J. biol. Chem.*, **177**, 429–438. (*173*)

VOLKIN, E. and ASTRACHAN, L. (1957). RNA metabolism in T2-infected *Escherichia coli*. In *The Chemical Basis of Heredity* edited by W. D. MC ELROY and B. GLASS, Baltimore, Johns Hopkins Press, pp. 686–695. *(239, 242)*

WACKER, A., DELLWEG, H. and WEINBLUM, D. (1960). Stahlenchemische Veränderung der Bakterien-Desoxyribonucleinsäure in vivo. *Naturwissenschaften*, **47**, 477. *(277)*

WAGNER, R. P., RADHAKRISHNAN, A. N. and SNELL, E. E. (1958). The biosynthesis of isoleucine and valine in *Neurospora crassa*. *Proc. natn. Acad. Sci. U.S.A.*, **44**, 1047–1053. *(165)*

WAHBA, A. J., MILLER, R. S., BASILIO, C., GARDNER, R. S., LENGYEL, P. and SPEYER, J. F. (1963). Synthetic polynucleotides and the amino acid code, IX. *Proc. natn. Acad. Sci. U.S.A.*, **49**, 880–885. *(256–7)*

WALDEYER, W. (1888). Ueber Karyokinese und ihre Beziehung zu den Befruchtungsvorgängen. *Arch. mikrosk. Anat.*, **32**, 1–122. (English translation entitled 'Karyokinesis and its relation to the process of fertilization' in *Q. Jl microsc. Sci.*, 1889, **30**, 159–281.) *(58, 325)*

WALKER, P. M. B. and YATES, H. B. (1952). Nuclear components of dividing cells. *Proc. R. Soc. B.*, **140**, 274–299. *(172)*

WATSON, J. D. and CRICK, F. H. C. (1953a). A structure for deoxyribose nucleic acid. *Nature, Lond.*, **171**, 737–738. *(174, 177, 194)*

WATSON, J. D. and CRICK, F. H. C. (1953b). Genetical implications of the structure of deoxyribonucleic acid. *Nature, Lond.*, **171**, 964–967. *(180–203, 228, 300, 331)*

WATSON, J. D. and CRICK, F. H. C. (1954). The structure of DNA. *Cold Spring Harb. Symp. quant. Biol.*, **18**, 123–131. *(180–1)*

WEIGERT, M. G. and GAREN, A. (1965). Base composition of nonsense codons in *E. coli*. Evidence from amino-acid substitutions at a tryptophan site in alkaline phosphatase. *Nature, Lond.*, **206**, 992–994. *(260–1)*

WEINBERG, W. (1908). Über den Nachweis der Vererbung beim Menschen. *Jh. Ver. vaterl. Naturk. Württ.*, **64**, 369–382. *(13)*

WEINBERG, W. (1909). Über Vererbungsgesetze beim Menschen. *Z. VererbLehre* **1**, 377–392 and 440–460. *(134)*

WEISBLUM, B., BENZER, S. and HOLLEY, R. W. (1962). A physical basis for degeneracy in the amino acid code. *Proc. natn. Acad. Sci. U.S.A.*, **48**, 1449–1454. *(257)*

WEISMANN, A. (1883). *Über die Vererbung*. Jena. (English translation entitled 'On Heredity,' in 'Essays upon Heredity and kindred biological Problems,' 1889, Oxford, Clarendon Press, pp. 67–105.) *(40)*

WEISMANN, A. (1885). *Die Kontinuität des Keimplasmas* . . . Jena. (English translation entitled 'The continuity of the germ-plasm as the foundation of a theory of heredity' in 'Essays upon Heredity and kindred biological Problems,' 1889, Oxford, Clarendon Press, pp. 161–248.) *(40–1)*

WEISMANN, A. (1887). *Ueber die Zahl der Richtungskörper und über ihre Bedeutung für die Vererbung*. Jena. (English translation entitled 'On the number of polar bodies and their significance in heredity' in 'Essays upon Heredity and kindred biological Problems,' 1889, Oxford, Clarendon Press, pp. 333–384.) *(61,66)*

WEISS, S. B. and NAKAMOTO, T. (1961). The enzymatic synthesis of RNA: nearest-neighbor base frequencies. *Proc. natn. Acad. Sci. U.S.A.*, **47**, 1400–1405. *(240)*

WELSHONS, W. J. and RUSSELL, L. B. (1959). The Y-chromosome as the bearer of male determining factors in the mouse. *Proc. natn. Acad. Sci. U.S.A.*, **45**, 560–566. *(76)*

WENRICH, D. H. (1916). The spermatogenesis of *Phrynotettix magnus*, with special reference to synapsis and the individuality of the chromosomes. *Bull. Mus. comp. Zool. Harv.*, **60**, 55–136. *(63, 114–7, 127)*

WESTERGAARD, M. (1958). The mechanism of sex determination in dioecious flowering plants. *Adv. Genet.* **9**, 217–281. *(76)*

WHITEHOUSE, H. L. K. (1963). A theory of crossing-over by means of hybrid deoxyribonucleic acid. *Nature, Lond.*, **199**, 1034–1040. *(274)*

WHITEHOUSE, H. L. K. (1965). A theory of crossing-over and gene conversion involving hybrid DNA. *Proc. 11th int. Congr. Genet.* 1963, **2**, 87–88. Oxford, Pergamon Press. *(278–281)*

WHITEHOUSE, H. L. K. and HASTINGS, P. J. (1965). The analysis of genetic recombination on the polaron hybrid DNA model. *Genet. Res.*, **6**, 27–92.
(279, 282, 284–5, 300, 326, 330)

WILCOX, M. S. (1928). The sexuality and arrangement of the spores in the ascus of *Neurospora sitophila*. *Mycologia*, **20**, 3–16. *(101)*

WILKINS, M. H. F. (1957). Physical studies of the molecular structure of deoxyribose nucleic acid and nucleoprotein. *Cold Spring Harb. Symp. quant. Biol.*, **21**, 75–88.
(177, 300)

WILKINS, M. H. F., STOKES, A. R. and WILSON, H. R. (1953). Molecular structure of deoxypentose nucleic acids. *Nature, Lond.*, **171**, 738–740. *(178, 179)*

WILKINS, M. H. F. and ZUBAY, G. (1963). X-ray diffraction study of the structure of nucleohistone and nucleoprotamines. *J. molec. Biol.*, **7**, 756–757. *(301)*

WILSON, E. B. (1896). *The Cell in Development and Inheritance.* New York, Macmillan.
(325)

WILSON, E. B. (1905). The chromosomes in relation to the determination of sex in insects. *Science, N.Y.*, **22**, 500–502. *(69)*

WILSON, E. B. (1909). Recent researches on the determination and heredity of sex. *Science, N.Y.*, **29**, 53–70. *(69, 71, 325)*

WIMBER, D. E. and PRENSKY, W. (1963). Autoradiography with meiotic chromosomes of the male newt (*Triturus viridescens*) using H³-thymidine. *Genetics, Princeton*, **48**, 1731–1738. *(276)*

WINIWARTER, H. VON. (1900). Recherches sur l'ovogenèse et l'organogenèse de l'ovaire des Mammifères (Lapin et Homme). *Archs Biol., Paris*, **17**, 33–199.
(62, 64, 327–8, 330)

WINKLER, H. (1916), Über die experimentelle Erzeugung von Pflanzen mit abweichenden Chromosomenzahlen. *Z. Bot.*, **8**, 417–531. *(330)*

WINKLER, H. (1930). *Die Konversion der Gene.* Jena, Gustav Fischer. *(264, 326)*

WITTMANN, H. G. (1962). Proteinuntersuchungen an Mutanten des Tabakmosaikvirus als Beitrag zum Problem des genetischen Codes. *Z. VererbLehre*, **93**, 491–530. *(259)*

WOODWARD, D. O. (1959). Enzyme complementation in vitro between adenylosuccinaseless mutants of *Neurospora crassa*. *Proc. natn. Acad. Sci. U.S.A.*, **45**, 846–850.
(217)

WOODWARD, D. O., PARTRIDGE, C. W. H. and GILES, N. H. (1958). Complementation at the *ad*-4 locus in *Neurospora crassa*. *Proc. natn. Acad. Sci. U.S.A.*, **44**, 1237–1244.
(215, 216)

WYATT, G. R. (1951). The purine and pyrimidine composition of deoxypentose nucleic acids. *Biochem. J.*, **48**, 584–590. (*174*)

WYATT, G. R. and COHEN, S. S. (1952). A new pyrimidine base from bacteriophage nucleic acids. *Nature, Lond.*, **170**, 1072–1073. (*174*)

YANKOFSKY, S. A. and SPIEGELMAN, S. (1962). The identification of the ribosomal RNA cistron by sequence complementarity, I. Specificity of complex formation. *Proc. natn. Acad. Sci. U.S.A.*, **48**, 1069–1078. (*293, 310*)

YANKOFSKY, S. A. and SPIEGELMAN, S. (1963). Distinct cistrons for the two ribosomal RNA components. *Proc. natn. Acad. Sci. U.S.A.*, **49**, 538–544. (*293, 310*)

YANOFSKY, C. and BONNER, D. M. (1955). Gene interaction in tryptophan synthetase formation. *Genetics, Princeton*, **40**, 761–769. (*165*)

YANOFSKY, C., CARLTON, B. C., GUEST, J. R., HELINSKI, D. R. and HENNING, U. (1964). On the colinearity of gene structure and protein structure. *Proc. natn. Acad. Sci. U.S.A.*, **51**, 266–272. (*224–6, 260, 262, 283*)

YATES, F. (1934). Contingency tables involving small numbers and the χ^2 test. *Jl R. statist. Soc.*, Suppl. 1, 217–235. (*30*)

YCAS, M. and VINCENT, W. S. (1960). A ribonucleic acid fraction from yeast related in composition to desoxyribonucleic acid. *Proc. natn. Acad. Sci. U.S.A.*, **46**, 804–811. (*242*)

YOSHIKAWA, H. and SUEOKA, N. (1963). Sequential replication of *Bacillus subtilis* chromosome, I. Comparison of marker frequencies in exponential and stationary growth phases. *Proc. natn. Acad. Sci. U.S.A.*, **49**, 559–566. (*197*)

YULE, G. U. (1907). On the theory of inheritance of quantitative compound characters on the basis of Mendel's law—a preliminary note. *R. hort. Soc. Rep. 3rd int. Conf. Genet.*, pp. 140–142. (*31, 37*)

ZAMECNIK, P. C. (1962). Unsettled questions in the field of protein synthesis. *Biochem. J.*, **85**, 257–264. (*248*)

ZAMENHOF, S., BRAWERMAN, G. and CHARGAFF, E. (1952). On the desoxypentose nucleic acids from several microorganisms. *Biochim. biophys. Acta*, **9**, 402–405. (*203*)

ZAMENHOF, S. and GRIBOFF, G. (1954). Incorporation of halogenated pyrimidines into the deoxyribonucleic acids of *Bacterium coli* and its bacteriophages. *Nature, Lond.*, **174**, 306–307. (*192, 228*)

ZELENY, C. (1921). The direction and frequency of mutation in the bar-eye series of multiple allelomorphs of *Drosophila*. *J. exp. Zool.*, **34**, 203–233. (*153*)

ZEN, S. (1961). Chiasma studies in structural hybrids. VI. Heteromorphic bivalent and reciprocal translocation in *Allium fistulosum*. *Cytologia*, **26**, 67–73. (*118–9*)

ZICKLER, H. (1934). Genetische Untersuchungen an einen heterothallischen Asko-myzeten (*Bombardia lunata* nov. spec.). *Planta*, **22**, 573–613. (*264*)

Index

α-helix, 214
α-particles, 145
aberrant tetrads, 264–6, 278–81
aberrations, chromosomal. *See* structural change
ABO blood groups, 134–5
abortive transduction, 270
Abraxas, 20–22, 71, 72, 322
acceptor RNA, 245
acentix chromosome, 122–5, 324
Acetabularia, 42–5, 235, 312–4, 318
Acrida, 117, 119, 321
acridine orange, 145
acridines, 56–7
acriflavine, 56
actinomycin D, 291, 312
acquired characters, 1, 12, 40–1
adaptor hypothesis, 244
adenine, 167, 173–5, 177
adenylosuccinase, 211, 215–7
Aerobacter aerogenes, 190, 195–6, 317
Agrostemma, 10, 320
alanine, 213, 236, 248, 252, 257–8, 261–2
aleurone. *See* Zea
Algae, 56, 258–9, 317, 318
alkaline phosphatase, 217, 261
alkaptonuria, 159
alkylating agents, 145
alleles, 9, 132–5, 204–211, 324
    complementation between, 211, 215–22
    heterokaryon test, 161–2
    recombination between, 155–8, 204–11, 226, 260, 263, 266–8, 283
Allium, 118–9, 319
allosteric inhibition, 307
Aloe, 114, 116, 319
Alosa, 172, 322
amber mutants, 223, 260–2, 292
Amblystoma, 172, 323
aminoacid code. *See* genetic code
aminoacids, 213
    mutation, effect of, 214–5, 219, 224–5, 260–1
    nucleotide triplets coding for, 257, 262
    sequence in polypeptides, 227–8
    synthesis of, 162–5, 220, 287–90.
aminopurine, 229–31
Amphibia, 296, 322
anaphase, 58, 60–6, 324
    bridge, 122–4
annelids, 259, 321
anthocyanin, 133, 159–60, 294, 302, 314
anthranilic acid, 162–3
antibodies, 134, 157
anticodon, 252, 324
antigens, 134, 157

antiparallel, 196
Antirrhinum, 11, 12, 39, 77, 315, 321
arginine, 161–3, 166, 213–6, 236, 254, 257–8, 261–2, 300, 312
Arphia, 69, 321
Ascaris. See *Parascaris*
Ascobolus, 266–7, 282–4, 318
ascus, 101, 263
asparagine, 213, 219, 236, 257, 258, 262
aspartic acid, 213, 236, 257, 258, 262
Aspergillus nidulans, 318
    adenine (*ad*) mutants, 204–6, 267, 268, 285
    arginine mutant, 166
    biotin (*bi*) mutants, 204–6, 207, 267
    chromatid interference, 111
    competitive inhibition, 166
    cytoplasmic variant, 55
    diploid strains, 204–6, 263
    heterokaryons, 46–47, 55, 204–6
    lysine mutant, 166
    mitotic crossing-over, 205
    negative interference, 267–8, 285
    nitrite mutants, 294–5
    para-aminobenzoic acid (*paba*) mutants, 267–8, 285
    recombination, 204–8, 263, 267–8, 280, 284–5
    white conidia, 46–7, 55
    yellow conidia (*y*), 204–5, 267
Aspergillus niger, 46–7, 318
assortive mating, 31
Astasia, 56, 318
Aster, 10, 321
ATP, 190, 245, 255
autoradiographs, 172–3, 181–8, 196–8, 200, 297, 314
autosomes, 75, 130, 324
auxotrophic mutants, 160–6, 203
Avena, 33–4, 319
Azotobacter vinelandii, 238, 317

β-galactosidase, 288–91, 307
Bacillus cereus, 291, 307, 318
    megaterium, 293, 312, 318
    stearothermophilus, 256, 318
    subtilis, 197, 318
back-cross, 9, 18, 21, 38–9, 55, 324
back-mutation, 135, 139, 165, 229–234, 283
bacteria, 167, 258–9, 295, 310, 317–8
bacteriophage, 168, 194, 270, 317
Balaenoptera, 228, 323
balanced polymorphism, 14
barley, 32, 140, 319
base analogues, 190, 223, 228